MENTAL HEALTH MANPOWER TRENDS

Joint Commission
on Mental Illness and Health

MONOGRAPH SERIES / NO. 3

Mental Health Manpower Trends

GEORGE W. ALBEE

A REPORT TO THE STAFF DIRECTOR, JACK R. EWALT

1959

Basic Books, Inc., Publishers, New York

Permissions

The author wishes to thank the following individuals, publishers and organizations for permission to quote from the material indicated:

American Nurses' Association: Facts about Nursing, 1955–1956, pamphlet, 1956.

American Psychiatric Association: Standards for Hospitals and Clinics, 1956; Fact sheets of the Joint Information Service.

Atlantic Monthly: Lloyd K. Berkner, "Wanted: A National Science Policy," January 1958; reprinted in K. Lansner (Ed.), *Second-rate Brains,* Doubleday & Co., Inc., 1958.

Columbia University Press: E. V. Hollis and A. L. Taylor, *Social Work Education in the United States,* 1951.

W. H. Cornog: "The Perils of Panic," in K. Lansner (Ed.), *Second-rate Brains,* Doubleday & Co., Inc., 1958.

John K. Galbraith: *The Affluent Society,* Houghton Mifflin Co., 1958.

McGraw-Hill Publishing Company, Inc.: In the Field of Education . . . Who Are Today's Capitalists? undated pamphlet.

The Mathematics Teacher: Nicholas DeWitt, "Soviet Science Education and Its Challenge," 51 (no. 2): 68, 70, 1958.

National Education Association: Teacher Supply and Demand in Colleges and Universities, 1955–1956 and 1956–1957, pamphlet, 1957; Teacher Supply and Demand in the Public Schools, pamphlet, 1958.

National League for Nursing: "Preparation of Nursing Leaders," *Nursing Outlook, 4* (no. 9): 517, 1956; Nursing for a Growing Nation, pamphlet, 1957.

Vice Admiral Hyman Rickover: Education in the Nuclear Age, speech delivered at New London, Connecticut, Dec. 6, 1957.

Social Work: J. W. Eaton, "Whence and Whither Social Work? A Sociological Analysis," *1:* 11, 1956.

Sidney G. Tickton: *Rebuilding Human Lives: The Rehabilitation of the Handicapped,* The Seventh Company, Inc., 1957.

Foreword

THIS IS the third of a series of monographs to be published by the Joint Commission on Mental Illness and Health as part of a national mental health survey that will culminate in a final report containing findings and recommendations for a national mental health program.

The present document constitutes a report of the project director to the staff director of the Joint Commission.

Titles of the monograph series, together with the principal authors, are listed here in the order of expected publication:

1. *Current Concepts of Positive Mental Health*
   Marie Jahoda, Ph.D., Basic Books, 1958. $2.75.

2. *Economics of Mental Illness*
   Rashi Fein, Ph.D., Basic Books, 1958. $3.00.

3. *Mental Health Manpower Trends*
   George W. Albee, Ph.D.

4. *Nationwide Sampling Survey of People's Mental Health*
   Angus Campbell, Ph.D., and Gerald Gurin, Ph.D.
   Survey Research Center, University of Michigan.

5. *The Role of Schools in Mental Health*
   Wesley Allinsmith, Ph.D., and George W. Goethals, Ed.D.

6. *Research Resources in Mental Health*
   William F. Soskin, Ph.D.

7. *The Role of Religion in Mental Health*
   Richard V. McCann, Ph.D.

[v]

These monographs, each a part of an over-all study design, will contain the detailed information forming the basis of a final report. From the data in the individual studies and other relevant information, the headquarters staff will prepare a summary document incorporating its findings and recommendations for national and state mental health programs. This summary document will have the approval of the Joint Commission before its publication in the form of an official report.

This final report will be published by Basic Books and transmitted to the United States Congress, the Surgeon General of the Public Health Services, and the Governors of the States, together with their representatives in the public health and mental health professions, in accordance with the provisions of the Mental Health Study Act of 1955.

Participating organizations, members and officers of the Joint Commission and the headquarters staff are listed in Appendix II at the end of the book.

The Joint Commission, it may be seen, is a nongovernmental, multidisciplinary, nonprofit organization representing a variety of national agencies concerned with mental health. Its study was authorized by a unanimous resolution of Congress and is financed by grants from the following sources:

American Association on Mental Deficiency
American Association of Psychiatric Clinics for Children
American Legion

American Medical Association
American Occupational Therapy Association
American Orthopsychiatric Association, Inc.
American Psychiatric Association
American Psychoanalytic Association
Association for Physical and Mental Rehabilitation
Carter Products Company
Catholic Hospital Association
Field Foundation
Henry Hornblower Fund
National Association for Mental Health
National Committee Against Mental Illness
National Institute of Mental Health
National League for Nursing
National Rehabilitation Association
Rockefeller Brothers Fund
Benjamin Rosenthal Foundation
Smith, Kline and French Foundation

Additional copies of *Mental Health Manpower Trends* may be purchased from the publisher or from book dealers.

JOINT COMMISSION ON MENTAL ILLNESS AND HEALTH

Staff Review

THIS REPORT concerns itself mainly with the supply and demand for psychiatrists, psychologists, psychiatric nurses, and psychiatric social workers in the United States, although it touches on related personnel as well. These four categories include the persons of high professional training whose efforts, in our present state of knowledge and following our present system of mental hospital care, count most in bringing about the recovery of increased numbers of persons with major mental illness. There are others of importance, too, but these mentioned are in the first line of a professionally competent attack on mental illness.

The author is Dr. George W. Albee, Professor of Psychology and Chairman of the Department of Psychology with a joint appointment in the Division of Psychiatry of the School of Medicine, Western Reserve University, in Cleveland. We asked Dr. Albee, who had made a previous study in this area, to do an extensive analysis of manpower trends in the mental health professions as one of the high-priority tasks in the national mental health survey of the Joint Commission on Mental Illness and Health.

Dr. Albee concludes, with frank pessimism, that sufficient professional personnel to eliminate the glaring deficiencies in our care of mental patients will never become available if the present population trend continues without a commensurate increase in the recruitment and training of mental health manpower. The only possibilities of changing this negative outlook for hundreds of thousands of mental hospital patients would require a great change in our social attitudes and a consequent massive national effort in all areas of education, including large increases in the number of mental health personnel, or a sharp breakthrough in mental health research.

That Dr. Albee finds the number of mentally ill as tremendous as we know it to be, and that he finds the numbers of persons available to treat mental patients as small as they are, can come as no surprise. We should have been surprised if he had not reckoned the numbers of mentally ill as large and our resources for helping them meager.

What he has succeeded in doing for the first time in a document of this magnitude and with great force and clarity is to relate the shortages in mental health manpower to the shortages in other categories of professional manpower, to the deficiencies in our system of secondary and higher education insofar as it relates to stimulation of our bright young people to go into professional careers, particularly in science. Dr. Albee believes that the trend in our social and cultural values has been anti-intellectual, anti-educational, and anti-professional.

Every page in this text should interest persons directly concerned with the future of mental health in the United States but Dr. Albee's Chapters I and IX, "Introduction" and "The Crisis in Education," will interest all conscientious Americans, whether or not they have any special concern for the mentally ill.

He first reviews the rise of modern man—his increased industrial productivity, his increased freedom from painful toil simply to stay alive, his longer, healthier life, his improved standard of living—and shows how these gains have depended on education and science, that is, man's capacity for systematic and creative thought.

From man's success in mass productivity has come a high respect for the producer and the rewards of manufacturing and selling the product, and also a collection of curious imbalances. The factory, the marketplace has brought us city life as the predominant pattern of living, and with it, crowding, tension, and conflict. It has brought us relative freedom from poverty as it previously existed, but it also has brought us a concentration of slums, skid rows, blighted areas, crime and delinquency, various forms of air, water, and environmental pollutions, and hideous damage to the natural beauties of our landscape.

Emphasis on liberty and the rewards of private initiative and enterprise—of primary importance to freedom-loving, prosperous, fortunate people—also gives us a deep-seated suspicion of government regulation and social planning. Leaders of industries who make and sell
frivolous (as well as essential) goods often make more money than
the leaders of government agencies engaged in essential services.
Skilled laborers earn more than public-school teachers. While expanding productivity, we have neglected our social responsibilities
and public services operated at the taxpayers' expense.

One manifestation of this deterioration of social responsibility is
our public mental hospitals. Their inefficiency as healing institutions,
as places where the mentally sick can receive the individual therapeutic attention our mental health professions know how to give, has
been repeatedly exposed in "snakepit" and "scandal" terms. Some
improvement has occurred in the last few years, but the public is only
now reaching the threshold of awareness of the kinds and numbers
of professional persons who would be needed to bring these hospitals
up to the level of care available in the typical voluntary or public
general hospital.

As Dr. Albee illustrates with a variety of indexes, the long-standing
shortage—in some instances, nearly complete absence—of compe-
tently and specially trained professional personnel in mental hospitals—particularly in many state hospitals—has been aggravated
rather than relieved by a tremendously increased demand for mental
health services in other agencies—for example, schools, courts, and
prisons—as well as in private practice.

The problem is not only the one with which every legislator is
personally familiar—the cry for increased appropriations—but also
the fact that we cannot find persons with the necessary professional
skills to fill the jobs that are budgeted. Surveys of State and county
hospitals have revealed budgeted positions for physicians and psychologists standing nearly 25 per cent unfilled. We are approximately
20 per cent short in filling budgeted jobs for psychiatric nurses and
social workers. In contrast, only 4 per cent of nonprofessional jobs
remain vacant.

Even if all available jobs were filled, the staffing of public mental hospitals would fall far short of the minimum standards for adequate care set by the American Psychiatric Association (these are truly minimum and not optimum or ideal standards). By this criterion, our hospitals are 20 per cent adequate in nursing staff and 36 per cent adequate in social workers. The adequacy is 45 per cent for physicians (with heavy reliance on foreign interns and residents) and 67 per cent for psychologists.

The present shortages are compounded in prospects for the immediate future by our remarkable population growth and the expectation that, with the increased birth rate and decreased death rate, the population trend will continue upward for many years to come.

What are the prospects for recruitment and training?

How about psychiatrists who, in the public's mind, are most closely identified with the diagnosis and treatment of mental illness?

PSYCHIATRISTS

The source of psychiatrists is young doctors, newly graduated from medical school or receiving intern training, who are in the process of making career decisions as to the special training they will seek. The proportion of full-time specialists who are psychiatrists or neurologists rose from 6 per cent in 1923 to 8 per cent in the mid-1950's.

The number of medical graduates has increased from 6,000 to 7,000 per year in the last decade. We do not know how many of these go into psychiatry, but we do know that about 600 complete resident training as psychiatrists each year. The net increase in psychiatrists is somewhat less, due to deaths, retirements, and foreign physicians returning home. Judging from the distribution of American Psychiatric Association members, only one-third of psychiatrists become full-time employees in hospitals or clinics. Another third enter full-time private practice, and the remaining third divide their time between private practice and salaried positions.

The total increment of new psychiatrists, as Dr. Albee points out, is not sufficient to maintain even the present ratio of one psychiatrist per 18,000 population, much less contribute toward fulfillment of the frequently quoted but wholly wishful estimate that today we need twice as many psychiatrists as we now have—20,000 instead of the present 10,000.

Because of the superior attractions of private practice, the greatest shortage—it is self-evident—occurs in the area where patients with major mental illness are concentrated—in public mental hospitals. One result has been a bidding by one state against another for the services of the small number of hospital psychiatrists available. The inevitable result is that those states with the least available money have the fewest psychiatrists.

The supply of psychiatrists is dependent, as we have seen, on the production of young doctors by our medical schools, as well as on what motivates a medical graduate to become a psychiatrist and, before that, what motivated the college graduate to become a physician. As yet, we are not too well informed on these motives, though we surely need to be.

PHYSICIANS IN GENERAL

A mental health manpower study, Dr. Albee stated, must be concerned also with the supply of physicians as part of the psychiatric manpower pool. Because the individual's mental health benefits from the protection of his general bodily health and from protection against the catastrophic effects of physical illness, adequate general medical care is indispensable. Furthermore, general practitioners and doctors in other medical specialties deal directly with a large element of emotional and psychosomatic illness in their own patients.

If the present trend of growth in the United States' population continues—an increase of approximately 3 million a year—then in another twenty-five years we shall have a population of 250 million instead of 175 million. Allowing for 4500 deaths and retirements per year, the present net gain in doctors is 3000 or less per year; this, on the basis of present plans in medical education, is not expected to increase by more than a few hundred a year. Thus, Dr. Albee stresses, we will add physicians at the rate of one per 1000 population as compared to the present ratio of one per 750. It is obvious, on this basis, that we shall fall further behind in the supply both of psy-

chiatrists and of doctors in general. This will further compound the
mental health manpower problem.

To increase the supply of physicians is a complex undertaking.
Our medical schools already face serious financial difficulties. There
has been strong resistance in organized medicine to Federal aid to
medical education. Leading medical educators support Federal aid
with safeguards against a rate of expansion that would reduce the
quality of medical students and of their professional education. The
question of the future demand for doctors aside, the *AMA News,*
official newspaper of the American Medical Association, editorializes
as follows (Nov. 3, 1958):

> To train more and better physicians, medical schools must augment the
> number of students admitted or additional school facilities must be provided.
>
> During the 1957–58 school years, there were 619 budgeted, unfilled full-
> time faculty positions in U.S. medical schools—an increase of approximately
> 90 per cent over the previous year.
>
> This presents a major problem. . . . Its magnitude, unless the trend is re-
> versed, has developed to the point where it may jeopardize certain aspects of
> medical education, research, and care in the period that lies ahead.
>
> If we cannot fill all of the full-time faculty positions in our present medical
> schools, how will new or expanded schools be staffed? . . .
>
> It would certainly be unwise to rush into a crash program for the whole-
> sale training of physicians that eventually would result in an over-supply of
> doctors and a greater shortage of physicists, chemists, and others in the scien-
> tific fields. But equally undesirable would be to face a shortage of physicians
> 10 or 15 years from now. . . .
>
> The needs must be carefully analyzed. They must be met as a result of
> sound developments based on the best possible knowledge. . . .

Whether or not a general doctor shortage now exists, or is coming,
has occasioned bitter debate for some years, but no one denies that
there is a shortage of psychiatrists or that psychiatrists must first
go to medical school. A great many innocent people who have had
the misfortune to fall mentally rather than physically sick have been
made to pay dearly through lack of needed medical and nursing
attention. The net result is that they must live their lives out in drab
institutional misery and deprivation.

PSYCHOLOGISTS

We have fared somewhat better in the total supply of psychologists, Dr. Albee reports. At the end of World War II, we had about an equal number of psychiatrists and of psychologists, over all. As the result of a phenomenal interest in psychiatry shown by physicians returning from military service, the number of psychiatrists doubled in the postwar decade. But, meanwhile, the number of psychologists quadrupled, with the result that there are now about 16,000 psychologists.

At first glance, this increase appears encouraging; in a way, it is. But only about one-third of all psychologists engage in clinical services, where their skills would count in the care of the mentally ill. The largest number are employed as college teachers. The second largest number of psychologists are employed by the Federal government, mainly for research, some of it related to mental health. Private industry employs a sizable number for aptitude testing and for personnel, management, and market research.

Albee attributes the larger supply of psychologists principally to a more favorable recruitment situation. Psychiatry must depend on a medical-school student, who is already a college graduate, to become interested in this specialty. In contrast, psychologists have direct access to undergraduates in college psychology courses, and the subject is a popular one. Thus, as college enrollments increase in the next fifteen years, psychology's manpower pool will increase. There is reason for optimism, he concludes, regarding a continued upward trend in supply. It may not be sufficient to meet the demand, however.

SOCIAL WORKERS

The prospects are not so bright in relieving the shortage of social workers. Part of the problem, this report indicates, is the lack of a clear-cut and favorable definition of the social worker's role, as the public sees him and as he sees himself.

To illustrate: The image of the physician as a friendly, helpful, healing figure is deeply etched in the average individual's mind. He is considered worthy of emulation; in fact, people envy him. The stereotype of the psychiatrist as peculiar or in some way different from other doctors persisted at least until the last war. Since then the psychiatrist's status as a member of the medical profession and a popular figure in our society has vastly improved; this is probably largely due to the psychiatrist's active role in public education, and the reading public's avid interest in human behavior. On recruiting grounds, it might be argued that there is still room for improvement.

The psychologist has been successful in making his profession appear attractive to youths in search of a career. His work is naturally interesting, for a like reason: human behavior, normal or abnormal, is interesting both in its psychological mechanisms and in its meaning.

But the social worker, who is a key figure in any clinic or hospital proposing to provide competent care of mental patients, including attention to his social and economic circumstances, presents a rather vague image in the minds of many people, it would appear. Indeed, we have observed misinformation and prejudice, as on the part of a state legislator who objected to the term "social worker" on the grounds that it implied socialism; "case worker" was acceptable to him, however.

Generally speaking, social work can be visualized as centering on the management of cases with the object of alleviating a crisis in the life of an individual, family, or group. This is done in a variety of ways, but always with the purpose of helping someone who needs help, without intent to use, control, or exploit him.

Only a tiny fraction of the 80,000 social workers in the United States are psychiatric social workers. The great majority, over all, are employed by Federal, State, or local governments. They are mainly college graduates, somewhat less than half of whom have had one, two, or, in some instances, more years of training in graduate schools of social work. Psychiatric social workers fall in the category with the highest training and are commonly regarded as an élite group in their profession. Because of the great shortage, there is a good deal of competition for their services and, therefore, there is apt to be a rapid turnover in any given job.

Dr. Albee reports an estimated need for an additional 50,000 social workers by 1960. Schools of social work train not more than 2000 a year. In the immediate past, these schools have not been able to fill their classes. The situation may improve somewhat with increased college enrollments, but the increase is not expected to meet estimates of need ranging from 4000 to 12,000 new social workers a year. Inasmuch as college students are not regularly exposed to social work as part of their undergraduate education, the schools of social work appear to lack any ready-made recruitment device.

NURSES

Nursing is the largest of the health professions. The nursing profession enjoys widespread social approval insofar as it fulfills the public image of a nurse as a tender, comforting figure who relieves the suffering of her patients.

A sizable number of high-school girls aspire to be nurses. Although there has been a general shortage of nurses for some years, recruiting efforts on the part of the nursing profession have been effective and the number of general nurses has steadily increased. The increase has not kept up with demand, mainly because of a 5 per cent annual drop-out rate, primarily due to marriage. As in social work, recruitment is handicapped by the prospect of relatively low pay in relation to professional training requirements, but working conditions have greatly improved.

This fairly wholesome outlook does not apply to psychiatric nursing. Although they have half of all hospital patients under their care or supervision at any given time, psychiatric nurses make up only 5 per cent of the nursing profession.

The best opportunity for recruitment occurs at the time, during the typical student nurse's three-year course of training in a hospital school of nursing, when she is assigned for three months to a psychiatric ward or to a mental hospital. What she finds, however, Dr. Albee remarks, is a kind of nursing duty quite different from her conception of bedside nursing. The psychiatric nurse's job is largely one of administration, teaching, and supervision of attendants. Her role often is more akin to management than to caring for patients, except in helping the physician in the administering of therapy involving technological skills.

This level of nursing duty, with its emphasis on teaching and supervision, is better served by the four- or five-year college nursing education programs, but there is a serious shortage of nurses with such advanced training. The annual requirement for nurses trained for leadership is 4000 by 1960, against the current output of 1000.

There is one nurse to every 53 beds in psychiatric hospitals compared to one to every 3 in general hospitals. When the comparison is limited to general duty nurses alone, it is one nurse for every 4 beds in general hospitals and one for every 141 in psychiatric hospitals.

If psychiatric nursing continues to attract only 5 per cent or less of hospital nurses, we may expect an increased shortage as time goes on.

PRACTICAL NURSES

The rise of the licensed practical nurse as an adjunct to hospital nursing service has been spectacular in general hospitals, and may be expected to continue. This movement, however, has been of little benefit to mental hospital patients. The typical practical nurse is an older, married woman with a family who wishes to work near home, usually in the hospital where she trained.

ATTENDANTS

The largest category of mental hospital personnel are attendants or psychiatric aides, as they also are called. They total between 80,000 and 90,000. Although there is some shortage, Dr. Albee reports, it is not great. In times past, attendants' jobs have been filled by untrained persons paid disgracefully low salaries. Although many skilled and devoted persons have filled these jobs, the lack of specific qualifications has made it possible for some persons with serious personality problems of their own to drift into this occupation. In recent years and in many states, the attendant's job has been considerably upgraded as the result of on-the-job training programs, increased pay, and improved working conditions. Dr. Albee could find no accurate data on the extent of this improvement. An intensive study of the use of attendants is badly needed.

PROFESSIONAL MANPOWER IN GENERAL

Albee reasons, quite logically, that we cannot evaluate the shortages of professionally trained manpower in the mental health field without at the same time contemplating the widespread shortage of highly trained persons in a variety of technical and professional areas. The reason is simple: We all draw on the same pool—namely, young men and young women who graduate from college. Any particularly successful efforts at recruitment in one field must necessarily be made at the expense of any other also reporting a shortage.

Any upward trend in the supply of any and all kinds of professional manpower will depend, then, on the strength of our educational system and the motivation of our youth in greater numbers to seek professional careers. The nature of a profession, with its emphasis on expert knowledge and specialized service to others, presupposes superior mental competence, moral responsibility, and advanced educational achievement.

At present, our system of education at both high school and college levels apparently fails to inspire students fully to utilize their brain power in ways that would prepare them for professional careers. There is, Dr. Albee states, a fundamental lack of appreciation and interest in intellectual achievement in our society and its schools and colleges.

Now suddenly we have been forced to the realization that the quality of our educational system has been on the downgrade for some years, Albee asserts. The trend in our high schools has been away from teaching the more difficult subjects involving mathematics and a basic understanding of science and toward life adjustment and immediate vocational skills. The same trend persists in college, where students poorly prepared in high school drift into courses that do not require extensive backgrounds in mathematics and the sciences. In short, some types of intellectual discipline have been sacrificed and science requirements softened.

Paralleling this deterioration of scholarly interest and lack of rewards for outstanding scholastic achievement in mathematics and science, we have witnessed the exodus of many of the best qualified secondary and college teachers to take higher paid jobs, usually in industry.

Unquestionably, the greatest professional manpower shortage is in teachers—competent teachers. From 1950 to 1955 there was a 57 per cent decline in our output of high school teachers in science and a 51 per cent decline in mathematics teachers. Of those that were produced, more than half decided against going into teaching.

Our schools and colleges are shockingly underfinanced and our teachers vastly underpaid. These facts have been dinned into the public's ear and are so well documented by so many different sources that they need no review here.

THE ROOT OF THE PROBLEM

The crisis that we face in education—and therefore in the training of professional manpower, and therefore mental health manpower— will become more acute, Albee points out, when the students who have swollen the enrollments of the public school system (with results, we should say, now made obvious to all who will listen) go on to our institutions of higher education.

But on the whole, the American public, this report states, appears incapable of recognizing the full implications of its educational problem and of becoming sufficiently alarmed to take the necessary degree of effective action. Educators have expressed alarm. Political statesmen have expressed alarm. Military leaders have expressed alarm. Industrial statesmen have expressed alarm.

What is the nature of this apathy?

Albee believes it arises in consequence of our industrial success and the abundant increase in consumer goods for a large majority of our people, with an attendant shift of emphasis to the importance of merchandising and the objective of a life of comparative comfort and ease.

Though high-quality education in reality is crucial to the maintenance of technological and scientific progress, both in our own consumer society and in military competition, it does not seem too important to most citizens. Our system of public schooling, Albee continues, has been responsive to—indeed, it is dependent on—people who are not at all impressed with the importance of intellectual achievement. Mediocrity has been the product.

In the end, the student's education must be financed by his parents, by him, or by society if he is deemed worthy. At present, higher education has become so expensive—the minimum cost of a college education is $6000 to $8000—that it has been priced out of reach of many parents and their children. Only a part of this cost is tuition, and tuition, in turn, pays only a small part of the cost of operating a college or university, which must spend several times more per student than the student himself pays.

As matters now stand, college faculty members indirectly subsidize a part of the cost of their students' education—out of the deficiency in their salaries as compared to those of persons of equal training in private enterprise. Albee reports that college teachers' salaries need to be raised at least 50 per cent in the next five years. Only in this way can competent faculty members be prevented from continuing to seek more remunerative jobs elsewhere, abandoning higher education as a sinking ship.

Dr. Albee distributes responsibility for the decerebrate trend in the American value system so broadly—both educators and businessmen share some of the burden of his criticisms—that we might better acknowledge that we all participate in the responsibility for the anti-intellectual and anti-educational attitudes that he charges. At least one member of the Joint Commission feels that one group which Albee does not scrutinize must share in the responsibility—the liberal arts professors. As this one critic states:

[The liberal arts professors] have simply been socially irresponsible . . . aloof from all concerns of public education, and even have allowed the colleges to become centers for the entertainment of the public. An assumption that liberal arts professors are brighter than the education specialists only makes more reprehensible their irresponsibility and their willingness now wildly to flail everyone but themselves. . . . Not since James and Thorndike has a respectable psychologist worried much about how kids learn in school. . . .

Albee does make this telling charge: those who go to Washington to fight Federal aid to education on the basis that public schooling is a prerogative of State and local governments often are the same ones who go back home and oppose increased state educational aid or bigger local school budgets. The problem seems to be one of coupling a dislike for taxation with a dislike for education. Through selfishness and ignorance, the education of our youth suffers.

Presuming lawyers, teachers, chemists, physicists, psychiatrists, psychologists, and other members of learned professions to be desirable members of our society, and also presuming that it is not wholly disgraceful to cultivate the brains God gave us, Dr. Albee cites a dramatic measurement of the amount of brainpower that is being wasted in the United States today:

Of 10,000 youngsters in an age group, 7880 enter high school, 5755 graduate from high school, 2016 enter college, and 1190 graduate from college.

Only about one in ten will enter the professional manpower pool, in other words. The above calculations take the students as they come, without respect to intelligence. The data reveals that this, as a matter of fact, is the way our colleges take them, contrary to widespread opinion.

Here is the situation when mental ability is taken into account:

Of 10,000 youngsters in an age group, 2000 are in the top fifth with respect to intelligence; 1963 of them enter high school, 1857 graduate from high school, 864 enter college, and 692 graduate from college.

The manpower pool of the mental health as of other professions depends (to a great extent) on the number of youths of superior mental competence who graduate from college and go on to graduate school. From the above figures, it would appear that only one in three of our brightest students enters the professional manpower pool, though we could assume that most of the remaining two-thirds pursue careers requiring outstanding intellectual ability.

Only a nation as well endowed and fortunate as ours could afford such a colossal waste. It is quite another question, of course, how long we can afford it.

The explanation for the number of students who, after entering high school, fail to obtain a college education lies in a complex of factors, including lack of interest, lack of inspiration, lack of self-discipline, poor study habits, lack of money. Both motivation and money are important, in that order.

Motivation comes either from one's parents or from a singularly good teacher, usually. Professional parents produce a larger percentage of children who enter professions. Many scientists report that their curiosity was originally stimulated by one teacher or another, in high school or college.

IS THERE A SOLUTION?

It is of some special interest to a national mental health study, we may say in passing, that our culture does not manifest a great respect for the mind. This conclusion certainly follows not only from the deficiencies in our education system that Dr. Albee demonstrates but from our lack of sufficient concern for those who are mentally sick. Our minds seem to be a small matter to us. This will constitute not only a bit of irony but a solid fact if we are unable to use our imaginations and creative energies in ways that will improve our value system and reverse the trend.

What can we do to reduce the mental health manpower shortage now or in the near future?

Examining Dr. Albee's chapter, "Implications for the Future," we find a number of possibilities, suggestions, and leads.

We can hope wholeheartedly for the first possibility that he entertains, without really counting on it, if we are guided by experience. The demand for professional services for the custody and continuous care of patients with schizophrenia or cerebral arteriosclerosis could be greatly reduced by a major breakthrough in the treatment of either of these conditions with a biochemical or other treatment that could be given to large numbers by a single therapist. Together, these patients fill the majority of our mental hospital beds. Whether or not this occurs depends principally on the brains and money used to study the problem.

We can agree with Dr. Albee that it would be unrealistic to pin all our hopes on such a research breakthrough. Both basic and clinical research should be supported to the maximum. But even with such support, we cannot count on increased purchasing power to produce the desired result. A characteristic of scientific research is that it ultimately produces results of benefit to us all, but we cannot predict when the result will come or even that it will be the one we were looking for. The time element is uncontrollable. There was a lag of forty years between the time Karl Landsteiner discovered the cause of poliomyelitis and the time John Enders and his associates found the way of cultivating the virus needed for effective vaccine production, although scientists worked on the problem of prevention regularly in the intervening years. The breakthrough often comes by chance. Sir Alexander Fleming was not looking for a penicillin when he observed it, and yet the antibiotics have made more difference in the control of infectious diseases than any other drug in medical history.

The development of the tranquilizing drugs and their helpfulness in the management of disturbed and agitated mental patients has been a source of encouragement in the care of the mentally ill. And yet, although the drugs and the hopefulness they offer make mental hospital employment more interesting and therefore more attractive, they do not relieve the need for professional experience and skills but increase it. These are not harmless drugs. Their effects must be closely watched and evaluated. In addition, they render persons hitherto out of contact with their surroundings accessible to psychotherapy, re-education and rehabilitation. Thus, they actually increase the need for trained therapists.

This brings us back to the need—so obvious that it is banal—of training more professional personnel. Albee notes that states and regions making an extensive effort to establish, strengthen, and support mental health training programs of one sort or another are at once in a more favorable position than those that do not. Training programs attract teaching talent and teaching talent attracts students. Students tend to stay in the area where they are trained. To be effective, of course, such programs need financial support and recruitment devices. We cannot disassociate any proposals for more training programs from the general shortage of persons to be trained, however.

Dr. Albee entertains the idea, as others have originated and discussed it, of creating a new helping profession in mental health. The training of a fully qualified psychiatrist requires thirteen or fourteen years beyond high school. The proposal is to create a new person carefully trained in psychotherapy but without the lengthy basic medical, general clinical, and advanced specialty training—a person to be trained in a maximum of four college years. Presumably, such a person would work under psychiatric supervision.

The dynamics of personality and behavior present a complex problem, and depend on an intricate interplay of multiple factors; even the physician and psychiatrist must evoke the utmost in knowledge and art to achieve a desired result. Many psychiatrists, knowing this, would view the proposal of a doctor-substitute with instant dismay. Yet the proposal deserves serious consideration of its advantages and disadvantages.

Furthermore, as Dr. Albee points out, the creation of a new profession begs the underlying question of how this person will be recruited and trained, and thus it returns us to the numbers treadmill. Such a person would have to come from the same shallow professional manpower pool as do all others.

Much thought has been given to the possibilities of changing the pattern of mental patient care to achieve more economical use of professional knowledge and skills. The Joint Commission has given the highest priority to its study in this area—*The Mental Patient and His Care*. This study will be the tenth volume in this series of monographs, to be followed by the Commission's over-all report. As a principle, we can state, as did Albee, that every professional person should do those things which most help the largest number of persons needing help. The crucial questions are *how,* and *for whom,* there being little agreement as yet on what methods provide the most help, or upon who needs help the most.

The possibilities for experiments are often foreclosed by the sheer lack of personnel in the face of hundreds and thousands of patients to be admitted and managed. The hospital staff's first responsibilities are to see they are fed, clothed, and sheltered in a humane manner and to see that as many patients as possible have treatment. For small staffs, this becomes more than a full-time job.

Yet we need to engage in an intensive exploration of methods of obtaining better staff utilization. The maximum benefits for the patient appear to be secured through the instruments of individual attention in a friendly environment. We know a great deal of a practical nature about the psychotherapeutic and re-educational process in the long-term, face-to-face uncovering and examination of the patient's problem, conscious or unconscious, and the exploration of how he sees the problem against the perspective of how the psychiatrist and outsiders might see it. Psychoanalysis has provided us with much basic information, some of which is subject to modification and adaptation to group therapy and environmental manipulation. This knowledge, plus information from the field of sociology on the nature of emotional forces among people in groups, provides further refinement of group manipulation of a therapeutic type.

Knowledge in analysis and sociology evokes fantasies of further research with the goal of dividing the task of treatment into distinct but interrelated jobs that might be handled by skilled technicians or subprofessionals. Such an approach would necessitate the presence of a highly skilled therapist to organize, guide, and support such workers. The analogy of treating the patient by assembly line techniques is tempting, but perhaps complicates rather than clarifies the proposed plan. At present, the complex steps involved in the process of treatment and cure in a large variety of mental or emotional illnesses is not sharply enough defined to permit this separation of a total process into separate but integrated units. Because the realization of such a goal would go a long way toward more efficient use of our professionals and the large numbers of attendants, aides, and their equivalents at the community level, this area deserves intensive research.

Nicholas Hobbs suggests experimentation with specially trained personnel similar to the French *educateur*. These persons would replace our present nurse and attendant staffing and theoretically would be more effective in management of patients, so much so that Hobbs believes the psychiatrists and psychologists could be limited to use in consultation and training, with little loss in therapeutic result for any patient and an extension of their scarce skills to many more. He specifically speaks of this experiment in hospital schools for children, but perhaps research could be done on using persons of this degree of training for the application of a therapeutic plan in discrete units. It may not work, but would be worth a try, and since the training requires approximately the time now used to train a practical nurse, it would be a major advance on the manpower front. This scheme is different in important aspects from other proposals to create "junior psychiatrists."

In closing this section perhaps the reader will find apt the admonition from *The Kingfisher and the Seabee* (Thurber): "You can't make anything out of cookie-dough but cookies."

THE MOTIVATION PROBLEM

The chief intent and value of *Mental Health Manpower Trends* has been to give us a bedrock statement of the nature, breadth, depth, and over-all significance of the manpower problem. From this bedrock it becomes the task of the Joint Commission as well as of all interested persons to erect a program that will help us locate, build, and fill our professional manpower pool. No recommendations have been spelled out in this report to the point that they could be considered a basis for action. This, in truth, is the function of the Joint Commission itself.

One might find some cause for regret, however, that Dr. Albee did not dwell at greater length on the subject of image-making. He did demonstrate how important this factor is.

He makes it clear that our potential reservoir of professional manpower—untapped manpower—lies in the able-minded high school students who are either not motivated or not financially able to go to college and thence seek a professional career. Two-thirds of this reservoir now leaks away.

It is apparent, of course, that any general solution of the professional manpower shortage must depend on new, greater, and more successful efforts to support our educational system from the ele-

mentary school all the way through the graduate school—from the
"little red school" to the "ivory tower," to use two stereotypes that
hardly exist any longer in reality.

But it is questionable how much of the needed support will be
forthcoming, out of either public or private funds, without important
changes in public attitudes toward teaching, toward study, and
toward people who try to use their minds in a rational manner. This,
as far as the general professional shortage is concerned, is the key-
stone in the nonintellectual facade our culture presents.

We have seen various studies of what high-school students and the
general public think of scientists and of their teachers. The images are
far from favorable, and often distorted or uninformed. Unfortunately, some of the studies are so designed that little other interpretation could be made. The better ones indicate that our youth is not
being encouraged to emulate professional people in a choice of
a career, or adequately informed of career opportunities in public
service pursuits. Yet we know full well that children are imitative,
and that what they become to a great extent is determined by what
we provide for them to imitate.

On the other hand, we know of no national effort that is con-
sciously, systematically, aggressively working at the problem of
creating favorable images of professional people among high-school
students, or even in making certain that all high-school students
have an opportunity to learn that they are desperately needed in
certain fields such as psychiatry, psychiatric nursing, and psychiatric
social work. There are many small efforts in this direction, to be sure,
but with the exception of the general nurse recruiting campaign, and
the well-financed programs of various industries to line up technological and scientific talent from high school on, we know of nothing
being done except in a fragmentary or circumstantial sort of way—
above all, nothing in the field of mental health itself.

Dr. Albee appears to have given us our cue in citing the importance
of contact between students and the content and representative of
a given subject in the case of psychology and psychologists. Few
subjects are of more interest to people than why and how they be-
have, as we already have mentioned.

If this same platform for image-making were moved back to the high-school level and perhaps somewhat broadened to involve teaching in the broad area of the behavioral sciences—psychology, sociology, anthropology, mental health—one would assume that in time it would make a difference in the number of high school graduates interested in seeking careers in one field or another involving the prevention and control of mental illness, or in basic research in human behavior. The task is one of creating more interest in working with people rather than with things. The public possesses generally favorable images of a doctor and a nurse, but this respect has not extended traditionally to the psychiatrist, the psychiatric nurse, or the social worker.

This prompts the question of who would provide such stimulation or models for imitation. We already are shockingly short of competent teachers in the sciences. Here we must allow our imaginations to run and improvisations to creep in.

What young psychiatrist, psychologist, psychiatric nurse, or psychiatric social worker would not be persuaded, if such a cooperative program was undertaken under joint educational and mental health auspices, to give an hour a week as a visiting teacher to lecture high-school students in his own neighborhood on some of the simpler elements and mechanisms of the individual, social, and cultural behavior of human beings? Not all would want to do so, and not all would be suited to this task, but with sufficient stimulation and willingness to overcome obstacles it could be done. Or so we believe.

Such a proposal would have to be tried and proved. But when we contemplate the number of highly trained, competent, and successful professional persons that can be found in various walks of life in most communities, and also contemplate the capacity of Americans who manifest community spirit and do voluntary work when called on, we must admit that we have approached the question of teacher shortages and bob-tailed curricula rather unimaginatively. Unless people who consider themselves intelligent and educated—even "eggheads"—take action of a sort that will win them respect and emulation in their communities, they will lose the battle against professional manpower shortages by default. And all of us, the non-intellectuals as well as the so-called intellectuals, will be the losers.

JACK R. EWALT, M.D., *Director*

Acknowledgements

IN THE SUMMER of 1956, Marguerite Dickey and I wrote an article about manpower trends in psychiatry, psychology, and social work. A single article on most subjects ordinarily is little noticed but because of the interest in the subject of manpower that has developed recently, particularly with respect to the sciences and professions, our modest article enjoyed an unexpected currency.

The embarrassing aspect of this sort of situation is that one later is called on to speak authoritatively in the absence of extensive knowledge. When I was asked to assume responsibility for writing the present draft of a manpower report, I accepted with some ambivalence because, while I looked forward to the opportunity of becoming better informed on manpower trends, I felt that others were much better qualified for the task. My solution has been to draw heavily on the work of real experts in the manpower field in preparing this report.

The reader will see at once my indebtedness to such genuine manpower authorities as Dael Wolfle, Morton Kramer, Sidney Spector, Ray Maul, Eli Ginsberg, and Daniel Blain. My thanks to them are genuine because their studies have been drawn on so heavily and so often. I have used materials from a number of important agencies—the National Institute of Mental Health, the Council of State Governments, the National Education Association, the U.S. Office of Education, the Bureau of Labor Statistics, and the National Science Foundation, to mention just a few. In addition, the various professional organizations have been exceptionally helpful in supplying information and perspective.

Four people made significant contributions to the preparation of the report, and I acknowledge their help with real gratitude: Angela Homme, Jay Greenfield, Inez Stuart, and Anna Schaffner.

The drawings illustrating the text were made with care and skill by Saul Isler and Harry Wadsworth.

Much of the early draft of the report was typed by Mary Courtney, and the final draft was prepared by Albert Clements. It is difficult to indicate how much I owe these two for their patience and perseverance.

Now that the report is completed I am all too conscious of the important things that have been left out. I am conscious, too, of the enormousness of the problems that face our Nation if we are to bring our services in mental health, and in the whole field of education, into balance with our efforts in other areas. Sometimes my biases as a college professor living in a salesman's world have interfered with objective reporting. But I hope the facts in the report are clear enough to permit the reader to see the problems for himself.

GEORGE W. ALBEE, PH.D.
Western Reserve University

Contents

List of Tables

List of Figures

MENTAL HEALTH MANPOWER TRENDS

I

Introduction

In THE LONG history of the existence of life on earth, one animal form after another has risen to a position of dominance on the world's stage and has then fallen back into oblivion. Each succeeding species has had some unique characteristic which provided its strength, though often such uniqueness or specialization limited the species' ability to adjust and thereby provided the seeds for its destruction.

Man's unique possession is his intelligence. Man, alone among the species, is able to form and to transmit concepts and to accumulate knowledge from generation to generation. Throughout most of his history, however, the accumulation of knowledge has been slow and man's ability to control his life and to plan his own destiny has been limited by the harsh demands of an unpredictable environment. John M. Keynes (1931, p. 360) points out that man's standard of living changed very little from the beginning of recorded history down to very recent times—say 250 years ago.

In many parts of the world, living conditions remain relatively unchanged still. But in those parts of the world where the production of food and manufactured goods has leaped forward following the Industrial Revolution, man has been freed from the necessity of long and arduous toil simply to stay alive.

With the level of production achieved in the Western world, it has been possible to excuse children, and large numbers of the adult population, from the requirement of daily subsistence toil. As a result, there has grown up a tradition of universal education for our young, and of employment in nonproduction occupations for many of the adults in our society.

Among the many benefits derived from the freeing of man from endless subsistence toil has been the growth and development of the sciences and professions.

At long last man has found time to cultivate and extend his intelligence. One important consequence is the rise of science. Science and its professional applications represent the use by man of the full power of his intelligence in an attempt to understand and control natural phenomena. There is nothing sinister, nothing mysterious, nothing unholy, about science. It is as emotionless and as objective as anything man ever does. If we believe in a real world, a world outside ourselves, and if we believe this world operates somehow lawfully, as we understand natural laws, then the more understanding man achieves of these laws the more he will be able to predict and control the natural phenomena of his world. And if man does not use science, if he does not use his power to think and conceive thoughts and to understand his world, then he is as doomed as have been the other species which strutted their moment on the stage and disappeared.

In addition to the attempt to discover the laws whereby his world operates, man has attempted to apply his knowledge for the benefit of himself and his children. Among the appliers of knowledge there have grown up specialists, professionals in particular areas who use their special skills and techniques to deal with specific problems. We will examine later the characteristics of professions in somewhat more detail.

Knowledge begets more knowledge. Most major scientific discoveries have led to varieties of applications, some of which have improved or increased the production of goods, thereby creating more time for the discovery of more knowledge and for further increase in services.

The scientific era is less than 300 years old. If we equate the time that man has been on earth to twenty-four hours, then active efforts in science have occurred for something like the last one-hundredth of a second. It is only during the last five one-hundredths of a second, for example, that we have had the chromosome theory. It is remarkable how much we have learned in the last few instants of our exist-

Per cent

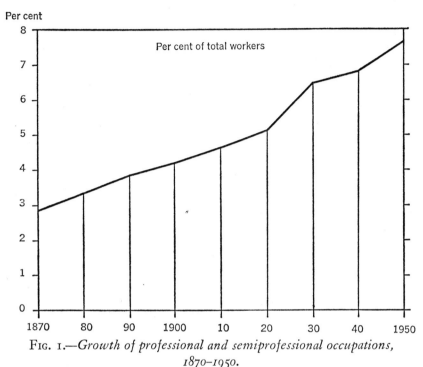

FIG. I.—*Growth of professional and semiprofessional occupations, 1870–1950.*

Source: U.S. Department of Labor, Bureau of Labor Statistics, 1957. *Occupational outlook handbook.* Government Printing Office, p. 51.

ence on earth in comparison to what we learned during all the rest of the day.

This accumulation of knowledge has direct and real consequences. Few will dispute seriously that an important factor in the achievement of our present standard of living is the controlled use of intelligence specifically directed to the solution of problems through the disciplines of science.

In the United States we have made tremendous progress, too, in the professional application of knowledge. We have achieved, for example, a remarkable decrease in infant and child mortality; and we have learned to control the infectious diseases of adulthood and middle age. A hundred years ago in the United States half of our children failed to survive to adulthood. As recently as the turn of

Millions

FIG. 2.—*Employment in goods-producing and service-producing industries, 1920–1955.*

Source: U.S. Department of Labor, Bureau of Labor Statistics, 1957. *Occupational outlook handbook*. Government Printing Office, p. 25.

the century, one child in four failed to reach adulthood. Since the turn of the century progress in medical science has cut infant mortality in our country to less than thirty in one thousand live births and has resulted in even more spectacular success among older children. Only one child in 2500 now dies between the ages of five and fourteen. If scientific research has achieved such phenomenal results in the struggle against unnecessary or premature death, what compelling reason is there why we should not achieve the same kind of results in the fight against other diseases, including the great plague of mental disorder?

The achievement, in the Western world, of comparative freedom from unremitting toil for large numbers of the members of society has not been without cost.

Social conditions are potent determiners of human attitudes. Now that we have more than enough goods to go around, poverty has ceased to be a crime. Unwillingness or inability to work no longer dooms a man to pauperism or to starvation; and physical or mental incapacity no longer requires that the individual so afflicted turn to beggary or be locked in a dungeon. We can support easily the unfortunates in our society out of our surplus, and so we do.

Another consequence of the revolution in the methods of production has been the movement of people into congested urban areas that are advantageously situated for the conversion of power and raw materials into finished products. The growth of cities has led to innumerable changes in living patterns and to increased demands on our people for adaptation. While no one can be sure which is cause and which is effect, there has been, along with increased urbanization, a substantial increase in the number of people whose behavior has required their separation from normal society or who themselves have felt incapacitated. The increase in mental disorder may be real, or it may be only a result of increased attention due to crowding, but there has been an increase.

Along with his intelligence, man has brought with him, in his fierce struggle to achieve dominance over other animals, an ortho-sympathetic nervous system constructed in such a way that, without his voluntary control, he can be instantly mobilized for a fight with an enemy or for escape from danger. This was an exceedingly useful mechanism to primitive man. But as civilization and urban living have developed, man has had to curb sharply his normal impulse to fight, and he has usually found that it is impossible to run away. But his nervous system still gets him ready for one of these actions in the presence of any emergency. Civilized man has had to learn to hold back primordial man, often at great cost to the body they both inhabit. Often the individual has not been able to withstand the fierce struggle that rages inside him when he cannot fight and cannot run away. Unfortunately, too, man's intelligence is often distorted and biased by the action of this nervous system.

In our search for brief historical perspective, another social force requires consideration. John K. Galbraith (1958) has written an incisive analysis of the power of traditional ideas in the economic world over our view of the present and future. Because production has been so crucial in the abolition of poverty and in the achievement of our high standard of living, we have continued to have an inordinate respect for production even after all of our important needs for the products of industry have been satisfied.

Man's memory for hunger and privation is long. Throughout the ages, and until very recently, man's wants were for food, clothing, shelter, and, as Galbraith emphasizes, for an orderly environment in which satisfaction of these needs might be sought. The production of food, clothing, and shelter of necessity has been an enterprise of individuals, and with the development of industrialization responsibility for the satisfaction of wants for these things has continued largely in the hands of private individuals. The provision of government, and the development of laws regulating the human enterprise, have been so fraught with difficulty, and so subject to exploitation of people and interference with human liberties, that man has come to respect the producer and suspect the governor. Despite the achievement of ample production and the development of checks and balances in government, we are still reluctant or, at least, hesitant to trust too far our welfare to the ministrations of government. This situation has led to curious imbalances. In a society with tremendous wealth, not only in the basic necessities, but also in other goods less and less central to fundamental human needs, we have often neglected, undernourished, or restricted the service and welfare activities provided by government, and in many cases by other nonproducers in society. The head of an industry producing the most frivolous or marginally necessary goods is rewarded far more generously than the head of a major governmental agency providing an essential service. By now, everyone knows that teachers are underpaid. Despite all protestations about the growth of the welfare state, we still give our greatest rewards to the businessman, the producer.

Our citizens enjoy an unbelievable variety of goods in the midst of strikingly inadequate social conditions.

The family which takes its mauve and cerise, air-conditioned, power-steered, and power-braked automobile out for a tour passes through cities that are badly paved, made hideous by litter, blighted buildings, billboards, and posts for wires that should long since have been put underground. They pass on into a countryside that has been rendered largely invisible by commercial art. (The goods which the latter advertise have an absolute priority in our value system. Such aesthetic considerations as a view of the countryside accordingly come second. On such matters we are consistent.) They picnic on exquisitely packaged food from a portable ice box by a polluted stream and go on to spend the night at a park which is a menace to public health and morals. Just before dozing off on an air mattress, beneath a nylon tent, amid the stench of decaying refuse, they may reflect vaguely on the curious unevenness of their blessings. Is this, indeed, the American genius? (Galbraith, 1958, p. 253).

MENTAL ILLNESS AND MENTAL HEALTH

Another project of the Joint Commission on Mental Illness and Health (Jahoda, 1958) has examined the requirements of a definition of mental health. The reader is referred to that report for a detailed discussion of the problems of definition.

We should look briefly, however, at this subject because it determines who shall be considered to be relevant manpower in the field of mental health.

The definition of mental illness is not especially difficult, though a number of problems need to be considered in certain peripheral areas of breakdown in normal human behavior. Ordinarily, we think of mental illness as an unusually persistent pattern of behavior over which the individual has little or no voluntary control; it differentiates him from his fellows; it incapacitates him; it interferes with his normal participation in life. The mentally ill individual often is caught in the grip of forces making him dangerous to himself or to others. In the milder case he may simply be unable to compete in the normal struggle for the satisfaction of his needs, and in the extreme case he may be unaware of himself and his surroundings and may be driven to acts which society finds incomprehensible and strange beyond belief.

Although mental illness has been recognized and described by writers throughout history, there were no real institutions for the care of people with mental disorders until sometime around 1800. The deranged were driven from place to place, locked in dungeons, and often left to starve or to die from exposure. Occasionally lone voices spoke out on behalf of these unfortunate people, but it was not until the end of the eighteenth century, when the French psychiatrist Philippe Pinel struck off their chains and brought them into the light, that any real concern was exhibited for their care or for the study of the causes of their condition. Progress has been slow until very recently and many of the old attitudes toward mental illness—fear, horror, and disgrace—still persist.

The large "insane asylums" that grew up to house the mentally disordered in the nineteenth century and the early years of this century too often have been looked upon with fear and distaste. Their very names have long been used to frighten children into obedience.

During the past seventy-five years progress has been made toward the understanding, description, and classification of mental illnesses. Although the older attitudes still persist, many believe that we are on the verge of tremendous discoveries which will go far to eliminate or prevent this age-old scourge.

Mental health is the positive side of the problem. Not only must our society be concerned with understanding and dealing with the problem of mental illness, but also it must become increasingly self-conscious about the positive mental welfare of its citizens.

We recognize that good mental health requires, in addition to the satisfaction of basic biological needs, as much freedom as possible from the unpredictable, capricious, and devastating blows of circumstance. To be mentally healthy, the human being requires a certain measure of both personal and extrinsic security, freedom from the threats of the devastation of war, depression, plague, and flood. He requires the positive rewards of appreciation, achievement, and self-realization. He needs some assurance that fate will not deal him an unexpected blow, plus the internal strength to survive such a blow if it falls and adaptability to avoid a second one if possible. He has come, in many parts of the civilized world, to expect education for his children, spiritual support from his religion, and protection from his government.

With the increased leisure time he has won, as a result of increasing productive efficiency, institutions and professions have come into existence which help to insure him against catastrophe and which help him achieve positive development of his interests and abilities.

The mental health professions, with which we will be chiefly concerned in this report, are psychiatry, psychology, social work, and psychiatric nursing.

These professions are of central importance to all those social institutions which have evolved to help the mentally disordered; to offer assistance to the needy, the inadequate, the incapacitated, and the unfortunate; to study the causes and the amelioration of suffering due to emotional disturbance; and to provide resources for research into all the complex problems of causation, treatment, and prevention of these disorders.

Kenneth E. Appel (1957, p. 363), 1954 president of the American Psychiatric Association, has defined mental health as ". . . the ability of people to meet and handle problems; to make choices and decisions; to find satisfaction in accepting tasks; to do jobs without avoiding them and without pushing them onto others; to carry on without undue dependency on others; to live effectively and satisfactorily with others without crippling complications; to contribute one's share in life; to enjoy life and to be able to love and be loved." He goes on to point out that "mental illness is the opposite side of the coin of mental health."

Many more than our four professional disciplines are involved in helping members of society to achieve mental health and to avoid or overcome mental illness. We will attempt to mention some of these other groups as we proceed to discuss manpower in mental health.

Detailed definition and discussion of our four mental health professions will be presented in succeeding chapters.

OVERVIEW OF MANPOWER SHORTAGES

Increasingly, there are signs that our society is ready to face the fact that a serious manpower crisis exists in a large number of specialized fields. Everything has been coming so easy for us for so long that, until recently, we have failed to notice that our system of education, upon which rests most of the achievement of our high standard of living, has been steadily changing its function in a direction that leads away from its original task of training the minds of our young in knowledge and its applications, and in techniques for the discovery of further knowledge.

Our society has grown so used to such a great variety of goods and services, to such a high level of technical productivity, and to the expectation of ready satisfaction of many of our health and welfare needs, that we have taken all of these blessings for granted. The time has now come for our discovery that such achievements do not occur by themselves, but are largely based on the effectively trained intelligence of our nation's brainpower.

The field of mental health faces a real manpower crisis. This seems paradoxical in view of the fact that our nation has many more trained mental health personnel per capita than any other nation in the world. Professional mental health services are available in some form to most of our citizens.

Shortages in many areas of living are largely a matter of aspiration. To the hungry man, there is only one shortage. To the society living on the verge of starvation, mental health personnel are a luxury far down its list of priorities. But in the industrial societies that have developed in Europe and the New World in the last century, services of many kinds have become important daily needs.

In a country with serious and widespread disease, whether it be malaria, yaws, tuberculosis, or typhoid fever, few voices are raised to demand that more psychiatrists be trained. But as, one by one, the plagues of mankind have been controlled in the West, the plague of mental disorder has been increasingly exposed to public view. Mental disorder is not an important cause of death. No one dies of schizophrenia. Schizophrenics die of pneumonia or of tuberculosis or of malnutrition or some other cause. While mental disorder is not an important cause of death, it is, in our society, the most important source of human incapacity and of manpower loss to the nation. Manpower in the mental health professions is insufficient to meet our society's current needs and demands. The prospect for the future, we shall see, is for more shortages.

WHAT IS A PROFESSION?

Much of the content of this report will be concerned with an examination of manpower trends in the mental health professions. We will look at the need for trained mental health personnel, at the present supply of people with special training in the field of mental health, and at the probable future supply of these people as they complete their specialized training and are prepared for work in the mental health field.

Although our preoccupation will be with mental health professional personnel, it may be useful to look for a moment at the origins and characteristics of professions in general. Over the years there have evolved numerous professions whose existence attests to the presence of a number of fairly definite social needs. Professions have identifiable characteristics, and one of the most obvious of these is that they satisfy existing social needs.

There are several accounts of the probable beginnings of the professions. Most social historians see them emerging out of the needs of primitive society for the discovery and transmission of knowledge about the world and for the explanation of natural phenomena. It is clear that the first criterion of all professions is knowledge.

Egyptian priest-astronomers, keeping a constant vigil in their temples, may have been one of the first organized groups to discover the power of knowledge. Having time on their hands, especially at night, and watching the stars in transit across the heavens, it is likely that such observation led to knowledge of seasonal fluctuations. By observing the coincidence of the juxtaposition of certain stars and the annual flood of the Nile, powerful knowledge became available to these priest-astronomers. To be able to predict floods in advance was to have knowledge of use to the layman but inaccessible to him.

This oft-quoted example of the beginning of a professional class in Egypt may be romance, but its point is clear. It illustrates one of the most important characteristics of any profession, namely, the possession of special knowledge useful to members of society.

In the present century a number of people have devoted much time and study to the sociology of professions. Abraham Flexner, who led the program for the extensive revision and improvement of medical education in the United States during the early part of the present century, wrote a great deal about his perspective on professions. In describing the characteristics of professions, Flexner (1915) stressed the intellectual nature of professional activities, their dependence on science and learning, and the necessary limitation in their scope and purpose. He pointed out that any profession, to be dignified by this designation, must have an intellectual or theoretical content which sets it apart from occupations whose principal special requirement is a motor skill or technique. As professions grow and develop, they solidify their intellectual content in such form that it can be taught to neophytes. A profession gradually becomes self-organizing, and strong in-group feelings develop among members of the same profession. A subculture forms, with its own symbols, values, and norms of behavior. Controlled entry into the profession is largely vested in the hands of leaders of the group so that neophytes are chosen with care and instructed into the mysteries of the special knowledge of the group.

Ernest Greenwood (1957) has built his approach to the nature of professions on the work of Flexner and of other more recent theorists. Greenwood stresses the importance of systematic theory and points out that whenever a group attempts to achieve the status of a profession it moves to an academic setting. While neophytes may be given special on-the-job training, much of their instruction is rooted in theory and in knowledge which can be taught only in the university. The importance of theory is apparent from the constant preoccupation of professionals with adding to their conceptualizations and with sharing pertinent discoveries. This sharing usually is accomplished by the publication of scientific and professional journals, by frequent meetings of members of the group to discuss new discoveries, by the recognized importance of refresher courses, and by other means whereby members of the group can be brought up to date on theoretical developments. The heroes of the profession are those who have added to the profession's theory. The attitude toward theory is usually critical rather than worshipful, and a constant attempt is made at improvement and refinement. All of this implies the importance of longer and longer curricula as part of the training of the neophyte, because members of the group come to believe the importance of theory is such that all details must be clear to the neophyte before he can be allowed to practice the skills or techniques involved in the profession. It is rare that a professional group will acquiesce to the suggestion that certain courses, or areas of knowledge, be deleted from the training of fledgling members of the group. We constantly witness an extension and broadening of professional training programs.

Another characteristic of professions differentiating them from other kinds of service occupations, in Greenwood's analysis, is the relative privacy and uniqueness of the knowledge and skills of the professional. This means that, in general, members of the public accept on faith the ability of the professional person to perform the service required. The general public, whatever its other special competences, has relatively little choice in the nature of the service received from the professional. The belief is accepted on both sides that the layman is unable to appraise or diagnose his own needs and therefore must rely on the appraisal or diagnosis of the specialist. In general, the layman comes to the professional with a willingness to put his welfare in the professional's hands. Because a client does not have the special knowledge necessary to evaluate the service rendered, there grows up a tradition that all professional service is competent, though perhaps one may be more competent than another. The professional in turn is expected to take an objective attitude toward the layman coming to him for service and certainly must not get personal gratification out of the relationship beyond the normal satisfaction of providing service and receiving his fee.

Because of the power over human welfare involved in the professional relationship, professional groups often seek the sanction of the community for their members to practice. Sometimes it is society that asks for certification of competence. This sanction or certification usually restricts the right of untrained people to use the name of the profession or to hold themselves as able to perform the services of the profession. Other forms of acceptance are sought from the community. The right to establish training centers and to accredit educational programs is asked of the community by professional groups in order to prevent unscrupulous or misinformed people from establishing short-cut training courses which leave out the theory so essential to professional training.

In seeking concessions from the community the professions generally take it upon themselves to police their own membership in such a way that no question will be raised about the public-spirited and public-protective nature of their activities. In the process of taking over this police power, professions develop ethical codes which are aimed at insuring the availability of competent service to members of the public irrespective to the public's ability to pay. Ethical codes also insure that new knowledge is immediately made available to all members of the group as soon as it has been shown to be valid, but prohibit the too early dissemination or use of techniques of questionable value.

In all this group activity, strong loyalties develop within the group and a special language grows up enabling the members to communicate with each other without revealing clearly their meaning to outsiders. The notion of the "career," a whole life of service in the particular profession, is held up as a model and is useful in recruiting neophytes into the professional culture.

All of these characteristics of professions are true, in varying degree, of the mental health professions. In considering trends and numbers of people available for work in the field of mental health most of our discussion will be oriented toward the mental health professions, though it will also be necessary to examine manpower trends in groups that do not fulfill the requirements of a profession.

At first thought it might seem possible to relieve the shortage of professional people by simply shortening training programs and by recruiting more students into the field through financial inducements. It will be clear from the complex nature of the professions and from the effect of this complex structure on the selection of applicants, and on the length of training, that such simple solutions to the problem of professional shortages are highly unrealistic.

CRITERIA FOR RECOGNIZING SHORTAGES

The National Manpower Council (1957, pp. 255 ff.) notes that shortages of skilled manpower may be viewed in at least three ways. One view focuses on the demands of a dynamic economy, with proliferating technical and scientific advances; the second view emphasizes the demands of a nation's people for more and better services and security, particularly in the areas of health and education; and a third view sees manpower shortages as road blocks to be overcome, standing in the way of society's objectives.

Shortages in one field cannot be viewed in isolation. There is ample evidence that the more technical, the more skilled, and the more complex the job, the greater our present and projected future personnel shortages for the occupational group trained to work at the job. United States Department of Labor data show clearly that shortages over the next ten years will be most severe in the professional and technical groups. A numerical increase in these categories of more than 33 per cent will be needed by 1965. Conversely, the number of unskilled jobs will decline some 3 per cent and the number of jobs for farmers and farm workers will decline more than 15 per cent by 1965.

What criteria may be used to determine whether shortages in any field actually do exist? The National Manpower Council lists a number of indices that have general applicability (1957).

The first of these is *an upward movement in wages or salaries*. Theoretically, when demand exceeds supply in any commodity, the result in a free market is an increase in price of the commodity. This does not always hold for manpower as witnessed by the relatively poor salaries offered nurses, teachers, college faculty members, social workers, and state mental hospital personnel, all of whom are in short supply. Even in engineering there are data showing that, although starting salaries are somewhat higher than the starting salaries of college graduates in general, this advantage is lost for engineers employed five years when this latter group is compared with others five years beyond college. Salary changes are slower, of course, in public or nonprofit institutions where many mental health professional people are employed. Furthermore, improvements in salaries in recent years have been quickly erased by inflation.

A second index is the *existence of demonstrated social need*. This criterion often implies the determination of some minimum number of personnel required to meet a standard. Shortages are then indicated by the number of trained people needed to reach this minimum. Many examples exist in the mental health field. Probably the best known standard of this sort is that devised by the American Psychiatric Association as a guide to staff needs of mental hospitals.

A third index of a shortage is the *existence of unfilled, budgeted positions in public and nonprofit enterprises.* There is little doubt about the meaningfulness of this criterion. In general, the creation of such job openings is subject to several stages of official scrutiny so that the existence of large numbers of unfilled jobs for which public funds are already available usually is a clear indication of personnel shortages. A number of studies are available which describe the existence of budgeted job vacancies in all of the professional fields in mental health.

Training requirements, or other qualitative factors, are a fourth indicator. Shortages are said to exist when vacancies are filled by persons who have not had the training judged necessary by boards or evaluation groups concerned with training standards. Many positions in social work and in clinical psychology, for example, are filled by untrained or inadequately trained personnel according to professional criteria set by the respective professional groups. Many physicians employed as psychiatrists in State mental hospitals do not meet the requirements for certification of the American Board in Psychiatry and Neurology. Many nurses in administrative or teaching positions do not have advanced professional training frequently judged essential by the nursing profession.

A fifth criterion is the *difficulties in filling specialist billets in the Armed Forces*. This criterion is similar to the third. It also applies to the inability of branches of the Armed Services to find research and development personnel in sufficient numbers to carry out programs for which funds are available. There have been occasions in recent years when more research funds were available than were spent in highly technical areas where trained mental health personnel are in short supply.

The last criterion, recently much in the public eye, is a *comparison with other countries*. The National Manpower Council points out that a recent yardstick for assaying shortages has been the use of data on numbers of people being trained in the various scientific and professional fields in the Soviet Union. The fact of substantial increases in the number of engineers, scientists, and physicians being trained in the U.S.S.R. has been used to point up the failure of our country to realize its intellectual potential in education.

In the course of our study of mental health manpower we will frequently refer back to these criteria. Let us examine them now in some detail.

Inflation and Professional Salaries.

Since 1940 the real income of nearly all employed persons has increased appreciably. Two exceptions are salaried civil employees, including large numbers of professional mental health personnel, and college faculty members. From 1940 to 1956 our industrial workers increased their real income, before taxes, by some 64 per cent. During this same period the real income of physicians increased 96 per cent and of lawyers 29 per cent. From 1940 to 1954 the real income of faculty members decreased 5 per cent. In the last couple of years there has been a massive effort to raise faculty salaries, as evidenced by the Ford Foundation grant and by local drives. Still, the improvement in real income of faculty members' salaries over 1940 is only 12 per cent in contrast to the gains indicated above. Meanwhile, in Russia, faculty members of educational institutions are singled out for special incentives, and the standard of living of this group exceeds that of most other groups.

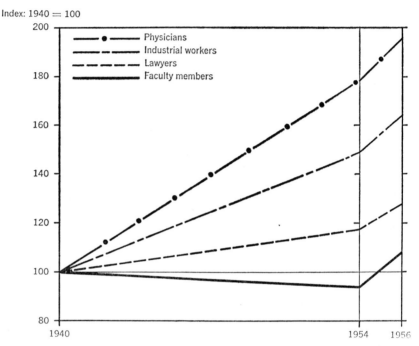

FIG. 3.—*Changes in real income before taxes, 1940–1956.*

Source: Business aid to our colleges and universities. (Undated pamphlet.) McGraw-Hill.

It is important to realize that the competence, vigor, and number of *future* scientific and professional manpower is dependent largely on the quality of their education. Yet as we shall see later one of the most serious problems we face is the declining quality of academic faculties whose job it is to train the next professional generation.

"In a free market, in an age of endemic inflation, it is unquestionably more rewarding, in purely pecuniary terms, to be a speculator or a prostitute than a teacher, preacher, or policeman," Galbraith notes (1958, p. 223).

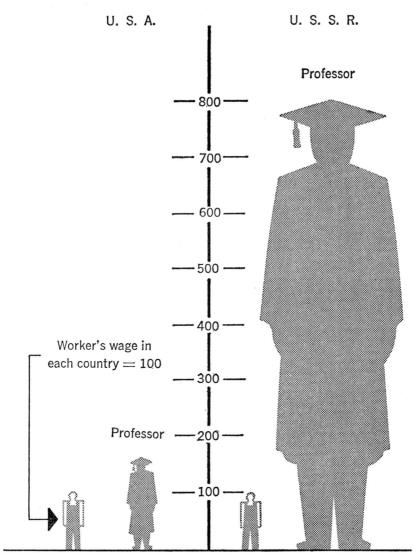

FIG. 4.—*In the field of education . . . who are today's capitalists?*

Source: In the field of education . . . who are today's capitalists? (Undated pamphlet.) McGraw-Hill.

For a number of years, the United States has been in the midst of a steady inflationary spiral. The rise in the cost of living has gone on month by month and year by year steadily undermining the purchasing power of the dollar. People on the fixed salaries of public agencies and institutions, pensioners, and others with fixed income, are the ones who suffer most from inflation. As Galbraith has shown, it is the public services that deteriorate most in the years of inflation.

"Nothing so weakens government," Galbraith (p. 266) says, "as persistent inflation. The public administration of France for many years, of Italy until recent times, and of other European and numerous South American countries have been deeply sapped and eroded by the effects of long-continued inflation."

Of course, as noted above, not all professional people suffer from inflation. Those who control their own fees and prices are able to adjust them to changes in the value of money. Psychiatrists, all physicians, lawyers, and other self-employed professionals who are in private practice, suffer less from inflation than do those who are on the fixed salaries of public agencies and institutions.

"In 1942 a grateful and very anxious citizenry rewarded its soldiers, sailors, and airmen with a substantial increase in pay," Galbraith recalls (p. 222). "In the teeming city of Honolulu, in prompt response to this advance in wage income, the prostitutes raised the prices of their services. This was at a time when, if anything, increased volume was causing a reduction in their average unit costs."

Any current figures on income for professional mental health workers, or for any other occupational group, are meaningful for only a very short time. Because we are in the midst of a continuing inflationary cycle the salaries earned ten years ago, five years ago, or even more recently, have an unreal appearance when read in the context of present earnings.

This is not to suggest that there has been any runaway increase in the salaries of professional workers, though undoubtedly they have increased as has the cost of living in general. Unfortunately, large numbers of professional persons who are on salaries do not find that the salaries increase as rapidly as the cost of living.

The point to be emphasized here is that figures cited for median earnings rapidly become meaningless. A better procedure would be to contrast the various professional groups on some sort of rank-order scale at any particular moment in time. Necessary data for this kind of presentation are not readily available though a few attempts are made later in our report.

According to the U.S. Department of Labor (1957, p. 44), the median income of all full-time workers over fourteen years of age in the year 1955 was $3801. This figure includes all the income of those who were employed full-time. There was a significant difference between men and women. The median earnings of full-time male workers was $4252 while the median earnings of full-time working women was $2719.

Now let us look at the earnings of some professional groups against this median standard to see if we can find evidence of the operation of supply and demand.

Information on the earnings of nurses varies in completeness and accuracy. There is marked variability from one part of the country to another. There are also differences in earnings between general duty nurses who have been trained in hospital-diploma programs and those professional nurses, many in teaching and administration, who have completed college training programs. A report by the Women's Bureau of the United States Department of Labor (by that Bureau together with the National Vocational Guidance Association in a survey of women college graduates in 1955) found that professional nurses averaged $3438 annually. In 1949 median earnings were $2127 (Perrott and Pennell, 1957, p. 11).

The mean net income of general physicians in 1951 was $12,500 a year, and in 1955 was $15,000. The earnings of psychiatrists were reported to be $17,300 in 1951 (Croatman, 1957).

According to the Bureau of Labor Statistics, beginning salaries of psychologists in 1956 were at approximately $5000 for new Ph.D.'s. A survey by the American Psychological Association in 1954 found the median earnings of all psychologists to be $6400. In 1949, median earnings had been $3572 according to Perrott and Pennell (1957, p. 11).

In social work, graduates of professional social work schools without previous experience were offered in 1955 a median salary of $3600. In many metropolitan areas the median annual salary of social workers who had completed their graduate training was approximately $4400, according to the Bureau of Labor Statistics (1957, p. 195). Social workers employed by the Federal government begin at $4525, after completion of social work school; those with two years of additional experience begin at $5440. Administrators in social agencies frequently earn much higher salaries.

Witte (1956) found a 35 per cent increase in the salary of the basic practitioner position in social work in public agencies between 1950 and 1954. But the median salary in 1954, at this level, was only $2760. Many of these workers were not graduate social workers, but significant numbers were college graduates.

According to the Bureau of Labor Statistics women graduating from college in June 1955, who were teaching in the elementary schools in 1956 earned an average annual salary of $3242. The Bureau estimates the average salary for all elementary teachers to be $3800 in 1955–1956. Teachers' salaries are generally lower in rural areas and higher in metropolitan areas.

According to the Bureau, secondary-school teachers had an average annual salary of approximately $4350 in 1955–1956. In some states the median salary was much lower and in some much higher.

A recent study (Tickton, Sidney G., 1957) gives some estimates of salaries in 1956 in several rehabilitation occupations and contrasts these salaries with earnings in a variety of railroad and industrial occupations (Table 1).

Tickton (pp. 12, 13) concludes:

The commanding fact which emerges from our research is this: the salaries today offered trained professional personnel in rehabilitation are inadequate. They compare unfavorably to salaries in comparable fields. They compare unfavorably with salaries for work which requires less training and responsibility. . . . Unless action is taken soon, our country will suffer from the consequences of an inadequate supply of professionally trained people in rehabilitation. By "an inadequate supply," we mean an insufficiency of trained people who can rehabilitate the thousands of handicapped Americans who *can* be trained and returned to work as self-sustaining citizens.

It is wasteful for the nation to neglect the human resources which are all around us.

Salaries of college and university faculty members vary with the type of institution and with the academic rank. According to a survey of the National Education Association the median salary for nine months of full-time teaching in 1955–1956 was $5243 for all ranks at all colleges and universities. Salaries ranged from an average of approximately $4000 for full-time instructors to an average of $7000 for full-time professors. The lowest salaries were paid by small non-public colleges and the highest by municipal universities, with the exception of some wealthy private universities.

In general, earnings are higher for those persons who are self-employed in contrast to those who are on salary; earnings are higher for those employed in private agencies in contrast to public agencies; earnings are higher for the more highly educated professional person and for those with experience; earnings are higher for men or for those professions predominantly male, and especially in urban areas; earnings are higher for those members of the profession who are specialized in contrast to those who are only generally prepared for employment.

Although earnings have increased for professional people in mental health, the increase has not been such as to be a clear-cut index of shortages, largely because of the complicating factors we have noted. Other professional groups in short supply have also improved their earnings in about the same amount in recent years, barely holding their own against inflation.

Severity of the Problem of Mental Disorder.

An estimate compiled by the Joint Commission's group studying patient care provides a quantitative estimate of the problem of mental illness:

One million seriously disturbed people are treated each year in the mental hospitals in the United States. Nearly as many more persons are treated in mental hygiene clinics, in other social agencies, and by private professional personnel. The total under treatment each year is 1,814,000.

It is estimated that, in any one year, some 10 per cent of the citizens of the United States need help with problems of an emotional sort (Commission on Chronic Illness, 1957).

Studies of army personnel indicate that mental disorders are the number one cause of disability separation, the fourth leading cause of noneffectiveness, and the eighth leading cause of referrals for medical treatment.

Half of the total number of hospital beds in the United States are occupied by mental patients.

The increase in mental disorder requiring hospitalization has grown faster than the increase in the general population over the last score of years. While the number of older persons in the general population has rapidly increased, the increase in hospitalized mental patients sixty years of age or older has been still greater.

On the other hand, as Daniel Blain points out, this phenomenon requires careful interpretation, for it may reflect increased utilization of mental hospitals more than any actual increase in mental disorders. Where more hospitals and beds have been built, there has been an increase in hospitalized patients, but in some states that have not expanded facilities, there has been no increase.

Once a person has been admitted to a mental hospital his chances of being released decrease precipitously as the length of time he has been in the hospital stretches out. According to data from the National Institute of Mental Health, the probability of a person's being released alive from a mental hospital decreases from an even bet, over all, during the first year to five-to-one odds against him in the second year. After five years the odds are ninety-nine to one against the patient. In the best mental hospitals, of course, as many as 50 per cent may be discharged in three months, and the rate for the first year may run as high as 75 to 90 per cent.

One of the more discouraging aspects of the problem of mental illness is its chronicity. Although half of the total number of hospital beds in the United States are occupied by mental patients, it is important to realize that this is not the same thing as saying that half of all the hospital patients in the country each year are mental patients. Turnover is rapid among most general hospital patients. Turnover is not rapid in mental hospitals. According to the National Institute of Mental Health, 40 per cent of the patients in State mental hospitals has been there ten years or more and 60 per cent of the resident population has been in the hospital for five years or more.

Some of these facts are illustrated by data in Tables 2, 3, 4, 5, and 6 in the Appendix.

Public concern about mental disorder is surprisingly mild. One important reason, as noted briefly above, for this lack of widespread concern is the fact that relatively few people ever die of mental disorder. The fact that half of the population of our mental hospitals is diagnosed schizophrenic, and the fact that this disorder accounts for a staggering number of man-days lost to industry, and a staggering total of tax dollars lost to government, does not alter the fact that when a schizophrenic dies the cause is heart disease, cancer, infectious disease, an accident, or some other disorder. We have heard a great deal about diseases that carry the label "No. 1 Killer," or "No. 4 Killer." But mental disease is hardly a killer at all. It is a torturer and a jailer, but not a killer.

Another likely reason for the lack of widespread public concern about mental disorder is the lack of visibility of most mental patients. Mental patients are easily removed from society and usually they are taken to a place some distance from society's main thoroughfares. Those psychotics who stay in the community generally are confined by circumstance to the diseased center of the city—to skid row, and to the cheap rooming-house belt surrounding downtown. Few molders of public opinion venture into these neighborhoods. Recent evidence (Hollingshead and Redlich, 1958) indicates that schizophrenia is several times more common in the have-not lowest socio-economic class than among the more influential upper class. It is small wonder that the problem is not one that thrusts itself into the public consciousness with any great force. Poliomyelitis victims are visible reminders of the dread effects of this disease. Mental cases, far more common, are seen rarely. The United States has been spending far more per year per patient for research on polio, cancer, and tuberculosis than for research in mental disorder.

Another reason for our psychological blindness to the subject of mental disorder may be found in the relatively poor prognosis for many of these diseases. Despite the cyclical swing of optimistic and pessimistic reports, the fact remains that a great many mental patients do not recover or even ever approach normality.

Much currency has been given to the notion that normal people are threatened or somehow repelled by mental patients and therefore put them out of sight and mind. There is need for research about this subject because a great deal of other evidence indicates that actually the general public finds abnormality exceedingly curious, intriguing, and interesting. Of course, interest may be related to the amount of personal involvement.

Whatever the priority of these factors, the observation continues to be valid that there is no strong grass-roots movement to eliminate this scourge.

In many parts of the world, mental disorders are masked by more immediate and attention-demanding disorders. The tolling of the bell may easily be masked by a strident whistle. Until the whistle is somehow shut off the bell is not distinguishable.

Neurologists tell us that often one pain can mask another. Neurologists can demonstrate this fact by giving a patient temporary relief from a chronic pain by putting one of his unaffected limbs into a container of ice water. The discomfort of the cold masks temporarily the regular pain. In many parts of the world mental disorders are masked, or screened out, by more immediate preoccupations with more painful problems. Further, there is evidence that many of the sophisticated forms of neurosis are luxuries of civilization. Persons genuinely suffering from neurosis sometimes have had their symptoms disappear during the stress of semistarvation or during incarceration in concentration camps. It is probable that in many parts of the world where the average daily caloric intake is below 2200 calories (over 66 per cent of the world's peoples get as little as this to eat, according to Huxley, 1957), there is relatively little inclination to be preoccupied with feelings of inferiority or ennui. People who have for centuries suffered from the enervating affects of malaria are likely to be less sensitive than we are to neurasthenia. Cultures where children are afflicted with the scourge of kwashiorkor due to protein-deficient diets are likely not to worry too much about temper tantrums.

Social scientists are largely agreed that there is a hierarchy of human motives that rests on the solid base of those needs which must be satisfied to maintain life. Food, liquid, sleep, and reproduction are basic to life. So long as the needs for these are denied satisfaction, little attention will be paid to more abstract needs. So long, too, as our society's needs are synthesized in the mass media, the whistle will obscure the tolling of the bell.

This discussion suggests that mental disorders are primarily the concern of civilized nations. Undoubtedly this is true. Probably one of the best indices of a country's standard of living is the ratio of psychiatrists to population. This is not to say that psychiatry is a luxury but that there is time and energy left for a concern with mental disorders only where production has reached the point at which the needs that must be satisfied to maintain life are largely accounted for.

Still another complication must be noted, despite the dimness of its dimensions. This complication involves the problem of how to determine the true extent of the need for mental health services. We are beginning to suspect that this need increases as the availability of professional service increases. There are many cultures, even among the industrialized nations of the world, where mental health services are all but unavailable at a strictly professional level. The people of these nations have other ways of giving and receiving emotional first aid, or long-term help, through institutions which have been replaced in the United States by professional groups and public institutions. Fifty years ago, we had fewer psychiatrists and virtually no psychologists, social workers, or psychiatric nurses as we know them today, and yet the 93,000,000 people living then in the United States somehow managed to live and die without the help these people might have given them.

Economists are beginning to suspect that a demand for consumer goods and services increases as fast as, or even faster than, our ability to produce them. Indeed demand may be created by the production process. It is quite possible that some of the demand for mental health services is growing because the supply of professional people is growing, though the demand has grown faster than the supply. Ordinarily we think this process happens in the other direction, that more people are trained to meet a rising social need.

In any event, such speculation is no justification for denying the real need for mental health personnel. Nearly two million persons with serious mental illness are real. The mental health professions must also deal with many kinds of people with problems besides those in mental hospitals. The dimensions of the problems of mental deficiency, alcoholism, drug addiction, broken families, juvenile delinquency, and similar palpable social problems are too real to be denied by verbal hocus-pocus.

There is no easy way to assess the extent of the present shortages in the United States of trained personnel in the mental health professions. Estimates have been made for the separate professional groups and for specific areas of concern. These will be presented later in detail.

Increasingly, spokesmen for the mental health professions, or for mental health lay groups, or for foundations concerned with large social problems, speak out about "the problems of mental illness." Usually they quote figures and ratios. Somehow, in our present age, we have become bored with figures, or at least blasé about their import. Still, no one has found a better way to describe the enormousness of the problem we face. Most of us know by this time that of every ten babies born this year one will spend some part of his life in a mental institution, according to figures of the National Association for Mental Health (1954). We realize that the Federal government is spending more for the pensions and treatment costs of psychiatric casualties among veterans than all the States combined are spending on psychiatric cases among nonveterans, according to the Ford Foundation (1955). Mike Gorman (1956) tells us that the bill for the hospitalization of those of our citizens in State mental institutions, inadequate as this hospitalization is, amounts to as much as a third of the operating budget in some of our largest and wealthiest states. He indicates, too, that for each of our three-quarters of a million mental hospital patients, there is another serious case in the community requiring treatment.

Mental health professional personnel are needed in many areas besides mental hospitals. There are other social needs equally critical. Large numbers of seriously disturbed people, children and adults, could use direct help. If their number is to be decreased in future generations, a massive research approach to these problems is urgently required. One of every five young men entering the military service has a juvenile court record; at least four million of our citizens are chronic alcoholics, and even larger numbers are problem drinkers; untold numbers of our citizens are suffering from incapacitating neuroses or from physical illnesses that have strong emotional roots or components.

For the future we shall see that the picture is equally grim. The rapid increase in our population and the deterioration of our educational institutions in general mean that fewer professional people will be available in the future unless drastic steps are taken.

A survey of all of the different groups requiring the professional help of mental health workers is beyond the scope of this report. But let us look for a moment at some of the kinds of people who are not actually mentally ill in the usual definition, but who do require professional time.

One recent study estimates that three-quarters of a million children under twenty-one have some orthopedic handicap. Another estimate is that there are nearly three million persons between the ages of fourteen and sixty-four with long-term physical disabilities. There are over 300,000 blind persons in the United States and there are 175,000 totally deaf persons. Many of these people require some kind of social assistance for maximum adjustment.

There is a steady increase in the number of children born out of wedlock. In 1954, this number was guessed to be 176,000 or nearly 4.5 per cent of all live births (F. DelliQuadri, 1957). Social agencies are often concerned with this problem because of the frequent emotional and financial difficulties involved. DelliQuadri described a recent study in Milwaukee indicating that more than three-quarters of the unmarried mothers in that area received some sort of social work assistance.

Adoption is another major problem requiring the competence of trained social workers and psychologists. Nearly 100,000 children a year are adopted. Especially difficult cases requiring more than the usual agency efforts include the adoption of the handicapped child and the otherwise hard-to-place child.

In 1957, there were almost fifty million men and women over forty-five years of age. This represents about 30 per cent of our total population. Nearly fifteen million persons are sixty-five years of age or over, and this group is increasing by some 400,000 annually. There is a differential in life expectancy between men and women. The ratio is approximately 87 men to 100 women after age sixty-five. By 1975 there will be three million more older women than men. As our median age increases there are all sorts of demands made for professional personnel from geriatrists to family service case workers. Vocational problems, emotional and mental disorders, and adjustment problems in general, increase with advancing age.

The trends in crime statistics are frightening. Many people believe that mental health problems contribute to the crime rate and cite these statistics as further evidence that the demand for mental health services is increasing.

According to the Federal Bureau of Investigation (1958, p. 72) in their Uniform Crime Reports, ". . . crime at 56.2 per cent above the 1950 level is rising four times as fast as the total population (up 13 per cent since 1950)." The figures on crime in 1957 are the highest in history; more than 9 per cent above 1956 and nearly 24 per cent above the average of the past five years. In 1957 there was a 12 per cent increase in burglary over the year before and increases in every other category of crime except murder and nonnegligent manslaughter which were essentially the same as the year before.

A further area of concern to criminologists is the sharp increase in the incidence of crime among our young people. Again the FBI notes (p. 70): "Assuming that the reporting cities have experienced a similar population growth, it appears that the percentage increase in arrests of young people is two and one-half times the percentage growth of their population group." Two-thirds of all the arrests for auto thefts are among young persons under eighteen. More than half of all crimes against property are among this group.

In examining arrest reports of 1220 police departments, the FBI points out that, of slightly more than two million arrests, 12.3 per cent were of young people under 18. This young group, however, makes up 47 per cent of the arrests for so-called Part One crimes

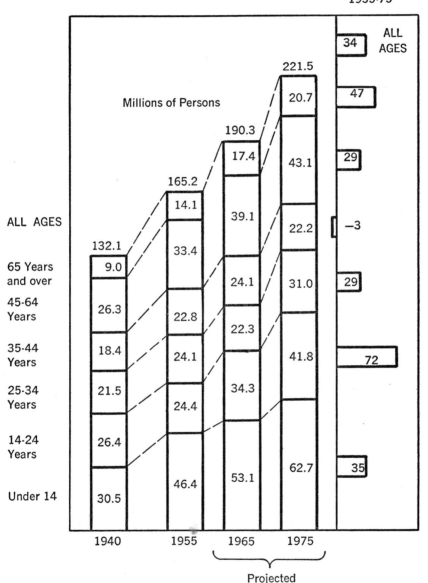

FIG. 5.—*Population changes by age groups.*

Source: U.S. Department of Labor, Bureau of Labor Statistics, 1957. *Occupational outlook handbook.* Government Printing Office, p. 16.

(murder and nonnegligent manslaughter, negligent manslaughter, rape, robbery, aggravated assault, burglary-breaking or entering, larceny-theft and auto theft).

Few will argue that the rise in criminal behavior, and especially its increase among our young people, is anything but alarming. Needed are improved recreational facilities, counselors and school psychologists in the elementary and secondary grades, expanded social service programs in both public and private agencies, trained probation officers, residential and out-patient treatment centers, and community clinics. More basic is the need for research investigations into the social conditions and injustices which are part of the roots of criminal behavior.

There are approximately 230 State and Federal institutions for adult offenders in the United States. There are, in addition, some 3000 jails and workhouses. In 1954 there were 183,000 prisoners in State and Federal prisons. Nearly 80,000 persons were sent to prison in 1954 and in that year less than 75,000 were released. There is a steady trend toward prison overcrowding due to longer commitments and decreased releases. Recent prison riots and self-mutilation by prisoners serve as reminders that all is not well.

Problems of parole and probation require the most able and skillful professional handling. Here is another area in which a professional group having real responsibility for mental health faces serious manpower shortages.

The World Health Organization (1952) estimates that there are something more than four and a half million alcoholics in the United States. About five and a half times as many men as women are alcoholic. Another estimate has approximately 4400 alcoholics per 100,000 population. The rate of alcoholism has been rising rapidly, increasing some 44 per cent since 1940. Because alcoholics are so often such poor therapeutic risks, and because social attitudes about alchoholism are not often compassionate, very few treatment centers are available for these people. There is a desperate need for more research and more professional therapeutic personnel in this field.

Nearly two million persons were eliminated from service in World

War II because of emotional difficulties. There are 50,000 narcotic addicts in the United States. More than a quarter of a million children are on the books of the juvenile courts each year. There are 400,000 divorces each year. More than two million serious crimes are committed each year. We do not maintain, of course, that divorce and crime are essentially or wholly expressions of mental illness, yet mental health is often involved, most would concede.

Let us return for a moment to consider the extent of serious mental disease. In round numbers, about one million patients are treated each year in our mental hospitals. At any one time three-quarters of a million persons are patients in these hospitals.

The cost of mental illness is staggering. In the Joint Commission's study of the economics of mental illness, Rashi Fein (1958) estimates the direct costs of mental illness in the United States to be more than $1.7 billion a year and the indirect costs to be $700 million a year. Fein shows that these are hard figures—in fact, underestimates—based on calculable costs only. Including these figures and making minimal allowances for certain items that cannot be reliably estimated, Jack R. Ewalt states that it is safe to assume that the direct and indirect costs of mental illness exceed $3 billion a year. Efforts to alleviate this drain on our resources are trifling. We spend a hundred million dollars a year for agricultural research, close to two hundred million dollars for medical research, and something like twenty million dollars for mental health research.

Mental Patients in Public Mental Institutions.

During 1957 the Joint Information Service of the American Psychiatric Association and the National Association for Mental Health (1958) found that expenditures per patient in State mental institutions had increased on the average by more than 10 per cent. During this period the consumer price index increased by only 3 per cent so these figures suggest that there was an appreciable gain during 1957 over the previous year. In terms of actual money spent, however, there is a long way to go. Expenditures in 1957 by states averaged $3.64 per patient, an increase from $3.27 in 1956. But at the same time 1957 expenditures in Veterans Administration mental hospitals were $10.31 per day per patient.

Another source (*Public Health Reports,* January, 1957) reports 1956 expenditures averaged $3.18 per patient in public mental hospitals. Table 7 lists the states in order of expenditure.

The Veterans Administration mental hospitals had an average of 71.4 employees per 100 patients in 1957 in comparison with 29.4 per 100 patients for the other mental hospitals in the United States.

Federal Mental Hospitals.

There were 428 Federal hospitals in 1955. Of the total, 161 were armed services hospitals; 173 were VA hospitals; sixty-five were U.S.P.H.S. hospitals; and twenty-nine were classified as "Other." All of the armed service hospitals were general hospitals. There were forty-one psychiatric VA hospitals, two psychiatric U.S.P.H.S. hospitals, and one "Other" psychiatric hospital serving the District of Columbia.

A larger proportion of Federal hospitals than both public and private non-Federal hospitals are devoted to psychiatric treatment. Slightly more than 10 per cent of all Federal hospitals are classified as psychiatric as compared to 8 per cent of non-Federal hospitals. This difference is even more impressive when we realize that almost 40 per cent of all Federal hospitals are general military hospitals. If we look at VA hospitals alone we find that nearly one-quarter of the VA hospitals are for psychiatric patients.

Although the proportionate number of psychiatric hospitals is higher in Federal than in non-Federal systems, the percentage of psychiatric beds in Federal psychiatric hospitals is smaller. About 50 of every 100 beds in non-Federal hospitals are in mental hospitals. In all Federal hospitals 36 of every 100 beds are in mental hospitals. Taking VA hospitals alone, we find that 48 out of every 100 beds are in psychiatric hospitals.

The proportion of mental patients in Federal mental hospitals is smaller also. Some 56 per cent of all the patients in non-Federal hospitals are in mental hospitals. The comparable percentages for all Federal hospitals, and for VA hospitals alone, are 50 per cent and 40 per cent respectively.

In judging the quality of a mental hospital, one important criterion is the turnover rate. We do not have any nationwide figures on the turnover rate as such, but to a large degree it can be inferred by comparing the average daily population with admissions during the year. As the annual increase in the average daily census is slight, the admission rate is a valid index of turnover. In all non-Federal psychiatric hospitals the admission rate is 46 per cent of the average daily census. In Federal psychiatric hospitals it is 70 per cent, and in VA hospitals alone it is 72 per cent. In non-Federal hospitals 1.6 per cent of all the patients admitted during a year are admitted to psychiatric hospitals. The comparable figures for the Federal hospitals, and for the VA hospitals alone, are 3.1 per cent and 8.1 per cent. It appears, therefore, that the Federal mental hospitals, especially those under the VA, have a higher patient turnover rate than the non-Federal mental hospitals.

At least half a million patients were admitted during 1956 to slightly more than 1100 mental hospitals, institutions, or services in the United States. At the end of the year about 7000 fewer patients were actually resident in the hospitals, the first time that the endless increase was reversed, giving hope that continued intensive efforts, and new therapeutic drugs and techniques, might bear fruit in the continuing struggle against mental disease.

Budgeted Vacancies in Non-Federal Public Mental Hospitals.

What is the present need for personnel in our non-Federal public mental hospitals? Detailed data are presented in Tables 8 through 13 in the Appendix.

At first view the situation does not look too serious. For every 1000 positions available, only sixty-eight were reported unfilled as of June 30, 1956. (These data are adapted from a study of the Council of State Governments, 1957, and from unpublished data supplied by the Biometrics Branch, National Institute of Mental Health.)

When we examine the number of vacancies for separate occupational groups, however, we find that a very high proportion of the vacancies are in the professional categories in contrast to the non-professional and maintenance personnel of the institutions.

Of slightly over 3000 available positions for physicians in State and county hospitals nearly one quarter (23.4%) were unfilled. A similar proportion of psychologists' positions were unfilled. Vacancies for psychiatric social workers and for registered professional nurses both ran to about 20 per cent of available positions. Some 15 per cent of positions for special therapists were vacant. These data are reported in detail in Tables 8 through 13.

The situation was better for the positions for nonprofessional workers. Of 3539 jobs available for nonregistered nurses (including student nurses) some 10 per cent were vacant. Only 4 per cent of nearly 70,000 jobs available for attendants and aides were vacant (Table 11).

If we count vacancies for all personnel having contact with patients we find that there are actually more reported vacancies for professional than for nonprofessional people. Nearly 21 per cent of professional jobs are vacant, numbering some 3500 vacancies. Only 4 per cent of nonprofessional jobs are reported vacant, numbering some 3100 vacancies. (The reader should remember that there are four to five times as many nonprofessional positions as professional positions in our public hospitals.)

There is a direct relationship between the amount of training required for a position and the proportion of vacancies existing in the position-category in our public mental hospitals.

The positions of physician and psychologist require the greatest amount of training. Shortages are most severe in these two groups. The positions that require the least amount of training (nonregistered nurse and attendant) are the easiest to fill. The middle groups, in the amount of training required (registered nurse, psychiatric social worker, and special therapist) are also between the extremes in percentage of vacancies.

It also is interesting to compare the vacancy figures of those occupations dealing directly with patients with the vacancy figures for administrative and maintenance personnel in the public mental hospitals. This latter group of occupations includes a wide range of positions from business director, accountant, and engineer, to skilled farm laborer and kitchen helper. The over-all employment figures for this heterogenous group are probably a good index of the over-all employment situation in the community. Of 45,471 positions available for administrative and maintenance personnel, 2669, or 5.9 per cent, were unfilled (Table 13).

There is, of course, no necessary relationship between the existence of vacancies in a State hospital system and the number of personnel available for patient care. Some of the states with the most favorable staff-patient ratios reported the largest number of vacancies. It is clear that many legislatures which are pressing for better care of people in public institutions may approve the creation of new professional vacancies faster than they can be filled. Other states, with budgetary problems or with little interest in or concern for their public institutions, may report few vacancies. Vacancies may result from inadequate salary schedules, poor working conditions, or other morale factors.

Table 14 shows the position of states according to the number of professional personnel per 100 patients. Table 15 also ranks the states, in terms of the number of full-time employees per 100 patients.

Nine states reported more than 10 per cent of their available positions vacant. These nine states, however, compare favorably with the other thirty-nine in employee-to-patient ratios. Five of the nine states which had many available positions had more favorable ratios than the United States average. Of these five, four are among the ten states with the lowest patient-to-employee ratios. Kansas, which has the most favorable ratio in the country, is one of the states with large numbers of vacancies.

So far we have been concerned with vacancies reported by the states—in most cases budgeted vacancies.

It should be noted, however, that even if existing vacancies could be filled the public hospitals would still be far below the minimum standards for mental hospitals set by the American Psychiatric Association.

Other Budgeted Vacancies.

It has been difficult to determine the existence of budgeted vacancies in other agencies and institutions than those reported above. Such estimates rapidly go out of date. At best all such surveys are prone to errors almost impossible to control.

One survey, reported by the Health Resources Advisory Committee (1956), counted 2500 budgeted job vacancies for medical and psychiatric social workers throughout the country. The Committee estimated that there was an accumulating shortage of 1000 workers each year in just these two social work specialties.

A survey of psychiatric services in general hospitals by Bennett, Hargrove, and Engle (1951) reported serious professional staff shortages in existing services, and they also found many other services that were physically ready to be put into operation but which could not be staffed due to manpower shortages.

Five years ago the Psychiatry and Neurology Division of the Veterans Administration did a comprehensive survey of its professional manpower needs, together with a projection of these needs to 1960. Subsequent experience has shown that these needs and vacancies were quite realistic and in some cases they bordered on the conservative side. To staff existing and allotted psychiatric and neurologic facilities by 1960 the manpower needs were sizable (Table 16).

Minimum Staff Standards and Personnel
Available in Public Mental Hospitals.

The American Psychiatric Association, after careful study, has made recommendations about the number of professional people and attendants needed in public mental hospitals. These standards represent the *minimum* considered necessary for adequate care and treatment of mental patients. The standards are relatively modest in conception, and few knowledgeable people have argued that they are in any way exaggerated.

For example, the standards recommend that there be one physician to every thirty patients on admission and intensive treatment services. To anyone familiar with these services this goal will seem most reasonable. The standards recommend one physician for every 150 patients on continued treatment services, and again this seems a modest aspiration.

They recommend one registered nurse to every forty patients on continued treatment, though it is necessary to note that nurses work only forty hours of 168 hours in a week, so that one nurse to forty patients means, on the average, one nurse to every 168 patients. The same qualification, of course, applies to the other professional groups. Table 17 summarizes the APA recommended minimum personnel ratios.

Recently, it has been suggested that the minimum standards are inadequate for psychologists and social workers. The number of psychologists in our mental hospitals has increased markedly in recent years largely because of an increase in the kinds of service demanded of them. The number of skills that the psychologists have brought to the mental hospital has likewise increased. No allowance has been made in the standards for the need for social workers to provide help to patients on continued treatment service and if this situation were corrected the need for social workers would be even greater.

The Joint Information Service (1957) found that not a single state is adequately staffed. No state even approaches the minimum standards.

Registered nurses are in shortest supply. For the United States as a whole there are less than one-fifth of the number of registered nurses required for minimally adequate staffing of mental hospitals.

The number of social workers was judged to be approximately 36 per cent adequate, but the reader will remember that social work standards are based on estimates which do not include the need for social workers on continued treatment services.

The number of physicians in public mental hospitals for the country as a whole was 45 per cent adequate, but it must be pointed out that a large proportion of this number is represented by foreign interns and residents with the inescapable problems, discussed elsewhere, that this group has in working in a different culture.

The hospitals had nearly two-thirds the number of psychologists recommended, though we have noted that some qualification of these standards is under consideration.

Nearly three-fourths of the number of attendants recommended were found to be employed. Once again we find validation for the observation that shortages are least serious for positions requiring the least formal training.

The Joint Information Service has calculated the total number of professional and nonprofessional personnel who would have been required (at the end of fiscal 1956) to bring the total number of personnel in all five categories in non-Federal public mental hospitals to minimum APA standards. Of this number more than 50 per cent of the shortage was represented by professional people. Data for the country as a whole and for the various states are to be found in the Appendix in Tables 18 through 23.

Needs in General Hospitals.

There has been a rapid and accelerating increase in the number of beds in general hospitals that are available to psychiatric patients. A recent survey by Bush (1957) found that nearly 600 general hospitals in the United States had facilities for the care of mental patients beyond just emergency admissions. This means that about 11 per cent of all general hospitals in the country have facilities for the treatment of mental patients. Half of all first admissions of mental patients in a given year were found to be to the psychiatric services of general hospitals. This does not mean that these facilities provide any sizable fraction of all continuing care of mental patients. They are a resource, however, for intensive treatment immediately following admissions. Often they enable patients to receive prompt care which enables them to return home. Many patients, however, go on to more custodial, less expensive hospitals.

Some 25,000 beds were reported available for psychiatric patients in general hospitals. Many leaders in the fields concerned with mental illness believe the development of psychiatric facilities in general hospitals to be an essential pattern for the future. They feel that the recruitment of competent staff is much easier in the context of the general hospital where contact with other specialties and with other professional groups often is more readily available.

Earlier studies have found that psychiatric services in general hospitals provide important amounts of training for mental health personnel. Although psychiatric beds in general hospitals account for only about one per cent of all of our nation's psychiatric beds, they are important as a first line of defense and as an active training resource. Most observers suggest that many more general hospitals ought to have psychiatric services both for in-patients and for patients who can be treated on an out-patient basis. Earlier surveys, however, have already established the existence of serious professional staff shortages. Some psychiatric units in general hospitals were found physically ready to be activated but closed because of a lack of personnel.

The trend is clear. There is a rapid increase in the availability of psychiatric beds in general hospitals and this trend shows no sign of abating. It seems probable that demands for professional personnel to staff these facilities will continue and will increase for the foreseeable future.

Needs in Mental Health Clinics.

According to Anita K. Bahn and Vivian B. Norman (1957), there were the equivalent of 1630 psychiatrists, 1356 clinical psychologists, and 2389 social workers employed in psychiatric clinics in the United States in 1954–1955.

If we define a full-time psychiatric clinic as a clinic with the equivalent of four full-time professional people (including the equivalent of one full-time psychiatrist, one full-time clinical psychologist, one full-time psychiatric social worker, and one additional full-time psychiatric social worker or other professional person) then we presently appear to have the equivalent of 1344 full-time clinics in the United States. The actual number of clinics is reported to be 1234, some having more professionals available than the standard clinic referred to. The advantage of the theoretical figure is that it provides a standard against which we can estimate needs for professional personnel for the future.

In 1955 the population of the United States was over 165 million. To have one psychiatric clinic for every 100,000 population (a ratio itself considered inadequate) we would have needed 1652 clinics instead of the 1344 equivalent full-time clinics described above. Three hundred and eight more clinics would take twenty-two more psychiatrists, 296 more clinical psychologists, and 915 more psychiatric social workers or other professionals (allowing for redistribution of present clinic manpower to fit the standard-sized clinic.)

The reasons for the greater shortage of psychiatric social workers are complicated but logical. At present just over one-half of the *full-time* staff members of psychiatric clinics are psychiatric social workers. But only thirteen per cent of the part-time staff members are psychiatric social workers. In other words, for a full-time psychiatrist and clinical psychologist there are two full-time psychiatric social workers, but for part-time psychiatrists and psychologists there are no proportionally equivalent psychiatric social workers. Of the total professional time now spent in psychiatric clinics, psychiatric social workers supply only 27 per cent.

By 1960 the population of the United States will be 177.8 million. If we want to keep up with the ratio of the equivalent of one clinic to every 100,000 population, we will need 126 more clinics in addition to those we are already short. This means further additional staff as follows: 126 new psychiatrists, 126 new clinical psychologists, and 252 new psychiatric social workers or other professionals.

By 1965 the population of the United States will be 190.3 million. Once again, to keep our ratio of clinics to population at 1/100,000 we would need still another 125 more psychiatrists, 125 more clinical psychologists, and 250 more psychiatric social workers or other professionals.

Now let us add up these needs. By 1965, in order to achieve and maintain the modest goal of one psychiatric clinic to every hundred

Millions

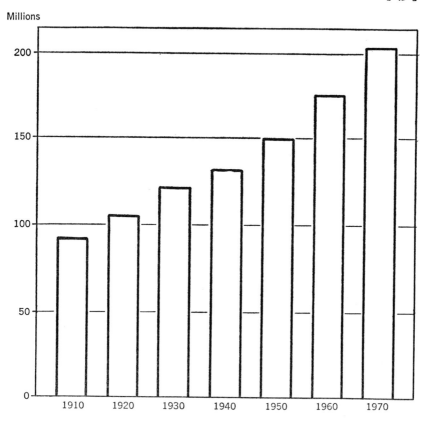

FIG. 6.—*Growth of the United States population.*

Source: U.S. Bureau of the Census, 1956. *Statistical abstract of the United States.* Seventy-seventh edition.

thousand of our population, we will need the equivalent of 273 full-time psychiatrists, 547 full-time clinical psychologists, and 1417 full-time psychiatric social workers or other professionals. There would be needed, of course, additional professional people to replace those who resign, retire, die, or otherwise leave the clinics. But, in general, these figures do not appear impossible of realization.

There are a number of difficulties associated with this picture. One clinic to 100,000 citizens is a purely arbitrary ratio, and actually is not far from the present ratio (1/122,000). It is probably both economically and morally defensible to say that four clinics per hundred thousand people would come closer to handling the needs of the nation than would one clinic per hundred thousand. What would it take manpower-wise to reach this goal? Immediately we see the tremendous size of the problem. By 1965, it would take close to 6000 new psychiatrists, 6256 new clinical psychologists, and 12,800 new psychiatric social workers or other professionals to reach this much more ambitious goal. Table 24 illustrates the relationship between the number of clinics and manpower needs for the future.

A second problem concerns the distribution of these psychiatric clinics. Only seven states and the District of Columbia have at present more than the number of professional man-hours per week needed to maintain a ratio of at least one clinic to each 100,000. Despite the above-described modest shortages which stand in the way of the goal for the nation of one clinic to each 100,000, this picture is unrealistic. The reason is simple. We cannot distribute the clinics arbitrarily. Large metropolitan areas and heavily urbanized states have more than their statistical proportion of clinics. Ninety per cent of professional man-hours available were in the standard metropolitan areas where less than two-thirds of our population lives. Let us ask the question another way: How many professional people would be needed to bring each state up to the 1/100,000 clinic-to-population ratio? This approach illustrates a frequent source of error in manpower estimates.

Table 25 supplies our answer. While we would need slightly more than a thousand professional people to bring the United States as a whole up to the ratio of 1/100,000, this picture changes when we attack the problem on a state-by-state basis. Let us (1) calculate the number of professional man-hours per week per 100,000 population now available in each state, then (2) find the amount this figure differs from 140 hours (the number needed for the desired minimum ratio), and (3) multiply this difference by the number of hundred thousand people in the state population. This procedure gives us the number of man-hours per week needed in each state (column 2). Dividing this figure by thirty-five hours (one professional, one week) and rounding to the nearest whole person gives us a total of 2500 people needed throughout the United States to bring each State up to the 1/100,000 ratio which we said above was a very modest goal.

Table 26 presents a rank order of the states according to professional man-hours available in 1955.

Representative Regional Estimates of Need.

Thirty per cent of the nation's civilian population resides in twelve midwestern states (Illinois, Indiana, Iowa, Kansas, Michigan, Minnesota, Missouri, Nebraska, North Dakota, Ohio, South Dakota, and Wisconsin). The people in these states receive 30.4 per cent of the total United States income. The Council of State Governments (1958) has worked out careful data on these twelve states. Let us use them as an example of some of the problems, resources, and present status of our mental hospitals. While the midwestern region is neither the best, nor the worst, in terms of manpower we will get some idea of the dimensions of the hospital manpower problem by referring to these data.

About 28 per cent of the average daily resident patient population in State hospitals is to be found in these midwestern states. One person in slightly more than 300 people is a patient in a State hospital at any given time. In 1956 there were 779 physicians and psychiatrists in the public hospitals of these midwestern states. If there had been enough to meet minimum standards of the American Psychiatric Association, 1491 *additional* physicians and psychiatrists would have been required. This means that the midwestern states are about one-third staffed for psychiatrists. Three hundred and twenty-five psychologists were employed in 1956 and 356 more would have been needed to meet minimum standards. Four hundred and ninety-two social workers were employed in 1956 in these midwestern states and 110 more would have been needed to meet minimum standards. One thousand six hundred and one registered nurses were employed in 1956 and 10,397 additional nurses would have been needed to meet minimum standards (Table 27).

A survey of *Mental Health Training and Research in the Western Region* by the Western Interstate Commission for Higher Education (1956) assessed the present resources, requirements, and prospects of eleven western states and Alaska. (Now, twelve states!) Covered in the survey were Alaska, Arizona, California, Nevada, New Mexico, Oregon, Colorado, Idaho, Montana, Utah, Washington, and Wyoming.

The survey located 1147 psychiatrists, 867 psychologists (including a number of school psychologists), 784 social workers, 1471 nurses, and 471 rehabilitative therapists, all of whom were engaged in mental health employment. These figures are not absolutely complete but cover the great majority of people employed in these categories in the western region, in State mental hospitals, Veterans Administration neuropsychiatric hospitals, institutions for the mentally defective, most clinics, general hospitals, and training centers.

The psychiatrists were distributed into three groups, roughly equivalent in size, including those (1) full-time in institutions, (2) full-time in private practice, and (3) some combination of these.

In the Veterans Administration neuropsychiatric hospitals some 62 per cent of the psychiatrists were certified by the American Board of Psychiatry and Neurology. Only 24 per cent of the State hospital psychiatrists were so certified. In general, the patient-staff ratio is considerably more favorable in VA as compared with State hospitals (1/81 vs. 1/247).

While the survey focused on the number of professionals needed to bring State hospitals up to VA levels, it should be noted that the latter are below APA standards.

To bring the State hospitals up to present VA psychiatric staffing would require 523 more psychiatrists. Approved psychiatric residency programs in the western region yield about eighty psychiatrists a year.

The Western States survey data on clinical psychology are difficult to evaluate because of the inclusion of an unspecified number of school psychologists.

All Veterans Administration neuropsychiatric hospital psychologists had the Ph.D. degree, but only 41 per cent of those in State hospitals had obtained the doctorate. One psychologist in ten in the State hospitals had only a bachelors degree. An additional 256 psychologists would be needed to bring the State hospitals up to VA levels. Approved programs in clinical psychology graduate sixty to seventy Ph.D.'s each year.

A total of 290 additional social workers is needed to raise State hospitals in the western region to Veterans Administration neuropsychiatric hospital levels in staffing.

Six graduate schools of social work approved by the Council on Social Work Education yield about 360 graduate social workers a year in all areas of social work specialization.

An unbelievable 3251 more nurses would be required by the State hospitals to raise the staff level of psychiatric nurses to present VA levels. As the number of nurses being attracted to state hospital employment is very small, this figure seems almost meaningless. Altogether some 3000 nurses a year finish their training in the region but relatively few go into psychiatric nursing.

We have noted that the use of VA staff ratios is far from an ideal standard. Most Veterans Administration neuropsychiatric hospital managers are very much concerned with shortages of trained personnel in these fields and in the present study reported a need for 25 per cent more staff in each professional category in these VA hospitals.

According to the Southern Regional Education Board there is a serious understaffing of mental health clinics, hospitals, and institutions for the mentally disordered throughout the South. In a 1954 report to the Southern Governors' Conference it was pointed out that, while the southern states have 3700 professional mental health personnel, the need is for 24,000 trained persons or about six times the present number. Funds were available at that time for some 750 additional positions which could not be filled.

At that time, southern universities and institutions were training each year approximately seventy-five psychiatrists, sixty clinical psychologists, seventy psychiatric social workers, and sixty psychiatric nursing specialists. These numbers were not, of course, enough to offer any hope that this output might catch up with needs. The report points out that the South would have to train five times as many persons as it is now training to meet its needs within the next decade.

According to a 1956 report of the Southern Regional Education

Board, there was a shortage of some 4000 psychiatrists in the southern region. The Board estimates that 1.9 per cent of all physicians in the South are psychiatrists in contrast to a national average of 3.3 per cent. Up to the beginning of the present decade, accredited medical schools in the South had graduated some 40,000 physicians of whom only 1.38 per cent became psychiatrists. At the present time, the South holds fewer than half of the young psychiatrists trained there. Furthermore, the proportion of psychiatrists trained in the southern region is proportionately less than the national average.

A summary of actions and recommended programs for increasing the number of psychiatrists in the South is available from the Southern Regional Education Board. In general, recommendations include strengthening training programs and increasing financial inducements for professionals and students.

Shortages of Mental Health Personnel in the Armed Forces.

There are no recent studies of shortages of mental health personnel in the military service, but discussions with a number of military personnel officials suggest that such shortages do exist. The Air Force reports unofficially a need for sizable numbers of psychiatrists and clinical psychologists. The Air Force also reports a need for psychiatric nurses but indicates that it anticipates filling this need through current procurement procedures.

A report from the Army indicates that it has been able to fill its authorization for psychiatrists through the doctor-draft program. It reports that nearly half of the physicians working in psychiatry are only partially trained. Efforts to recruit physicians into the Regular Army Medical Corps to undertake psychiatric residency training have not been very successful. The Army also reports an expanding need for clinical psychologists, with only half the total authorization on active duty. A program of support for graduate students in psychology was instituted in 1957 in an attempt to replenish losses of clinical psychologists.

Admiral B. W. Hogan (1958) describes the mental health manpower situation in the Navy as follows:

The Navy Medical Department is now experiencing a significant shortage of psychiatrists. It is anticipated that approximately 15 per cent of our psychiatric billets will be vacant by January 1, 1959 because of our difficulties in recruiting medical officers who are trained in psychiatry. The critical shortage of psychiatrists should be alleviated to some degree in the summer of 1959 when physicians who have been deferred for civilian residency training under the Berry Plan come on active duty.

Although the numerical shortage in psychiatrists will be somewhat alleviated by the Berry Plan, the Navy is still faced with a very significant problem. Within the next few years, there will be an extreme shortage of psychiatrists who have both the professional and military experience required to serve as chief of service in our hospitals. It is considered that this shortage of senior psychiatrists will become our most pressing mental health manpower problem.

The personnel situation with regard to clinical psychologists is equally and, in some ways, more critical than that for psychiatrists. By January 1, 1959, there will be approximately a 15 to 20 per cent shortage of clinical psychologists. Inasmuch as these individuals are no longer under pressure of being drafted into the Armed Forces by the time they have completed the academic work and internship required for a Ph.D., and inasmuch as the pay for the newly appointed military psychologist does not compare favorably with the financial remuneration in civilian life, it has been found extremely difficult to interest well-trained psychologists in the naval service. Unless some reasonable and adequate means is devised for alleviating the increasing shortage in military clinical psychologists, it may reasonably be anticipated that this situation will reach such proportions within the next two to three years as to seriously impair the Navy's neuropsychiatric program.

All psychiatric social workers engaged in dealing with naval personnel are either Civil Service employees or representatives of the American Red Cross. While our neuropsychiatric program has not suffered from a shortage of psychiatric social workers because of difficulties in recruiting, shortages of personnel have, on occasion, resulted because of budgetary limitations in the various naval hospitals.

No particular problem exists with regard to supply of psychiatric nurses which is unique, alone, to that specialty of nursing.

The Soviet Race for Knowledge.

The availability of professional manpower in any particular branch of the public service, or in private practice, is fundamentally dependent on the number of bright young persons coming to the professional schools. Diversion of persons from one branch of service to another, or from one type of professional training to another, does not alter the manpower picture in its over-all aspects. The important consideration basically is the number of persons entering the pool for distribution in the various areas of need. The social and cultural values of a particular society or segment of it will often play a major role in determining not only the size of the pool but the distribution of its members. It is felt that we can learn much by examining the way other peoples have handled this problem in other times or in other settings. At the moment, there is a considerable interest in this country about the developments in the Soviet Union. The material to be quoted here illustrates the point that it is necessary to take positive steps to bring persons into the manpower pool. No attempts will be made to discuss the possible shortcomings of a totalitarian system of education. It is used rather to illustrate the fact that, if a people approach a problem in a planned and organized way, a desired result can often be achieved.

In a report to the National Press Club, the United States Commissioner of Education, Lawrence G. Derthick, described (1958) his sobering experience in seeing firsthand the all-out effort the Soviet Union is making in the field of education.

Among the facts he reported are the exceptionally capable teachers who are highly selected and who have the highest pay and prestige of any professional group, the small size of classes, the active participation of parents in education, and the difficult curriculum. Commissioner Derthick further reports the ground swell of Soviet public opinion which is supporting an all-out educational effort. The Russians, he says, plan to overtake and pass the United States by investing in the education of their young people at the expense of everything else. The widespread instruction in foreign languages, in science, and in mathematics exceeds anything offered in all but a very few schools in this country. Derthick summarizes with the statement: "We are today in competition with a nation of vast resources, a people of seemingly unbounded enthusiasm for self-development and fired with a conviction that future supremacy belongs to those with the best-trained minds, those who will work hard and sacrifice."

The United States is in an educational race, all unwillingly and often unknowingly. The Russians are on the track and running while American slug-a-beds wrap themselves more snugly in pleasant dreams. The Russians are convinced that their planned society, which includes all-out educational efforts, will defeat us in the end. As Derthick points out: "This conviction is basic to all of their efforts and all of their plans for the future. Education is paramount. It is a kind of grand passion—this conviction that children, schools, and hard work will win them their place in the sun, and on the moon."

It is necessary to realize that it takes a long time to train a professional person. Some of the cultural reasons for this lengthy process were discussed in the first chapter, but there still remain additional functional requirements of preparation and of sequence which stretch out the process of educating scientists and professional personnel. If it takes eight to ten years after high school to educate a scientist or a professional person plus another five to ten years to season him with experience, then we realize that the Soviets are likely to get much farther ahead before we can possibly start catching up. They recognized some time ago the competitive value of education.

As Nicholas DeWitt (1958) points out:

The Soviet effort is a persistent drive. It is not an overnight feat. It is not just a passing fancy which, like an unpleasant rumor, can be stopped or silenced or forgotten at will. The Russians are not playing hide-and-seek. They are in dead earnest in their ultimate objective that, if not today or tomorrow, then in a decade or generation or two hence their absolute technological, economic, and military supremacy will triumph. Their educational program, they think, is aiding them in this goal. This is what they openly profess and preach, and they live and act accordingly. This *is* their goal. And anyone who does not realize this plain, hard fact is playing the fool.

DeWitt goes on to point out that, while the total number of graduates of higher educational institutions was approximately the same in both the United States and Russia in 1957, the Soviets turned out more than twice as many scientists and engineers, and this has been going on now for at least six years. In the Russian ten-year general educational school about half of all the hours are devoted to instruction in science and mathematics.

"Every pupil," DeWitt says, "*has* to take five years of physics, six of mathematics, three of biology, four of chemistry, six of foreign languages, and so on. Either the youngster succeeds in passing the required subjects or, if he fails, he is out, and is absorbed by an elaborate system of trade and vocational schools."

Whatever the gloomy facts about how the Soviet Union is forging ahead in the education field, our reaction is predictable. The argument runs as follows: the figures quoted are not true, but rather are one more example of the lies and distortions we have come to expect—and even if they *are* true the quality of their education is really not very high—and even if the quality of their education *is* high ours is better!

This head-in-the-sand attitude cannot indefinitely protect us. Somehow in our increasing preoccupation with technology and production, we have forgotten that both of these are based on intelligence and knowledge. Yet our government, like most of our major businesses, has neglected the support of the educational facilities which should have been providing us with new ideas, new products, new perspective.

It is hard for us to imagine that there may be a time when the United States is all but forgotten in history. But unless we use all the wisdom we can muster, and unless we properly educate most of the intelligent children we bear, history tells us that oblivion can be our fate.

Lloyd Berkner (1958) says: "In 1956, big business invested something like thirty-five billion dollars in new capital. Yet it contributed only $100,000,000 to education. Certainly private investment in the men that must man our industry and government to insure its pre-eminence is comparable to the importance of other forms of capital investment."

Toynbee (1950) tells a most arresting story about Assyria. In 400 B.C., one of Cyrus' armies moved back from the Tigris River toward the Black Sea. It passed the cities of Kalah and Nineveh. Rather, it passed the *former* cities of Kalah and Nineveh, because they were empty of life. The soldiers were amazed at the size and complexity of these empty cities, but neither the soldiers, nor the few poverty-stricken people living outside the massive walls, knew the names of the cities nor their history. Less than three centuries before, Assyria had been the greatest nation in the world, and these were two of her mightiest cities. It is as though two centuries hence an army should march up the east coast of North America and find the ruins of Philadelphia and New York and be astonished by their size and complexity and yet not know the names of these cities nor have ever heard of the people who built them or the nation in which they were located.

This is a grim and disquieting thought. Is there any alternative to the present course we are following, a course which seems to lead us sooner or later over the cliff? Perhaps we are in the grip of historical forces beyond our control.

If we survive, we will survive because of our use of intelligence. While man's unique possession is his intelligence and his capacity for conceptual thought, he shares with other forms of animal life the tides of passion—of love, hate, fear, and the violent winds of ignorance and prejudice. These are strong adversaries to the intellect. As Freud himself pointed out, the voice of the intellect is soft. It is frequently drowned out by our passions. But as Freud insisted, the voice of the intellect persists. Our intelligence, in the words of Karl Menninger (1955), ". . . has the qualities of eternity. When the tumult and the shouting die, and the captains and the kings depart, thought remains. No great nation has ever put its confidence in thought; steel has always been preferred. Perhaps that is only because our earth is young, our civilization still green. But we are older now, and should be wiser."

POPULATION CHANGES AFFECTING THE FUTURE DEMAND FOR MENTAL HEALTH PERSONNEL

Manpower needs in mental health are affected by another important factor, the growth in our population. In a static population, policies that lead to an increase in the number of people completing their professional training would be expected to narrow the gap between need and the personnel available. But in a growing population we find that efforts to increase service often result only in our being able barely to keep up if, indeed, we are not outdistanced by growing demand.

The population of a country depends in large measure on both the birth rate and the death rate and on the relationship between these two rates. The population of the United States is increasing both because our birth rate has shown a sharp increase since 1940 and because there has been a slight but appreciable decline in the death rate over the past twenty-five years.

We are witnessing a world population explosion because high birth rates, heretofore largely neutralized by high death rates, have continued unabated while public health measures and other innovations have sharply reduced death rates.

It has taken seventy years for the population of the world to double to its present size of approximately 2.7 billion people. Other things being equal, our world's population will double again in the next forty-two years and will redouble in about eighty-four years. This means that we are rapidly approaching the population figure of seven billion which many experts believe to be the absolute maximum that the earth can support.

It took nearly seven thousand years for the number of people on earth to increase from some ten million to our present figure of 2.7 billion.

Two things are happening in our population. In recent years there has been an enormous boom in the number of babies born and a gradually increasing life span. This means that the population pyramid is getting broader and broader at the base at the same time that it gets taller. The large number of babies and the increasing number of old people present changing demands for professional skills. More school teachers, child psychiatrists, and pediatric nurses will be needed and more persons who have specialized in the fields of gerontology and geriatrics. More child psychologists, school psychologists, school social workers will be sought. With improved understanding of the causes and treatment of infectious diseases the pattern of skills demanded of physicians also changes.

Concurrently with the increasing median age of the population, and with the arrival of larger and larger numbers of infants, we are witnessing a population migration to urban centers. For complex reasons, not entirely understood, there is a higher incidence of mental disorders and emotional turmoil in urban areas.

Because we know the number of females in the United States who will be in the eighteen to thirty-four age group (the age range of women bearing 85 per cent of the country's babies) ten years hence, we can make very accurate predictions with respect to this factor. There are, at present, something like 19.5 million young women at this fertile age. Ten years from now this number will be increased by more than three million. Twenty years from now there will be thirty-two million fertile young women in this age group. This simply means that the number of babies, the number of school children, the number of demands of an expanding population will continue to grow at an explosive rate.

We face no temporary manpower emergency. When, at long last, the pressure of the demand for educational facilities from elementary schools through professional schools forces us to take drastic action, we will find that it is only the beginning. The pressures of expanded demand for educational facilities, and more importantly for teachers and college faculty, will grow to the point where our present shortages will seem trivial.

OTHER FACTORS AFFECTING MANPOWER SHORTAGES

The Concentration of Professionals.

So far we have been concerned with evidence that shortages exist on a national or state level for mental health personnel and that these shortages will increase.

Another factor which must be considered in assessing shortages is the strong tendency for professional people to go to urban areas and to stay there. This means that more serious shortages exist in rural states and regions than is evident at first.

People who live in cities are likely to have professional services available in far greater degree than people living in rural areas. Hospitals, clinics, and social agencies, especially the large, well-staffed research and training centers, are usually found in urban areas. Social work is an urban profession, historically and functionally. Psychologists, nurses, psychiatrists, and other professional mental health workers tend to live and practice in cities.

Let us cite some representative evidence for this tendency so that our discussion of the need for professional people may be held in perspective. Training more people, at a faster rate than at present, would result, in all probability, in little improvement in the manpower situation in rural areas.

There is, for example, a relationship between the density of population of an area and the availability of health services to people living in that area. In fourteen standard metropolitan areas (as defined by the Bureau of the Census) with one million or more people there were, in 1950, 180 physicians per 100,000 people. In contrast, the rate was 113 per 100,000 people for standard population areas under 100,000. The rate for the United States as a whole was 127 physicians per 100,000 population. The per capita income for the metropolitan areas was $1598; the per capita income for the areas under 100,000 population was $1360.

When another method of delineating population areas is used, these differences in health services are even more striking. Using this latter method involves the classification of areas within states on the basis of their proximity to densely populated areas. We find that metropolitan and adjacent counties have 147 physicians per 100,000 people and isolated counties have 76 physicans per 100,000 people.

A great amount of urbanization is characteristic of psychologists. Metropolitan and adjacent areas have 4 psychologists per 100,000 people while isolated areas have one or less.

One other pertinent observation needs to be recorded because it has implications for the future: physicians (and probably other professional people) in rural areas tend to be older (27 per cent are over sixty-five) than physicians in metropolitan counties (8 per cent are over sixty-five).

There are eighteen cities in the United States, each with a population of more than a half million. In these cities live slightly less than 18 per cent of our total population. Yet in these cities there are nearly 40 per cent of our total psychiatrists (Table 28). It must be recognized, of course, that these cities serve as a resource for their urbanized environs, though counting all the people in their greater urban areas still brings their population up to only 28 per cent of our total population. And we must remember too that an appreciable number of psychiatrists we have not counted live in the urban areas but outside the city limits. The most obvious case of the latter is Beverly Hills, which boasts nearly as many psychiatrists as Los Angeles. The situation is similar in Chevy Chase and Bethesda for Washington, D.C., and for the cities in northern New Jersey and southern Connecticut for New York City, to cite other examples.

In another examination of the distribution of psychiatrists, the Joint Information Service (1957) calculated the relation of population to psychiatrists for each of fifteen metropolitan areas with a population of over one million in 1956. According to these figures Washington, D.C., had the most psychiatrists to population (one to 6000), with greater New York, northeastern New Jersey, and greater Boston following close behind. The metropolitan area with the poorest representation was Buffalo, New York, where there was one psychiatrist to each 27,300 people. For all fifteen metropolitan areas there was one psychiatrist to each 10,600 persons and for the rest of the United States, excluding these areas, there was one psychiatrist for every 29,000 persons. It should be noted that the relatively good showing of Washington, D.C., is somewhat artificial in view of the large number of administrative and non-practicing psychiatrists employed there.

This concentration of psychiatrists in urban areas is even more apparent if we look at those who are specialists in psychoanalysis and who are members of the American Psychoanalytic Association. As Table 29 indicates, more than three-fourths of all the country's psychoanalysts are to be found in the ten largest cities. Sixty-three per cent are in New York, Chicago, Los Angeles, Boston, and Washington.

Another approach to the problem of the distribution of mental health personnel is suggested by this evidence that psychiatry is an urban specialty. Census data are available on the extent of urbanization of the states. That is, data are available to permit the classification of states into a rank order according to the extent that their populations live in urban as contrasted with rural areas. When we compare the ten states with the most urban populations with the ten states with the most rural populations, we find a startling difference (Table 30). In the ten most urbanized states there is one psychiatrist for every 12,200 people; in the ten least urbanized states there is one psychiatrist for every 43,800 people. These urbanized states have slightly less than four times the population, seven times as many hospitalized mental patients, and more than fourteen times as many psychiatrists as the nonurbanized states. Indeed, we find a rank order correlation of .77 between urbanization and ratio of psychiatrists to population for all the states (see Table 31).

Although there is a more or less direct relationship between the total population of states and their number of psychiatrists (see Table 32, rho = .87), there are many examples of small urbanized states with favorable psychiatrist-to-population ratios, and of large nonurbanized states with poor psychiatrist-to-population ratios. Connecticut and West Virginia are nearly the same in population, but Connecticut has one psychiatrist to every 8900 of its citizens while West Virginia has one to every 66,100. Connecticut has about twice as many patients in mental hospitals as West Virginia and 8.4 times as many psychiatrists.

These findings are not meant to suggest, of course, that there is any direct causal relation between urbanization and number of psychiatrists. Both may be related to regional wealth, educational facilities, per capita income, or other variables. Nor is the patient census a good index of demand for psychiatrists; still, about half as many people per thousand are in mental institutions in the rural states while these states have only a quarter as many psychiatrists per thousand persons. Some of these relations will be evident from Tables 33 and 34 in the Appendix. The urbanized states tend to have a much higher per capita income, somewhat higher average number of years of schooling of their citizens, and higher mental hospital admission rates; they spend more on mental patients and have slightly more employees in ratio to patients in their mental hospitals.

We have reported at length on the urbanization of psychiatrists. The same sort of evidence could be cited for the other mental health professions.

Although these data indicate that professional people are concentrated in urban areas and especially in our largest cities, it should be noted that analysis of the distribution of the professionals could be carried still further. Even within a large city there is marked variation in the regional distribution of professional people. Some neighborhoods or sections of the city have many professionals, and other sections or neighborhoods have few. In Greater New York, for example, the ratio of physicians to population is one to 440. Manhattan, however, has one physician for every 208 people; Queens has one physician for every 660 people; and the other boroughs are less well supplied with physicians.

Manpower studies usually are made to discover the *availability* of people trained in some capacity. Our data require that we keep certain reservations in mind with respect to the *availability* of mental health professionals. Not just psychiatrists, but social workers, nurses, psychologists, and other professional people tend to go to urban areas and to stay there. Professional services are far less accessible to persons separated by distance, physical and social, from the trained professional.

*Selective Factors Involved in the Movement
of Students into the Mental Health Professions.*

The future supply of professional people also depends on how successful the professions are in recruiting students in the various fields.

It is not surprising that relatively little objective information is available concerning the multiplicity of factors involved in determining the movement of young people into specific occupations. Viewed in historical perspective, it is only during the past few moments in human history that any meaningful vocational choice has existed for significant numbers of people. The majority of mankind still spends its days in the endless struggle to obtain the basic necessities of life and any discussion of occupational choice needs to be tempered with the realization that we are talking about a psychological luxury beyond the reach of a majority of mankind. With more than half of the adult population of the earth functionally illiterate and with a large proportion of the remainder still in the grip of tradition-directed patterns of culture dictated by economic want, vocational choice is a privilege enjoyed by a proportionately minor fraction of the earth's people.

Universal education is an exceedingly recent concept. It is an even more recent achievement. Now that the productive capacity of many countries has reached the point where leisure is available to children no longer needed in the fields or factories it has been possible to permit children to attend school and to free an increasingly large number of adults from the production of goods in order that they may teach. During the last thirty years in the United States, there has been a steadily decreasing distance between the number of people employed in goods-producing activities and service-producing activities. According to the Bureau of Labor Statistics, the number of people employed in service-producing activities surpassed the number of people employed in goods-producing activities for the first time in history during the present decade.

During the past eighty years there has been an enormous expansion of the professional and semiprofessional occupations. The number has increased from less than half a million in 1870 to more than six million in 1956. This represents a growth three times as fast as that of the total labor force. According to the Bureau much of this growth has been due to the development of new professional fields. The four leading professions in 1870 were teaching, the ministry, the law, and medicine. These four traditional professions employed three-quarters of all professional workers in 1870 but represent only some 40 per cent of the total today. Science and engineering are the professional fields responsible for much of the rapid growth. Other new professions such as social work, clinical

Millions of Workers

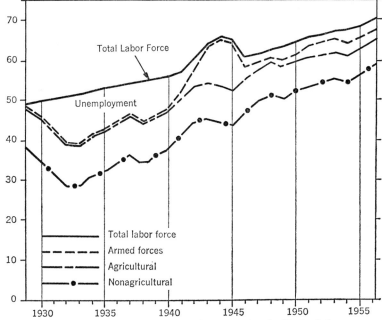

FIG. 7.—*Growth and changes in employment in the United States.*

Source: U.S. Department of Labor, Bureau of Labor Statistics, 1957. *Occupational outlook handbook.* Government Printing Office, p. 23.

psychology, and personnel management were all but unknown before this century.

The growth in the number of professional people of course has paralleled a tremendous growth in the output of our higher educational institutions. Professional work, by definition, requires extensive higher education. As noted above, it has only been in certain fortunate areas of the world and in very recent years that the production of the necessities of life was sufficiently bountiful to free significant numbers of adults from the necessity for constant struggle for production.

Social scientists have been concerned for a number of years with the factors which determine the choice of a particular occupation or profession. Suggested answers have ranged from the view that occupational choice is largely accidental, and is influenced by arbi-

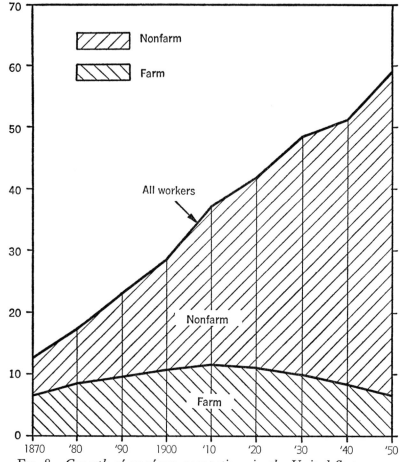

FIG. 8.—*Growth of nonfarm occupations in the United States.*

Source: U.S. Department of Labor, Bureau of Labor Statistics, 1957. *Occupational outlook handbook.* Government Printing Office, p. 24.

trary factors, to the purely psychological view that such factors as interest and conscious or unconscious motivations are important in such determinations.

Recently a group of social scientists (Blau et al, 1956) spent some time in a seminar working out a conceptual scheme to account for occupational choice. This seminar, sponsored by the Social Science

Research Council, worked out a heuristic approach to the problem of occupational entry. On the basis of their discussions and examination of the literature the group felt that entry by young people into a particular occupation was determined both by personal factors and by factors characteristic of the occupation itself. While a large number of factors are important in both sides of the equation, they indicated their belief that there were four crucial considerations in each.

So far as the individual is concerned, the occupational choice depends on (1) the amount of information he has about fields available to him, (2) his technical skills and abilities, (3) his social characteristics, and (4) the orientation of his value system.

On the other hand the characteristics of the occupation which are crucial involve (1) the demand for people in the field, (2) the actual functional requirements for success in the field, (3) the nonfunctional requirements for success in the field, and (4) the reward system.

Without going into the details of all the interesting ramifications of this conceptual scheme, it is apparent that a great deal of research could profitably be done on various factors in each area of determinants of occupational choice. This is as true for the mental health professions as it is for occupations in general. It is clear that large numbers of people cannot choose to enter the mental health fields if information about opportunities in each of the mental health professions and occupations is not widely disseminated and available in such form as to be clearly understandable by young people who have not yet committed themselves to a career pattern.

We also need to recognize that many of the technical skills required of personnel in the mental health fields are poorly identified and described. Thus, it is very difficult to survey the manpower pool for the existence of skills essential to success in training for any of the major mental health occupations.

It is apparent, too, that our pervasive orientation toward mental health has a number of class-determinant biases or class-influenced philosophies. It would be important for research to establish how much the values and philosophies of the field of mental health contribute to the effective activity of members of these occupational groups. Studies are necessary to determine both the rewards and satisfactions which are essential to the job-satisfaction of people already engaged in work in the mental health fields and patterns of satisfaction that would need to be changed in order to attract more students into these areas.

We will cite some data later in this report to show how many potential professional students are lost because of our failure to encourage large groups of young people to go on for more education.

We are a long way from being able to define the important factors and their interrelations responsible for the movement of young people into the mental health professions. Certain factors are so obvious that they seem not to require discussion. Other factors are subtle but nonetheless powerful. Research in this area has been piecemeal and unsystematic.

A student enters a field of professional activity if he has information about the opportunities afforded in the field, interest in the activities required by the professional work, aptitudes for succeeding in the various training programs and in the selective devices employed by the field to screen and train its recruits, motivation which can only be satisfied by the achievements, intellectual and cultural, represented by the professional discipline, and values that are compatible with the values of the professional culture.

There are many complex problems involved in attempting to describe the motivations, abilities, interest patterns, and values of persons who enter the mental health professions. Because, for example, all fledgling psychiatrists are selected from the pool of physicians, and mostly from recent medical school graduates, there is a temptation to use studies of the characteristics of medical students as a source of information about psychiatric residents. But because only something like 8 per cent of new medical school graduates enter residency training in psychiatry, these people can very well represent an exceedingly different group than medical graduates in general. In the same way, it seems probable that those nurses who accept jobs in psychiatric centers, representing as they do a very small percentage of the total number of nurses trained, are different in many ways from the average nurse. Clinical psychologists and psychiatric social workers probably differ in many respects from members of the parent population from which they are drawn.

Certain broad descriptive characteristics are possible. Members of the mental health professions, as well as members of professions in general, have intellectual ability well above average. They tend, on the whole, to be more interested in people than in things and most studies find that they report a curiosity about human behavior. We will examine, when we discuss each profession, some of the findings of studies with respect to each of the professional groups.

The attractiveness of professional fields depends in part upon the widespread existence of an attractive, oversimplified image of the profession that can serve as a model for the fantasy vocational choices of young people. Numerous vehicles of mass communication carry such models for certain professions—medicine and nursing in particular. Comic strips which feature a physician, a nurse, a lawyer, or a detective, and television and radio dramas using these figures provide important information to school children in the process of deciding about their careers.

One of the problems to be resolved by the mental health professions is the absence of a widespread image of the role of the mental health professional. A number of studies indicate that high school students have relatively little information about career opportunities in the mental health professions. Confusion exists about the difference among psychologists and psychiatrists and psychoanalysts, and for many high school students the career of the social worker is little known or understood.

Studies have shown that a decision to enter one of the mental health professions is usually made sometime during college. Kenneth E. Clark (1957), for example, found that a very high percentage of psychologists reported that they first thought about psychology as a career during their college period, with most of this group not thinking about psychology as a lifework until their last two years in college. One advantage psychology has in comparison with other mental health professions is its direct contact with college students. Nearly every college student takes at least one course in psychology, so the intrinsic interest of the subject matter can be presented directly to possible recruits to the field. Both psychiatry and social work rarely have such opportunity except as the subject matter of these latter fields is included in other courses in psychology, sociology, and related fields.

Psychiatric nursing is in a somewhat different position in that the majority of psychiatric nurses are recruited from students who have completed hospital-diploma programs during which they have had field-work placement in a psychiatric service.

It is important to note that in Clark's study the factor which professional people reported to be most influential in their career choice was the influence of a particular teacher or the interest aroused through particular courses. This would mean that those fields not having direct access to the pool of prospective students are at a serious disadvantage in recruitment. A great majority of students who decided to become psychologists had prior career commitments in other fields and had to go through the process of changing their minds in order to enter the field of psychology. It is virtually certain that career commitment changes are necessary for people entering the field of social work, and possibly to some extent, psychiatry. In another section we will examine in somewhat more detail the problems of recruiting nurses into psychiatric nursing. We may note here, however, that there is evidence that the widespread image of the nurse that attracts many high school girls and is responsible for their career choice of nursing differs in many ways from the experiences of student nurses in their psychiatric field placements. In other words, psychiatric nursing differs markedly in content from most other forms of nursing and it is the simplified image of these other forms that has been attractive, with the result that student nurses are preselected in such a way as to make them prove unlikely recruits for the field of psychiatric nursing.

The Number of Accredited Schools.

The availability of professional manpower is dependent to a large extent on the number of places (and their capacity) where new members of the group can be trained. For the professions this means accredited professional schools.

One of the characteristics of professions mentioned earlier is their tendency to seek from society the right to evaluate and accredit their own training programs. This is true of the individual professions, including the mental health professions, and is more generally true of our educational institutions.

As William K. Selden (1956) has pointed out, large-scale financial assistance is generally available only to those higher educational institutions having accreditations. Industrial gifts and grants from private foundations in general go to those educational institutions which are on the approved list of various accrediting agencies.

There are other advantages to being accredited. In a wide variety of professional fields, from architecture to veterinary medicine, state laws require that the individual seeking a license to practice must be a graduate of an accredited institution.

Professional training in the mental health fields necessarily involves accrediting of both the universities with training programs and the special programs or schools within the university where individual members of the profession receive their training.

There are six regional associations of colleges and universities and all of these have accepted responsibility for accrediting colleges and universities within their particular region. In general this kind of evaluation is based on an institution's faculty, curriculum, physical facilities, and over-all policies.

A wide variety of professional associations operate accrediting groups. According to Selden, the following professional programs are examined by professional accrediting agencies: architecture, business, chemistry, dentistry, design, engineering, forestry, journalism, law, library science, medicine, music, nursing, optometry, pharmacy, psychology, public health, social work, teacher education, veterinary medicine. The approach of professional organizations is generally a segmental approach, in that little attention is paid to the over-all quality or characteristics of the educational institution, but rather most attention is focused on the school or department training the fledgling members of the professional discipline concerned.

Professions must insure that the schools training new members of the profession conform to all of the requirements for the transmission of theory, information, and skills. The public largely has come to recognize the importance of accrediting procedures. Accreditation has a universal tendency to work toward improving standards by bringing inadequate training programs up to some minimum standard. Accreditation tends to limit the number of new members of the professional group trained but compensates for this limiting tendency by insuring that adequate training is achieved.

The lure of status and prestige of the professions is a constant temptation to the establishment of training schools offering more rapid or easier entry into a professional field or into an area where it is difficult to distinguish the practitioner poorly trained from the well trained. Diploma mills and unaccredited programs are often money-making operations. They are very difficult to control because often they include in their courses or titles some reference to religion; this makes them all but immune because of our strong feeling against interfering with the freedom of religion.

The voluntary self-regulation by professional societies of their training programs generally assures the public of good quality professional training. One must be careful to point out, however, as medical thinkers occasionally do, that certification by a board or specialty society does not guarantee competency or superiority, any more than lack of it guarantees incompetency or inferiority. As a matter of fact, if certification of one kind or another were a requirement for eligibility to win the Nobel Prize in Physiology and Medicine many who have made original discoveries or outstanding contributions to humanity would have been disbarred from consideration. Indeed, one man who won the prize in medicine within the last ten years lacked an academic degree of any kind! But here we are speaking, for the most part, of the brilliant persons and individualists who dare to be different. Observed one humble genius: "But who could examine *me?*"

Hollis and Taylor (1951) point to three different kinds of accrediting procedures that are common.

First, the stronger training centers of a profession join together in some sort of a membership arrangement in which they establish criteria for membership in their group which other centers must meet in order to become affiliated. Later these membership conditions are spoken of as accreditation.

A second kind of professional accreditation is done by a group operated and controlled by practitioners in the field. An example is the *Council on Medical Education and Hospitals* through which the American Medical Association accredits medical schools.

Thirdly, the accrediting body may consist of some sort of joint council or committee representing several of the special interests involved in the maintenance of professional educational standards. An example here would be the *Council on Social Work Education*.

For the past several years professional schools conforming to all requirements for accreditation by the respective professional groups in mental health have been far below capacity in the number of students enrolled. This should be taken as another index of shortage if we accept the argument that our society needs maximum output from its educational facilities.

The prospect for the future is quite different. Our professional schools will be flooded with applicants when the oncoming wave of students reaches the level of education of these schools.

II

Prospects in Psychiatry

INTRODUCTION

A PSYCHIATRIST is a physician with special training in the understanding and treatment of mental illnesses and emotional disorders.

The past fifty years have seen profound changes in the role and functions of psychiatrists in our society. Psychiatry has moved out of the asylums and into the consciousness of the average American. By the turn of the present century, psychiatry was a well-established medical specialty. (It actually constitutes the oldest organized group of medical specialists in the country, the American Psychiatric Association having been established in 1844.) It was composed almost entirely of the superintendents of mental hospitals in the beginning. These mental institutions housed and cared for those members of society afflicted with the major psychoses—people so severely and obviously deranged that they had to be kept in locked wards. The hospitals largely were custodial institutions, and were referred to as "asylums" and their inmates were usually called "lunatics" and "insane."

The psychiatrist in the public mental hospital usually was responsible for all of the treatment, including the actual medical care, of the several hundred to several thousand patients in his institution. As the system evolved, he experienced isolation from his medical colleagues and from other professional groups. He had to endure low salaries and low prestige. In spite of these drawbacks some able and sincere physicians went into psychiatry and laid the foundations for our present clinical treatment of severe personality disturbances. In general, however, a relatively small number of

[72]

physicians entered the field and little organized training for this specialty existed.

With the growing influence during the early decades of the twentieth century of American psychiatrists Adolf Meyer and William A. White, and with the growing influence in Europe of Sigmund Freud, a massive change in psychiatry, and in the attitude of the informed public toward psychiatry, began to be shaped. At the same time, exciting new discoveries in neurology and biochemistry inspired that group of physicians interested in the biological and organic side of mental disorder.

During the first World War psychiatrists came into contact with "shell shock," the traumatic neuroses caused by the stress of combat, and with other emotional disturbances augmented by the stresses of wartime. Psychiatry began to take an interest in the treatment of less severe emotional disorders. During the twenties a whole series of significant developments occurred in psychiatry. Out-patient clinics were established and the influences of psychoanalysis, psychobiology, psychosomatic medicine, and neurology all began to be felt. Psychiatry also began to be interested in the treatment of children. These changes all had the effect of bringing psychiatry out of the mental hospital as its exclusive locus of work. In 1934, the American Board of Psychiatry and Neurology was established. This body functions as an examining board whereby properly trained and experienced physicians can be evaluated and certified as qualified for the practice of psychiatry or neurology or both.

During the thirties further advances occurred in the understanding of psychological disorders; new treatment techniques were introduced such as insulin shock, metrazol shock, and electro-convulsive therapy. Research was increased and the viewpoints of psychosomatic medicine became increasingly important in training and in treatment in both psychiatric and general hospitals. The private practice of psychiatry increased and the establishment of out-patient psychiatric clinics continued.

World War II caused the public, and the mental health professions, to be acutely aware of the tremendous extent of mental illness in our society as well as the need for doing something about it. The large number of recruits rejected for neuropsychiatric reasons, and the large number of soldiers discharged for emotional unsuitability, served to underline the great need for trained physicians in the field of psychiatry. These experiences, further, served to lessen somewhat the notion that mental illnesses only happen to marginal members of society. Finally, the war created an enormous population of veterans eligible for psychiatric care because of service-connected or service-aggravated emotional disorders.

One result of the heightened interest in psychiatry has been the growth of the American Psychiatric Association. It has shown a steady increase since the war. From 4000 members in 1946 the membership has increased to over 10,000 at present (Table 35 and Figure 9).

In 1923, slightly more than 6 per cent of all physicians who were full-time specialists were in psychiatry and neurology. By the middle of the present decade, something over 8 per cent of full-time specialists were in psychiatry and neurology and of this group about 60 per cent were diplomates of the American Board of Psychiatry and Neurology. Table 36 indicates the yearly total certified by this Board.

It should be noted that over the past thirty-five years an increasing proportion of all physicians enter some specialty. In effect, this means that there are more specialists today than there were thirty-five years ago; and a slightly larger per cent of this larger number of specialists are in the fields of psychiatry and neurology.

The number of full-time specialists in psychiatry has increased somewhat faster than might have been expected from the over-all rate of increase in the number of medical specialists in the past twenty-five years. Nevertheless, the increase in psychiatrists has been spectacular only since World War II and it has not been as great as in some other specialties such as internal medicine, surgery, and obstetrics-gynecology.

Education and Experience Requirements of Psychiatrists.

All psychiatrists are physicians with additional training in the diagnosis and treatment of mental disorders. This means that they

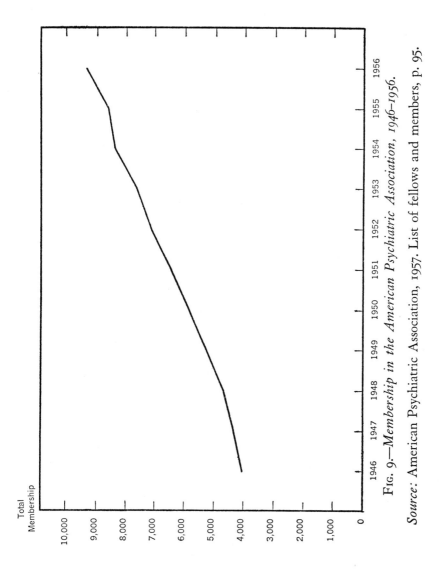

Fig. 9.—*Membership in the American Psychiatric Association, 1946–1956.*

Source: American Psychiatric Association, 1957. List of fellows and members, p. 95.

are graduates of medical schools, have completed internships, and usually have had a residency in a mental hospital.

The educational requirements for fully qualified psychiatrists are long and arduous. After completing high school, the typical student finishes three to four years of college, four years of medical school, and a year of internship by the time he is licensed by a state board to practice medicine. Following licensure, the physician who aspires to practice in the specialty of psychiatry generally seeks a residency in an approved hospital or agency concerned with the diagnosis and treatment of mental and emotional disorders. This residency may last one year, or it may last five; the average is somewhere near three years.

If a physician wishes to qualify for examination and certification as a psychiatrist by the American Board of Psychiatry and Neurology, he must obtain three years' resident training in an approved training center plus two years' practical experience. Thus, we see that it takes thirteen or fourteen years of work beyond high school, ten years beyond graduation from college and six years beyond graduation from medical school before an individual can consider himself fully qualified in the eyes of his peers. As a rule, all this cannot be accomplished before the age of thirty, and it often takes longer as the result of interruptions—for example, military service, illness, or lack of money.

Such certification is not required for the practice of psychiatry. As we have noted, 60 per cent of those physicians who limit their practice to psychiatry are so certified. Many of the psychiatrists in state mental hospitals are not so certified.

Training Standards and the Evaluation of Training Programs in Psychiatry.

The term psychiatrist is actually applied to several groups of physicians with very different levels of training. A physician with one year of practice in a mental hospital may be elected to associate membership in the American Psychiatric Association and may practice psychiatry. Board-certified specialists in psychiatry, as we have noted, are a much more highly trained and specialized group. They have completed at least five years of training and experience in their specialty and have passed a series of difficult written and oral examinations. Still another group of psychiatrists are the psychoanalysts; they have completed, in addition to regular psychiatric training, a personal analysis and a number of supervised training analyses together with additional specialized courses and seminars. We shall have more to say about psychoanalysis below.

These differences in training should be sufficiently clear to indicate that we need to qualify our use of the term psychiatrist with some indication of the nature of his training and certification.

The *Council on Medical Education and Hospitals* of the American Medical Association is the principal accrediting group for medical education in the United States. Members of the Council are elected by the House of Delegates of the AMA. Among the functions of the Council are the accreditation of medical schools and the approval of both internship and residency programs. The *Advisory Board for Medical Specialties* was established by the AMA in 1934. The Board advises the *Council on Medical Education and Hospitals* on matters relating to the medical specialties. The Board coordinates regular medical education and gives official approval to the various medical specialty examining boards that have come into being over the years. Membership on the Board consists of elected representatives of the various specialty examining boards together with members from other national medical organizations interested in medical education and certification.

The various specialty examining boards must themselves be approved by the Council and by the *Advisory Board for Medical Specialties* on the basis of standards formulated by the Council. At present there are nineteen approved examining and certifying boards, one being the *American Board of Psychiatry and Neurology,* established in 1934.

The primary purpose of the specialty boards is to certify practitioners and to specify training standards. The boards advise physicians who desire certification with respect to their course of study and training, determine whether candidates for voluntary certification have received adequate preparation as defined by the Board, provide comprehensive written and oral examinations to determine the competence of such candidates, and certify the qualifications of those who successfully demonstrate their satisfactory training and knowledge. The boards stimulate the development of adequate training facilities by aiding the *Council on Medical Education and Hospitals* in setting minimum standards of education and training in the specialties and by evaluating the residencies under consideration by the Council.

An institution applies to the Council for approval of a residency training program in psychiatry. The Council then conducts a survey of the institution to determine whether the residency complies with the Council's "Essentials of Approved Residencies and Fellowships." A report of the findings of the survey is submitted to the specialty board concerned for its recommendations. Approval may then be granted by the Council.

Subspecialties in psychiatry are not specifically approved by the *American Board of Psychiatry and Neurology*. Psychiatrists are examined in neurology, and neurologists are examined in psychiatry, and certification usually is in one or the other of the two fields; there is no specific certification in child psychiatry or psychoanalysis made by this Board.

Child psychiatry is a subspecialty in the field with widespread recognition, but it is not accredited as such by the *American Board of Psychiatry and Neurology*. The *American Association of Psychiatric Clinics for Children* does evaluate clinics for training approval—but only those clinics that are members of the Association. As training in child psychiatry ordinarily begins at the third year of graduate psychiatric training, and as two years of residency training approved by the *American Board of Psychiatry and Neurology* are prerequisite to training at an AAPCC clinic, training in these clinics generally has been credited by the *American Board of Psychiatry and Neurology* as a third year of residency. This arrangement also applies to other training centers in child psychiatry that are not members of the AAPCC but which meet the requirements for residency training of the American Board.

A further complication of this picture is provided by the Ameri-

can Psychoanalytic Association. It approves and accredits psychoanalytic institutes and training centers on the basis of requirements
defined by the Association. This group establishes minimum requirements for applicants for training, certifies those who successfully complete training, and defines the procedures whereby certified analysts become recognized as qualified specialists within the
psychoanalytic field.

PRESENT AND FUTURE MANPOWER PROSPECTS IN PSYCHIATRY

We have seen in the first part of this report that there is no simple
way of assessing shortages in the mental health professions. The
number of psychiatrists a country needs is dependent on the aspirations of the people and on the standard of living of the country.
No simple statement of need has meaning. On the basis of our examination of the various indices of manpower shortage we can say,
however, with some confidence that there are not nearly as many
psychiatrists in the United States as there should be. We have found
no one who would argue with this statement.

There is, in the United States, approximately one psychiatrist to
every 18,000 people. This does not mean, of course, that psychiatrists
and people are evenly distributed within the country. In the northeastern section of the country there is one psychiatrist to 11,000
people but in the southern region, if we do not include the District
of Columbia, there is one psychiatrist to each 34,000 people. Certain states are relatively well off in the availability of psychiatric
service and other states have next to no service available. Data
illustrating these relationships are to be found in Table 37 for the
various regions, and on a state basis. Also in the Appendix, Table
32 illustrates the relationship between the size of a state in population and the number of psychiatrists available. Ranking the states
according to population and according to the number of psychiatrists results in a rank order correlation of .87, indicating substantial
relationship.

A Congressional Inquiry on Mental Illness conducted by the

House Committee on Interstate and Foreign Commerce (1953) concluded its hearings with the judgment that the country needed at least twice as many psychiatrists as were available. It does not seem likely that such an increase in the number of psychiatrists available is in prospect for the foreseeable future. Blain (1956) shows that we are gaining only some 450 psychiatrists a year after allowing for loss to the profession due to death and retirement. At that rate of gain, he figures that it would be twenty years before we would be able to double the number of psychiatrists in the country. But as we have seen, our population continues to grow, and the demand for mental health services continues to increase, so that our need for mental health professional personnel rises along with whatever increase in supply is occurring.

There are other facts suggesting that Blain's figures on our rate of gain in psychiatry are too optimistic. Gorman (1956, p. 150) calls attention to the following: "Of the approximately 450 doctors who complete the three-year psychiatric residency, an average of 250 each year immediately go into private practice. This leaves public psychiatry with about 200 recruits, little more than enough to replace the older psychiatrists who die off or retire."

Because of the tendency of young psychiatrists who are completing their training to go into private practice, the shortage of psychiatrists is most acute in public and nonprofit hospitals and agencies and in psychiatric research. Earnings in public agencies, as we have noted, tend to be considerably lower than in independent practice. The same low salaries are the case in research positions, almost all of them salaried positions. The Group for the Advancement of Psychiatry (1955, p. 2) says: "Despite increased facilities and sums available for research in psychiatry, the present trend of psychiatric trainees is to enter into the practice of psychiatry, with emphasis upon psychotherapy and the shock therapies, rather than to undertake research."

There is one additional pessimistic factor to be considered in attempting to ascertain our rate of gain or loss in psychiatric manpower. A sizable proportion of those young psychiatrists in residency training are foreign citizens, graduates of foreign medical schools, who enter the United States under the provisions of the United States Information and Exchange Act of 1948. They are required to return home upon completion of their education, although many find a way to apply for citizenship; unless they remain in the United States, they do not represent any real gain in permanent psychiatric manpower. This group inflates figures on the number of psychiatrists completing training. While they do offer service to the institutions and agencies in which they serve as house officers they do not stay on as staff members in any great numbers.

It seems clear from the foregoing that the prospect for the future is a continuing decline in the number of psychiatrists available for public agencies and institutions. One result has been that states raise salaries and begin competing with each other for the small number of personnel available and willing to work in public hospital settings. *Time* (1955) quoted the governor of Indiana as saying: "Eventually we will have to stop this bidding against each other. There has got to be some common ground of salaries and mutual consideration . . . These interstate raids on mental-health institutions for personnel sometimes get to be like the raids to build up rival football teams."

Factors Affecting the Supply of Psychiatrists.

What are the chances of our increasing our future supply of psychiatrists? Can a significant increase be achieved?

The number of psychiatrists completing their training is related directly to the number of young physicians graduating from medical school who decide to specialize in psychiatry and who enter residency training in this field. In recent years the status of psychiatry has improved enormously and strenuous efforts have been made, directly and indirectly, to encourage more young physicians to enter into psychiatric training. Despite these efforts, there has been no significant increase in the percentage of all medical residencies that are in psychiatry. Table 38 in the Appendix indicates the number of first-year residencies filled in all medical specialties and the number of first-year psychiatric residencies that were filled during the past several years. About 8 per cent of all first-year residencies are filled by medical school graduates pursuing graduate education in psychiatry. If we examine the data for *all* residencies filled (first year through fifth year), and for all psychiatric residencies filled, we find the percentage fairly constant at around 9 per cent .

These figures suggest that there is not likely to be any sizable increase in the number of psychiatrists because there is no sizable increase in prospect in the number of physicians completing their medical education. This subject is discussed in some detail below. For the moment, we need only remember that, because all psychiatrists must be physicians, the number of people who enter psychiatric training is directly affected by the number who complete their medical education.

The number of medical school graduates has increased from some 6000 a year during the first three years of this decade to nearly 7000 during the past three years. Table 39 shows the relationship between the number of medical school graduates and the number of first-year residents in psychiatry. The average over the past five years suggests that the number of first-year residents in psychiatry is equal to approximately 10 per cent of the number of medical school graduates that year.

If we estimate the number of medical school graduates for the next few years, using information on present freshmen class size in medical schools, and present attrition rates, we can predict that the nation's medical schools, including our newly established schools, will be turning out almost 7500 physicians a year by 1965. This does not offer much hope for any sizable increase in the number of psychiatrists.

While this method of estimating future psychiatric manpower may be conservative, it is difficult to see how any serious error is involved. If we were to double the size of classes in our medical schools, or if we were to double the number of schools, 10 per cent of the additional graduates entering psychiatry would not enable us to catch up with our estimates of need. There is little prospect, as we shall see, of any such large increase in medical school graduates.

Of course another way exists to increase the number of psychiatrists in training. If a larger proportion of medical school graduates

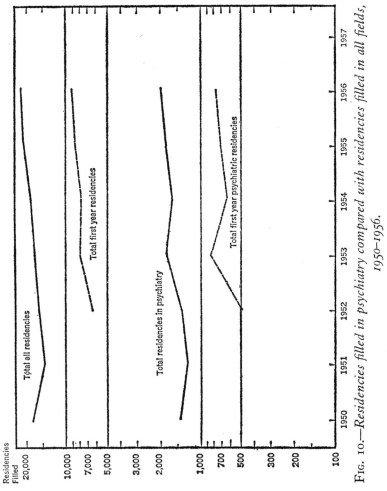

Fig. 10.—*Residencies filled in psychiatry compared with residencies filled in all fields, 1950–1956.*

Source: Journal of the American Medical Association. Annual residency issues.

were to be recruited into psychiatry the same result would be accomplished as would be the case if we continued to get essentially the same percentage of an increased number of medical school graduates. Again the data do not support the possibility of this increase in recruits coming about. Table 40 indicates that the per cent of available residencies filled in psychiatry has consistently been smaller than the per cent filled of residencies in all specialties. Other medical specialties have expanded residency opportunities too, and they are at least as successful as psychiatry in recruiting students.

Each year more residency programs are approved and more residencies are offered throughout the country. Since the end of the Second World War the number of residencies offered in psychiatry has nearly doubled. Table 41 indicates the number of residencies in psychiatry offered and filled at the first-year level and at all levels for the past decade.

This table, when considered alone, suggests that approximately 70 per cent of first-year residencies in psychiatry are filled year by year and slightly more than this percentage of all psychiatric residencies are filled. Taken by themselves these data would suggest that there has been a rapid increase in the number of psychiatrists trained and that the prospects for the future are fairly good. But there is a catch, as already indicated.

Foreign Physicians in Specialty Training.

The hidden factor that deflates our optimistic picture is the rapid increase in the number of foreign physicians who have been accepted as house officers in hospitals in the United States. This increase masks a plateau in the number of United States physicians in advanced training (Table 42).

In recent years there has been a marked increase in the number of foreign physicians entering the United States for graduate medical training. During the past several years the number of foreign physicians in all medical specialty residencies has increased rapidly until they now account for at least one fourth of all residencies filled (Table 43 and Figure 11). Without them, hospitals would be faced with even greater numbers of unfilled house staff positions—even *with* them vacancies are now running to 30 per cent for internships and 20 per cent for residencies.

In psychiatry, some 25 per cent of residencies filled are occupied by foreign physicians, as indicated by Table 44 and Figure 12. In 1956, 28 per cent of approved psychiatric residencies were vacant despite the presence of these physicians from abroad. Without the foreign trainees, 45 per cent of all available psychiatric residencies would have been unfilled.

If one quarter of the physicians now in residencies in psychiatry are from abroad and will return home when their training is completed (and this is the requirement of the law), then we must revise our estimates of future psychiatric manpower downward some 25 per cent if these estimates are based on the total number of residents finishing their training. (There is some uncertainty about how many of these foreign citizens remain in the United States after their training is completed. Recent evidence, not complete, suggests that increasing numbers do remain here and apply for citizenship.)

The Joint Information Service (1957) reported a recent survey of psychiatric residency training in the United States. In August, 1956, they counted 2074 physicians who were psychiatric residents in 215 training centers in this country.

Of this number, graduates of foreign medical schools comprised 33.2 per cent of all the residents in training in psychiatry. It is important to note that some of these graduates of foreign medical schools were American citizens who had studied medicine abroad although it is certain that a majority of the group were foreign citizens.

Nearly half of all the residents in psychiatric training were in the New England and the Middle Atlantic States. Half the residents were in their thirties and an additional 35 per cent were under thirty years of age.

Nearly a fourth of all physicians in state mental hospitals were residents and most of these were foreign trained. More than half the foreign trained physicians in psychiatry found residencies in the state hospitals, but significant numbers (23 per cent) were in uni-

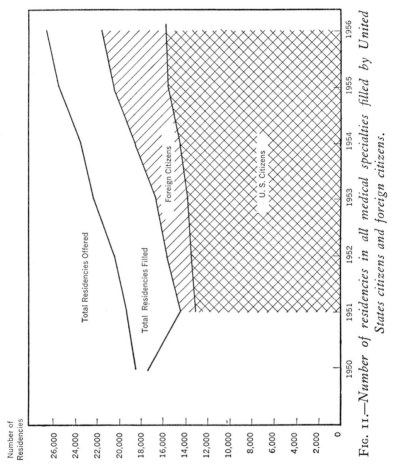

Source: Health Resources Advisory Committee, 1957. Unpublished data.

FIG. 11.—*Number of residencies in all medical specialties filled by United States citizens and foreign citizens.*

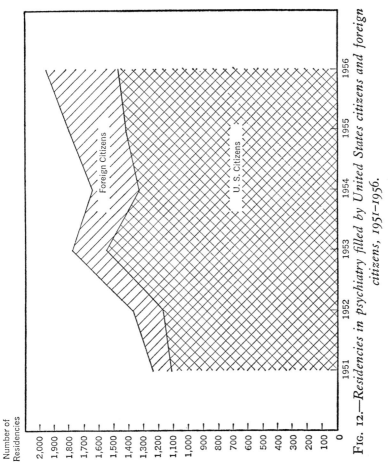

FIG. 12.—*Residencies in psychiatry filled by United States citizens and foreign citizens, 1951–1956.*

Source: Journal of the American Medical Association. Annual residency issues. Health Resources Advisory Committee, 1957. Unpublished data.

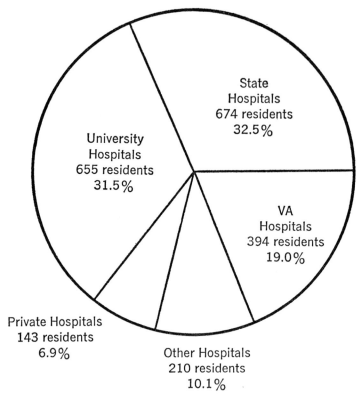

FIG. 13.—*Distribution of psychiatric residents by type of training center,*
1956.

Source: Joint Information Service of the American Psychiatric Association
and the National Association for Mental Health, 1957. *Physicians train-*
ing in U.S. psychiatric training centers, August, 1956, p. 2.

versity affiliated centers and 11 per cent were in other hospitals and
centers.

Some 900 of the 1400 hospitals in the United States with approved
graduate medical education programs (in all specialties) had one
or more alien physicians in training. About half of these alien
physicians were concentrated in New York, Ohio, Illinois, and New
Jersey. New Jersey had 68 per cent of its house staff filled by alien
physicians. In the five-year period from 1950–1951 to 1955–1956, the
number of alien physicians increased 280 per cent from 2072 to 7873.

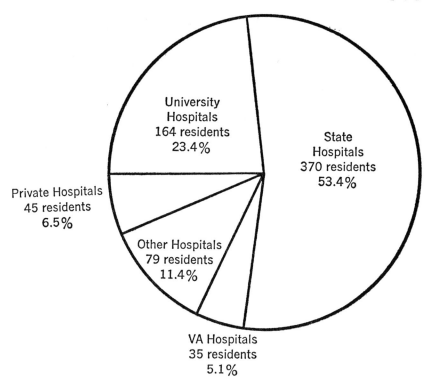

Fig. 14.—*Distribution of foreign-trained physicians in residency training in the United States, 1956.*

Source: Joint Information Service of the American Psychiatric Association and the National Association for Mental Health, 1957. *Physicians training in U.S. psychiatric training centers,* August, 1956, p. 3.

In this same period the citizen-physician group in house staff positions decreased about 1 per cent. Tables 45 and 46 show the distribution of alien physicians by region and state.

Where the total number of residents in medical specialties increased from slightly more than 18,000 to slightly more than 21,000 (16 per cent) since 1950, all of the increase is accounted for by the alien physician group which increased more than 300 per cent during this time. As a matter of fact, the number of citizens taking residencies decreased by more than 7 per cent during this same interval. These data (from *Hospitals,* 30, January 16, 1956) are not in exact agreement with data from the Health Resources Advisory Committee (1957) cited in Table 43. But the discrepancies are not large and the implications are the same. The total of medical residencies filled by United States citizens has not increased over this decade.

Selection of Psychiatric Students.

Aspiring psychiatrists are a highly selected group, drawn from a very rigidly defined pool of prospects. A psychiatrist is first of all a physician. Psychiatric residents must, therefore, have completed their training in medicine. In general, competition among medical specialties is such that medical school graduates interested in specialties have little difficulty finding an approved residency in the specialty of their choice.

A very large number of vacancies exists on hospital staffs. In spite of the presence on hospital staffs of 6000 foreign interns and residents in 1956 there were that year more than 7000 unfilled internships and residencies. This means that the selection of people who enter psychiatry is largely self-selection. These individuals have already completed a long succession of academic and other hurdles. Now they are selected largely because they are interested in a specialty field. Certain highly regarded psychiatric training centers receive many more applications for residencies than they can accept, but this is the exception rather than the rule. It is very probable that almost any physician seeking a residency in psychiatry will be able to find some sort of residency training.

In spite of the popular notion that most psychiatrists are a little peculiar, the Menninger Study (Holt and Luborsky, 1958) found that a great majority of psychiatric residents were normal, healthy, conventional, and well-adjusted people. Applicants for residencies who are seriously disturbed are either screened out in advance or tend not to complete their training. The few disturbed people who do go through some kind of psychiatric training program have been found to drift away from psychiatry into general practice because of their inability to find and maintain a satisfactory practice in the field.

The Changing Status of Psychiatry.

The status which a medical specialty enjoys cannot help but affect the number and the kind of medical students attracted to the specialized field.

The status of psychiatry within medicine has improved markedly in recent years, although most observers see some continuing cleavage between psychiatry and the rest of medicine.

Early in this century, and before, the practice of psychiatry did not attract many outstanding students, limited as it was to employment in large mental institutions where the primary responsibility of the physician was diagnosis and custodial supervision. With the introduction of psychoanalytic training in this country there was a sharp change in the kind of student attracted to the field. According to Knight (1953), physicians in training as psychiatrists during the 1920's and 1930's tended to be an individualistic, introspective, and intellectual group, most of whom were attracted to the theoretical, and relatively esoteric, field of psychoanalysis.

With the movement of many psychoanalytic psychiatrists into medical education, and with the improved status and popular acceptance of psychiatry following World War II, the type of student attracted to residencies in psychiatry has again changed. Holt and Luborsky suggest that the young physician choosing psychiatry today is no longer in any sense "peculiar," but rather is following a socially approved and prestigeful path. Because of this change they suggest that present-day residents tend to be less preoccupied with theory, less introspective, and on the whole, perhaps, more ordinary. They are no longer avid readers of the psychoanalytic literature but rather they complete assignments and training requirements as quickly as possible. Most of them look forward to private practice as their goal.

Cost of Training in Psychiatry.

It is extremely difficult to calculate the cost of specialty training in medicine. The cost of eight years of college and medical school varies enormously depending on the college chosen and the medical school attended. State universities tend, on the whole, to be less expensive both at the undergraduate and at the professional school level than private universities. Following completion of college and medical school, the aspiring psychiatrist accepts a year-long internship at very low pay. In 1955, according to the Bureau of Labor Statistics (1957), the average intern earned $120 to $170 a month depending on the location of the hospital. Some of the best teaching hospitals pay little or nothing. Residencies in psychiatry are also not sufficiently remunerative to allow the aspiring psychiatrist to keep out of debt. Many psychiatrists spend ten to fourteen years after high school completing their training. The cost of this training in tuition and living expenses together with lost earnings during this period make psychiatry one of the most expensive professional fields. While stipends for psychiatric residents have been pushed upward and exceed most other specialty stipends they still are insufficient for most residents to make ends meet.

There are signs that medical school administrators are looking with some question on the increasing pressures that are being brought to bear on medical school students and graduates in attempts to expand training programs in psychiatry.

Dean William W. Frye of the School of Medicine at Louisiana State University cautioned the Conference on Psychiatrists sponsored by the Southern Regional Education Board (1956) that a medical school's major function is rounded undergraduate training, not specialized training. Further, Dean Frye said, increased financial support and emphasis on psychiatry unbalances the program. Stipends in psychiatry, he felt, are out of line with those in other medical specialties.

PSYCHOANALYSIS

There are two main streams of thought and theory within psychiatry in the United States today. One group of psychiatrists emphasizes organic (somatic, neurological, biochemical) and constitutional factors in mental disorder and approaches the problem of treatment with drugs, physical techniques, and surgery. A second group of psychiatrists emphasizes the psychological approach to etiology, diagnosis, and treatment. Occasionally both views are combined in one person, who has been able to integrate them, but this is the exception.

Because of the growing strength and influence of psychoanalysis, we will look for a moment at the manpower situation in this highly specialized field. Our failure to take special note, in a similar way, of those areas of psychiatry which emphasize a different approach is partly due to the lack of available studies and partly because the organic and constitutional approach represents a mainstream of psychiatry.

One other reservation needs to be noted about our discussion of psychoanalysis. We use available data on members of the American Psychoanalytic Association. There are other groups of professional persons practicing various forms of psychoanalysis not recognized by this Association. We have not the time, or the skill, to trace the intricacies of doctrinal disputes and professional disagreements about methods and qualifications in psychoanalysis. The reader is cautioned that there are other analysts not counted and other approaches to analysis not mentioned. In any event the number of people involved is not large—we are neglecting hundreds, not thousands.

There has been a slow but steady growth, both in numbers and in acceptance, of psychoanalysis in the United States. This has been true despite frequent bickering and schisms both between psychoanalysis and the outside world, and within the field itself.

In 1908, Abraham A. Brill returned from Bleuler's analytically oriented clinic in Zurich filled with enthusiasm for the new method. He entered the private practice of psychoanalysis in New York, thus becoming America's first full-time practicing analyst.

A year later, in 1909, G. Stanley Hall invited Freud to deliver a series of lectures at Clark University. It was the first official academic recognition of his work and Freud's five lectures "On Psychoanalysis" are now considered classics. Freud later wrote of the satisfaction the experience gave him: ". . . in Europe I felt myself as an outcast—here I perceived myself accepted by the best men as an equal." (Oberndorf, 1953.)

The American Psychoanalytic Association was founded in 1911 with eight members. By 1925, it had thirty-three members. These early years were marked by frequent doctrinal disputes within the various groups interested in analysis and, down to the present, internal struggle and debate has continued in several local groups. Despite these internal problems, the number of members of the American Psychoanalytic Association has increased from year to year to its present 754 members, as of November 1958 (see Table 47). In addition, there are 888 students in training institutes recognized by the Psychoanalytic Association.

By 1936, the American group was ready to break away from the International Psychoanalytic Association, especially in order to set its own standards for training institutes. The American group notified the International Association two years later that it would no longer recognize membership in a foreign psychoanalytic society as sufficient evidence of competence for practice in the United States. The withdrawal of American support, the emigration of many European analysts, and the beginning of World War II sharply reduced the effectiveness and influence of the International Association. The focus and center of psychoanalysis shifted to the United States. For example:

	International Membership	American Association Membership
1925	210	33
1931	307	68
1952	762	448
1958		754

One of the principal sources of contention between American and European schools of thought on psychoanalysis was the question of lay analysis, quite acceptable in Europe. The founders and early advocates of psychoanalysis in the United States had been medically trained and as time passed the requirement of previous medical training came to be a shibboleth to American analytic institutes, this despite Freud's frequent and increasingly embittered objections to the American position. While some exceptions have been allowed, and are still made, to the requirement of prior medical training, and while some potentially strong nonmedical analytic groups have come into being, by and large the pattern has continued to be held. Admission to formal analytic training, with the exceptions noted, requires graduation from a Class A medical school, a year of internship, and a year of full-time training in psychiatry. Prospective psychoanalysts must sign a pledge not to represent themselves as analysts until authorized to do so by a training institute of the Association.

These restrictions, together with the years of training required for completion of all requirements, including at least 300 hours of personal analysis, and 200 hours of supervised analysis, mean that the production of psychoanalysts is a very slow process.

The pattern of development of formal training in psychoanalysis has historical origins to be found in the reactions to the antipathy that European medical schools displayed toward Freud's work at the turn of the century and in the succeeding decades. It became the custom for those interested in psychoanalysis to first have a didactic analysis in a training center separated from a university. The first formal analytic institute was organized in Berlin in the 1920's. Trainees at the institute had their own didactic analysis and also instruction in theory and practice. This pattern largely has been followed since.

In the United States a similar pattern has developed with analytic institutes growing up independently of universities and of psychiatric training centers. Problems have arisen because many residents in psychiatry want psychoanalytic training concurrently with their residencies. Psychiatric training centers near analytic institutes have had little trouble attracting residents, though problems arise in supervision, in service, and in financing training. On the other hand, residency centers far removed from psychoanalytic institutes have, on the average, fewer applicants. Relations between residency training centers and analytic institutes are moving slowly toward more integrated programs though many exceptions still exist. The Group for the Advancement of Psychiatry (1955) notes this trend toward integration and expresses concern that changes are being based on inadequately supported opinion rather than on objective study.

A recent study reported by Potter, Klein, and Goodenough (1957) has obtained information about the financial problems and hardships encountered by psychiatric residents, especially those in analytic training, or who plan to enter analytic training later.

The study obtained information from some 700 trainees in psychiatric residency programs and in analytic training centers. Complete anonymity was permitted the respondents and the sample on which the study was based included at least 70 per cent of the students.

The sample was almost evenly divided between trainees in psychoanalytic institutes (349) and residents in psychiatric training centers (335). Nearly half of the psychiatric resident group was in personal analysis. This means that, at the time of the study, three-quarters of all psychiatrists in training in the geographic areas and training centers concerned were in analysis. (It should be noted that there is some bias in this figure, in that the twenty-eight residency centers surveyed were those near analytic institutes.) Moreover, a large majority of the residents not in analysis hoped to secure this training later.

Analytic training is expensive. The median expenditure for personal analysis for those in training was $3000 a year, though for some the cost was as high as $5000. Ninety per cent of the young physicians in analysis paid $15 or more an hour for their own analysis, and 40 per cent paid $20 or more. Further, we should remember that after the young physician finishes his personal analysis he must undertake control analyses in which he pays his supervising analyst at approximately the same rate per hour as he paid for his own analysis. Tuition for required psychoanalytic courses adds an average of $850 a year for those in the institutes.

In addition to these training expenses the resident must pay his living expenses and, as three quarters are married and half have children, he must find ways of supporting his family during his lengthy training. The median living expenses of residents in the survey were $4000.

Let us look at the financial problem of a typical psychiatric resident who is in his second year of a three-year residency. He has begun his personal analysis in order not to delay by two or more years his eventual completion of training. His living expenses are $4000 a year. His analysis is costing him $3000 a year. But his pay as a resident is only $3000 a year. This means that by the end of his third year as a psychiatric resident he will be several thousand dollars in debt unless (1) he is wealthy, (2) his wife is able to work, which often means delaying having a family, (3) he can get a stipend or grant from some source, or (4) he engages in private practice in addition to his full-time duties as a resident and in addition to the time and energy required for his personal analysis.

Actually the survey found that few residents had enough savings to see them through and at least two-thirds expected to be in debt at the end of their residencies. Half of the group in analysis had received gifts or grants, though generally these covered only a fraction of the deficit. Nearly all of the married residents without children reported income from their wives' employment and nearly a third of those with children reported that their wives worked.

The residency training is supposed to be a full-time educational experience. Yet from 40 to 75 per cent of all third-year residents in analysis or analytic training admit on the questionnaire participation in private practice. Psychiatric residents not in analysis report much less private practice.

There are several problems associated with our present system of analytic training. The medical graduate aspiring to become an analyst must look forward to years of low income and high expenses, stretching through and beyond his residency training. Usually he must undertake some private practice to augment his income during his analytic training and even during his psychiatric residency. As a result of the geographic restrictions imposed by the need to remain close to the analytic institute, he tends to build up personal and professional ties which restrict his later mobility. This results in a heavy concentration of analysts in geographic areas near the institutes. The length of training means that the newly certified analyst is thirty-five or forty before he begins to practice and usually he has built up sizable debts so that he concentrates on earning a large income.

Among the ways the report suggested to improve the financial problems of the student in analytic training are (a) increased loans and grants to students, (b) lowered fees for personal analyses and control analyses, (c) combining psychiatric and psychoanalytic training in residencies, (d) arrangement for supervised private practice to be part of residency training, (e) absorption of analytic training costs by medical schools and hospitals through use of staff analysts.

Appel (1957) points out cautions that are necessary in viewing our American enthusiasm for psychoanalysis. Analysts can handle only a few cases a year. As a result, psychoanalysis as a form of treatment is now limited to students in training analysis, part-pay patients in institutes and clinics, and patients who can afford the heavy expense involved in private analytic treatment.

Appel believes that the popularity of psychoanalysis in the United States, in contrast to many European countries, is because it fits in with our ethos to the effect that anything is possible and can be accomplished. He points out, too, that psychoanalysis is good business and profitable. This is not to say that Appel, or most leaders of American psychiatry, are opposed to psychoanalysis. The problem is a failure in widespread realization of the relative inaccessibility of psychoanalytic treatment for most citizens (see Tables 29 and 48). "One thousand analysts cannot make much of a dent in this problem except through teaching, research, public education, and the creation of optimism in public demand for more psychiatrists," said Appel.

While the American Psychoanalytic Association continues to grow steadily (Table 47), it is most unlikely that analysts will ever be available in sufficient numbers to be of any real importance in the *direct* therapeutic alleviation of the problem of mental disorder. Rather, psychoanalysis has had its most fundamental effect in providing an orientation and conceptual framework which professional workers in the field of mental health can use in their daily work. The gradual adoption of analytic theory in large segments of psychiatry, social work, education, and other fields has had far-reaching consequences. As Kaufman (1950) has shown, most psychoanalysts are occupied with teaching duties in addition to their work with patients. He reports that nearly 60 per cent of the members of the Association were teaching in various centers not including the analytic institutes. If the latter group is counted then only 12 per cent of all analysts have no teaching duties.

Surveys of residency training centers in psychiatry have shown the widespread use of analytic formulations of mental disorder in psychiatric training and the high incidence of aspirations to analysis by psychiatrists in training.

Far from being outside the pale, psychoanalysis now occupies a strong place in the mainstream of American psychiatry, many of whose leaders are themselves analysts.

III

Manpower Prospects in Medicine

THERE ARE at least two compelling reasons why a survey of mental health manpower should concern itself with the supply of physicians, both at present and in prospect.

The first reason, already mentioned, is that the supply of psychiatrists is intimately bound to the number of physicians trained. Because all psychiatrists must have completed a medical education, the number of persons finishing medical school represents the limited manpower pool from which new psychiatrists may be recruited.

A second reason for being concerned with manpower in medicine is broader in scope. Every definition of mental health includes some reference to the importance of freedom both from unnecessary concern with health and for protection against the catastrophic effects of illness, or, on the larger scale, for victory over the widespread plagues of mankind.

For both of these reasons, therefore, we will look briefly at manpower prospects in medicine. Few subjects are so emotionally loaded as the questions of whether or not there are enough physicians in the United States and whether or not the availability of medical service is increasing or decreasing with our growing population.

ARE THERE ENOUGH PHYSICIANS?
WILL THERE BE ENOUGH?

The United States population is growing by approximately three million people a year. If this growth is maintained, and most population experts think that it will be maintained for a number of years, there will be some 250 million people in the United States within twenty-five years. This growth in total population exceeds, proportionately, the anticipated growth of the nation's medical school enrollments and graduates.

According to the Bureau of Labor Statistics (1957), some 4500 physicians die or retire each year. Nearly 7000 physicians now graduate from our medical schools annually, and it is expected that by 1960 some 7300 will graduate each year, with a small continued increase expected thereafter. It is important for us to note that our present rate of increase in physicians represents a gain of only some 3000 physicians a year. This is not enough to keep up with the increase in the population of the country. We are preparing physicians in the ratio of one to 1000 people for the increase in our population (taking into account the need for replacement of physicians leaving the field in the general population); the ratio for the general population is now one to 730 people.

The implications of this divergence are bitterly debated among proponents of different views concerning the adequacy of medical service at present and projected.

One view holds that, as new drugs and improved clinical techniques become more widely available to physicians, the number of patients that a doctor can treat increases enormously with no decrease in quality of medical treatment. The opposite view is that the nation will find itself confronted before long with a tremendous shortage of physicians unless drastic steps are taken soon to increase the supply of medical school graduates to the point where some sort of balance may be kept between total population and physicians available. The group arguing that there is no real problem believes that distribution of physicians, rather than their number, is the major difficulty to be solved.

Proponents of the view that there are enough physicians, but that they are not properly distributed, argue that if relatively small numbers of physicians were relocated there would be no difficulty. F. G. Dickinson, Director of the Bureau of Medical Economic Research of the American Medical Association, points out that scarcely ⅛ of 1 per cent of the population of the country is more than twenty-five

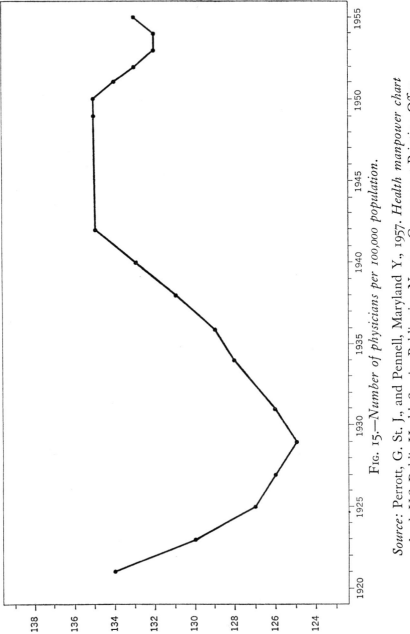

FIG. 15.—*Number of physicians per 100,000 population.*

Source: Perrott, G. St. J., and Pennell, Maryland Y., 1957. *Health manpower chart book.* U.S. Public Health Service Publication No. 511, Government Printing Office.

miles from the nearest doctor in active practice (see Clark, M., 1958). No one can say what is the ideal distance.

An increasing number of people take an opposite view. Recently the *New York Times* (Clark, M., 1958) quoted Dudley Kirk of Population Council as saying that the medical profession should anticipate a tremendous increase in the demand for medical services, and that too few physicians were being trained to meet this demand. Howard A. Rusk (1958) said: "To maintain our present physician-population ratios—one to every 730 persons—we will then [1975] need 315,000 physicians. We now have approximately 225,000 and our current rate of increase is around 3000, compared to a need of around 5250."

It seems highly improbable that the medical schools will soon be turning out the 10,000–15,000 new physicians a year that would be required to keep up with population growth. The medical schools have a number of serious financial problems, and there are strong resistances within organized medicine, for other reasons, to a sharp increase in the number or size of medical schools. While it has been possible to recruit some physicians from Canada, Europe, and Asia, these sources are not altogether satisfactory because of different standards of training, particularly among the European and Asiatic universities, and also because of the serious need for physicians in most foreign countries.

It seems probable that we will continue recruiting foreign physicians although opposition to the practice of using foreign residents has been growing in recent years. A typical criticism is one by McCormack and Feraru (1955), who complain about the quality of medical training of physicians from abroad. These writers indicate in strong terms their concern about the large and impersonal lecture classes that comprise much of the medical training of physicians from many foreign countries, and they go so far as to see in these visitors a serious threat to the safety and well-being of our hospital patients. On the other hand, some medical spokesmen have expressed gratification over the fact that the United States now has an opportunity to repay in kind for the reverse flow of students during the earlier part of this century when many American students studied in the medical centers of Europe.

One of the favorite arguments used in debating the question of whether the United States is training enough physicians involves a comparison between "then" and now. The difficulty is in deciding how to choose the proper "then." For example, Turner (1955) argues that larger numbers of physicians are being trained now in comparison with then. He says: "While the population of the nation has approximately doubled during this period [1900–1954], in the forty-four years since 1910 student enrollment in approved schools of medicine increased from 12,530 to 28,229, which represented a total increase of 125.8 per cent. In 1910 there were 3165 physicians graduated from approved medical schools as compared to 6861 in 1954, the latter figure representing an increase of 114.6 per cent."

The difficulty with these figures is to be found in the expression "approved schools of medicine." Abraham Flexner (1910) completed his well-known investigation and report on medical education in the year that Turner uses as a base for his comparison. Flexner classed sixty-six schools as Class A "Approved" and sixty-five others Class B and C "Unapproved" schools. In 1910 the "Unapproved" schools had 8996 students enrolled. If we add this group to the enrollment in the "Approved" schools this brings total enrollment to 21,526. If we use this latter figure as a basis for comparison with "now," this would mean an increase in enrollment of only 36 per cent instead of the 125.8 per cent quoted above. The "Unapproved" schools had 1275 students who graduated in 1910 making a total of 4440 new physicians turned out by all schools. The increase to 6861 in 1954 would therefore be just 55 per cent rather than the 115 per cent Turner quotes.

It is true that many graduates of Class C schools were not especially able or well-trained physicians and they were denied licenses in many states. If we compare only the graduates of A and B schools with present rates, something Turner himself does in another article, we find that enrollments have increased 69 per cent and medical school graduates 89 per cent during the period in which the country's population has doubled.

As justification for these alternative comparisons it can be pointed out that graduates of B and C schools were considered physicians in 1910 and as such were counted by the Census; they performed and practiced. They also joined the American Medical Association which in 1910 had a membership of 121,484. By 1950, the AMA membership was 201,277. The AMA membership increased 66 per cent during the period when the population of the country doubled.

Several new medical schools in the United States and Canada are in the process of getting under way so that the total output of students will increase somewhat for the next few years. After that, unless some drastic action is taken soon, we can only conclude that the supply of physicians will decrease in proportion to the population.

Most of the quoted ratios of physicians to population use the total membership of the American Medical Association in ratio to the total population of the country. It is necessary for us to note that a fairly large proportion of AMA members do not actually practice medicine. Many physicians are in full-time research, others spend most of their time teaching, and still others are in administrative positions or service jobs where little of their time is devoted to the practice of medicine.

PROBLEMS OF MEDICAL EDUCATION

There are in the United States seventy-eight approved medical schools with full four-year curricula, four two-year basic science schools, and three new schools with provisional approval. The operating budget of these eighty-two medical schools exceeds 110 million dollars per year. Student tuition accounts for some 20 million, or less than one-fifth of their total expenditure. The balance must be made up in various ways. In the case of state and city schools, much of the difference is appropriated from tax revenues, and in the case of private medical schools much of the deficit is made up from endowments, grants, and gifts. With our continuing monetary inflation, the income from all sources continues to be less than required. Resistance to increasing appropriations on the part of legislatures means a tightening of the belt for state and municipal schools while private medical schools must look to gifts and subscriptions to make ends meet.

Another problem of medical schools, which ultimately will raise costs, is the pressure for increased faculty salaries. Despite the prestige that traditionally has gone with faculty appointments to medical schools, it is increasingly difficult to recruit highly qualified teachers on a full-time basis. Part-time lecturers and demonstrators in medical schools are on the increase. The low salaries tend to be an obstacle to the recruitment of topflight faculty on a full-time basis. Some schools arrange for their faculty members to earn additional income each year by taking off time for private practice, or by permitting faculty members to use their offices to see private patients. In either case, the medical school loses because the time ordinarily devoted to research and study is now used for personal income. According to the *JAMA* (1958, November 16), there were 331 budgeted, unfilled full-time positions on medical school faculties, an increase of 30 per cent in two years. Faculty salaries will have to be raised or the quality of medical education will have to decline.

In addition to the shortages of physicians on the staffs of medical schools, there is also a growing shortage of trained specialists in the basic sciences on which the practice of medicine rests. In another part of this report we have pointed to the growing shortage of people trained in basic sciences such as biology, physiology, anatomy, physics, psychology, and sociology. Deficiencies in preprofessional education cannot help but be reflected as difficulties later for the professional schools. The decline in the quality of preprofessional academic work of medical students is evident in Table 49.

Because of the high cost of medical education, the shortage of faculty members, and the resistance to any sharp increase in the number of persons trained, it seems unlikely that we will be able to keep up with the demands of an expanding population in terms of medical manpower.

As the Association of Medical Colleges has pointed out, the need for physicians is not likely to be met by expanding existing medical school enrollments. The largest contribution can only come from the establishment of new medical schools.

Yet it takes from eight to fourteen years between the decision to form a new medical school and the graduation of its first group of physicians. A program must be planned, buildings constructed, and a faculty found, before students may be admitted. At the present time several new schools of medicine are in various phases of this process and others have recently expanded or are now expanding from two-year to four-year programs.

There is one other source of physicians we have not yet considered. It is the group of United States citizens enrolled in foreign medical schools. During 1954–55, for example, there were 1730 American students in foreign medical schools. This is the equivalent of three or four additional medical schools. The large majority of these United States students were studying in five countries: Switzerland 490, Italy 343, Canada 332, the Netherlands 125, and Belgium 103. This represents a sharp increase in comparison with pre-World War II figures. Plans are now being worked out by the American Medical Association to evaluate physicians trained in foreign universities to insure that they are trained as well as students in this country.

One of the reasons for the decreasing proportion of college graduates who apply for admission to medical schools (Table 50) is to be found in the high cost of a medical education. Medical education is the most expensive of all forms of professional education. It requires at least nine years—four years of college, four years of medical school, and one year of internship. For training in a specialty in medicine the time is increased by the addition of three or more years of residency in an approved training center.

Four years of college plus four years of medical school costs $10,000–15,000. According to *The New York Times,* the median cost of medical school alone is increasing from its present figure of $7200. Although most medical schools have scholarships and student loans available, relatively few students finish their training without incurring large debts and relatively few have funds to finance their own training. The cost of a medical education does not end when the student completes medical school. His internship, and perhaps his residency, rarely pay enough for the young physician to support himself let alone a wife and family. Additional funds must be borrowed or somehow found to finance the long years of specialty training. It is little wonder that a large proportion of physicians who complete their training go into private practice where income is best, rather than accept jobs in public agencies and institutions, or in teaching, or in research, where salaries lag far behind what the physician may earn in his own practice.

THE TREND IN APPLICANTS
TO MEDICAL SCHOOL

Throughout this decade, the medical schools have been faced with an ebb-tide manpower pool of college graduates from which to recruit their freshmen classes. The trend over the past several years has been for medical schools to accept a higher and higher proportion of their applicants. Figure 16 shows how the relation of applicants to students accepted has changed.

Medical educators have been seriously concerned over the decline in the number of applicants because this has reflected, very probably, some loss in over-all ability.

Ebaugh and Barnes (1956) warned: "Most of us have failed to be aware of the alarming fall in the number of applicants for admission to medical schools. For the year 1948–1949, the height of the postwar boom in applicants, there was . . . a ratio of applicants to admissions of 3.6 to 1. By the year 1953–1954, the ratio of applicants to admissions [was] 1.97 to 1." Other medical spokesmen have warned that "the calibre of applicants to medical schools is falling" (Funkenstein, 1955), and that those schools with geographic restrictions "had to 'scrape the bottom of the barrel'" (Stalnaker, 1955).

Actually it means very little to say that there are two applicants for each entering place as a freshman in medical school. As a matter of fact, certain schools have no problem in choosing from a large number of applicants. In 1957, for example, Harvard reported over 10,000 applications for 115 places in its first-year medical class. Generally it has been the State schools which restricted admission to residents of the State that have had difficulty filling their freshmen class.

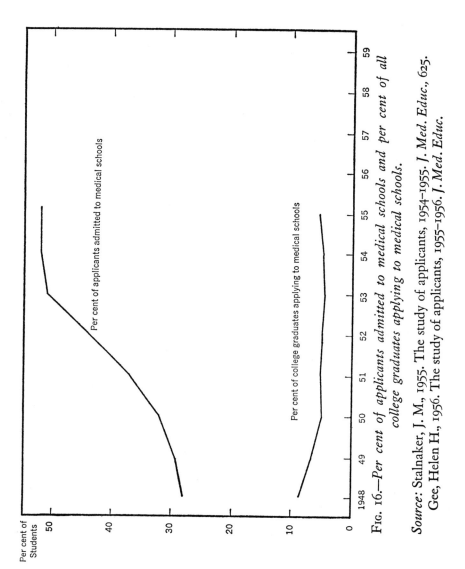

FIG. 16.—*Per cent of applicants admitted to medical schools and per cent of all college graduates applying to medical schools.*

Source: Stalnaker, J. M., 1955. The study of applicants, 1954–1955. *J. Med. Educ.,* 625. Gee, Helen H., 1956. The study of applicants, 1955–1956. *J. Med. Educ.*

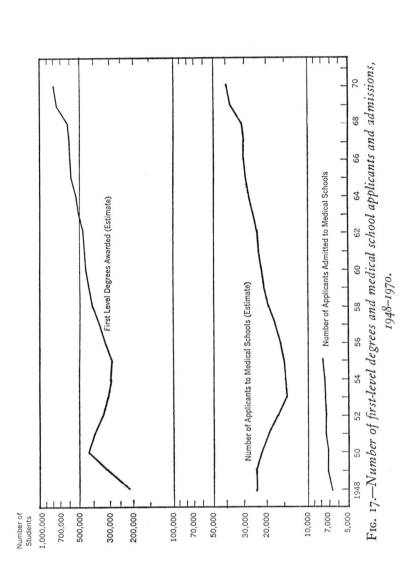

Number of Students

1,000,000
700,000
500,000

First Level Degrees Awarded (Estimate)

300,000

200,000

100,000
70,000
50,000

Number of Applicants to Medical Schools (Estimate)

30,000

20,000

Number of Applicants Admitted to Medical Schools

10,000
7,000
5,000

1948 50 52 54 56 58 60 62 64 66 68 70

FIG. 17.—*Number of first-level degrees and medical school applicants and admissions, 1948–1970.*

Source: Stalnaker, J. M., 1955. The study of applicants, 1954–1955. *J. Med. Educ.*, 625. Gee, Helen H., 1956. The study of applicants, 1955–1956. *J. Med. Educ.* U.S. Department of Health, Education, and Welfare, Office of Education, yearly. *Earned degrees conferred by higher educational institutions.* Government Printing Office. U.S. Department of Health, Education, and Welfare, Office of Education, 1957. *Estimate of degree trends*, dated February 19. Committee on Interstate and Foreign Commerce, House of Representatives, Eighty-fifth Congress, 1957. *Medical School Inquiry.* Government Printing Office.

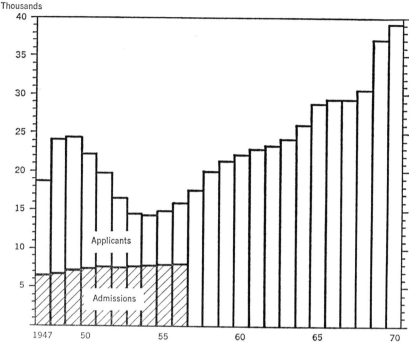

Fɪɢ. 18.—*Medical school applicants and admissions and estimates of future applicants.*

Source: Stalnaker, J. M., 1955. The study of applicants, 1954–1955. *J. Med. Educ.*, 625.

Gee, Helen H., 1956. The study of applicants, 1955–1956. *J. Med. Educ.*

U.S. Department of Health, Education, and Welfare, Office of Education, yearly. *Earned degrees conferred by higher educational institutions.* Government Printing Office.

U.S. Department of Health, Education, and Welfare, Office of Education, 1957. *Estimate of degree trends,* February 19.

Committee on Interstate and Foreign Commerce, House of Representatives, Eighty-fifth Congress, 1957. *Medical School Inquiry.* Government Printing Office.

The number of applicants to medical schools rose slightly in 1956 to 15,518. It now seems likely that the lean years are over and as the number of college graduates increases the medical schools will find increasing numbers of students applying for admission. This should also mean that they will be able to select better students. It should

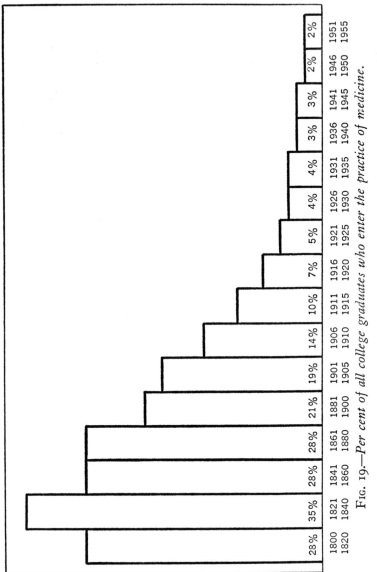

FIG. 19.—*Per cent of all college graduates who enter the practice of medicine.*

Source: Data obtained from U.S. Office of Education and from U.S. Public Health Service.

also mean that within the next decade or two qualified applicants will be available for whatever expansion of medical training occurs. Table 51 in the Appendix indicates the number of first-level degrees awarded and contains estimates of the number to be awarded to 1970. If we take 5.1 per cent (the average of the past five years) as the per cent of college graduates who apply to medical school it will be clear that there will be no shortage of applicants for the future. By 1970, considerably more than twice as many applicants will be seeking admission to medical school in comparison with current numbers.

According to Dael Wolfle (1954), one young person in 400 got a degree in medicine early in this century. In recent years the proportion has been almost exactly the same. However, fifty years ago 14 per cent of all academic degrees were granted to medical students but now only 2 per cent go to medical students.

While the implications of the trends and currents in medical education will be debated, we cannot escape the conclusion that we are likely to have fewer physicians in proportion to population in the future than we do now. This will act to limit the number of new psychiatrists trained. Whether it will mean any decrease in the availability of medical service we will leave for the reader to decide.

Finally, we must recognize that the physician not specially trained in psychiatry—the general practitioner, the internist, the pediatrician, among others—is occupied frequently with the care of emotional problems. The support and reassurance of the understanding physician is of crucial importance in the mental health of large numbers of our citizens. Any trend which promises to reduce this contribution to the nation's mental health must be seen as a serious problem.

IV
—————

Manpower Prospects in Psychology

INTRODUCTION

Psychology usually is defined as that branch of science concerned with the study of behavior. Psychology occupies a position somewhere between the natural sciences and the social sciences and often is classified administratively into one or the other of these areas. Many studies of degree trends in American higher education classify psychology separately because of its mixed antecedents.

Historically, psychology grew out of a mixture of English empiricism and German physiology. The first psychological laboratory was founded at the University of Leipzig in 1879. The early interest of psychology in human sensation and perception rapidly grew to include a wide variety of other components of behavior. The first American psychologists who established laboratories in the universities in this country were either educated in Europe or drew heavily on the work of European psychologists. The growth of the testing movement, with especial emphasis on intelligence testing, required increased concern with methods of measurement, especially in the field of statistics. A preoccupation with rigorous scientific method provided the early psychologist with his best defense against criticism from more secure sciences.

Psychology's struggle to achieve a separate identity has led to preoccupations with theory and method. Probably the unique contribution of the psychologist has been his acquisition and use of research skills in exploring the dimensions of human behavior.

Two quite different orientations in psychology have grown up in the United States. The behaviorism of Watson, with its emphasis on objectivity, and the psychoanalysis of Freud, with its insistence on the value of intensive study of the individual, provide two of the important components of the developing pattern of American psychology.

Until recent years, psychologists had been employed primarily by higher educational institutions. Some important applications of psychology to selection and to individual case-study had been made prior to 1940, but during World War II the field was called on to undertake research and service in a wide variety of real problems of selection, classification, evaluation, and rehabilitation.

Since World War II there has been a mushrooming growth of the applied areas of psychology; the employment of psychologists outside the academic setting has increased so rapidly that this group now represents a majority of psychologists.

Because psychologists are employed in such a wide variety of jobs, and because there are so many different areas of human behavior on which psychologists may focus their attention, it is difficult to provide a clear picture of the field of psychology as a whole. Also because of rapid changes in the function and emphasis of large groups of psychologists, and changing requirements in their education, predictions for the future have less certainty than was the case for psychiatry. Psychology is a broader, less clearly defined field than the other mental health professions. Structurally, it is more like chemistry or engineering than psychiatry or social work.

Another difficulty, for our present purpose, is the problem of deciding who should be included in this examination of manpower trends. What areas of psychology relate to mental illness and mental health? Should we include only clinical psychologists, the group whose training and employment are most specifically directed toward working with the mentally disordered? It is certainly defensible for us to include people working in vocational guidance, in school psychology, and in rehabilitation. But what about those psychologists concerned with mental health in industry, or those concerned with research into fundamental psychophysiological problems such as color vision in animals?

In some of the succeeding data, we will use degree trends in all of psychology as reported by the United States Office of Education. The reader should keep in mind that some of these people completing graduate training are concerned only peripherally with mental illness and mental health. On the other hand, because our knowledge of human behavior increases with new discoveries, and because research methodology developed in one area finds applicability in other areas, we may argue that this use of total degree data is justified.

In some of our discussion of psychology we will report information on the membership of the American Psychological Association. Recent surveys reported by Clark (1957) have suggested that the membership of the American Psychological Association seriously underestimates the number of psychologists in the country. For every two members of the APA, Clark found three other people, similarly employed, who were not APA members. These findings, based on several community surveys, give some indication that the number of psychologists employed in the mental health field is considerably larger than the total number of APA members. For the most part these nonmembers have completed less academic training, and they probably are less identified with professional psychology than members of APA. But the reader should bear in mind that the discussions of trends in psychology based on APA data represent minimum figures.

Some idea of the rapid growth of psychology in the United States will be obtained in Table 52 and Figure 20. There are now four times as many members of the American Psychological Association as there were immediately following World War II.

Twelve years ago Wolfle (1947) pointed out that the American Psychological Association had increased by some 6 per cent a year from its founding in 1892 until 1920. From 1920 to 1947, the Association grew at about 10 per cent a year. Extending the 1892–1920 curve, Wolfle predicted 6500 members of the Association by 1950 (actually there were 7273), 16,000 members by 1960 (there will be at least 19,000), and 40,000 members in 1970. As we shall see below, degree trends are such as to make this latter figure quite realistic.

We have noted that the character of psychology has changed with

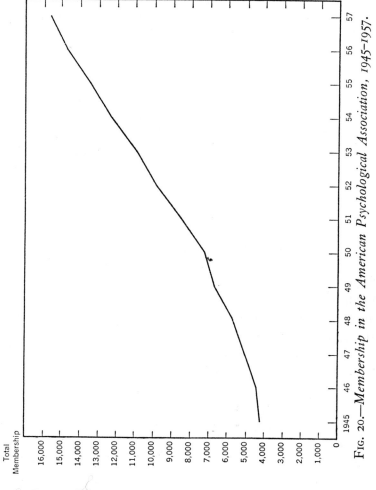

FIG. 20.—*Membership in the American Psychological Association, 1945–1957.*

Source: Letter from E. L. Hoch, Public Information Office, American Psychological Association, March, 1958.

its rapid growth. A major change has been the burgeoning of the applied areas of the field. In a recent survey of this growing profession, Clark (1957) suggests a number of reasons for the progress and change in psychology. He points to our advances in statistical knowledge, to improvements in surgical techniques, to the development of new and synthetic drugs, and to developments in electronics, all of which have resulted in marked increases in research activity in psychology. Further, the tremendous social demand for diagnostic and therapeutic services in the care of the mentally disordered has likewise served as a source of great stimulation to psychology.

The number of psychologists that can be trained is not restricted by the kind of limiting factors in the size of the pool of potential recruits that binds psychiatry in an iron restraint. Graduate schools have been able to step up sharply the number of psychologists trained, and psychology has the further advantage of being the only mental health profession (with some possible exceptions for social work) with direct and continued access to young people in college. The value of recruitment of the first course in psychology, and of personal contact with undergraduates, has not been sufficiently emphasized. Figure 21 illustrates the somewhat steeper growth curve of psychology in comparison with social work and psychiatry.

Clark suggests that the amount of financial support for research and training in psychology has been one of the most unexpected and nurturant developments in the last decade or two. It is hard to determine the total amount of financial support for psychological research and training, but the yearly reports of Young and Wilson in the *American Psychologist* give some idea of the sizable support available. For the last several years the Federal government has supported psychological research at a rate of approximately ten million dollars a year. Clark guesses that a national total of at least twenty-five million dollars a year is being spent on psychological research.

In training, other support has been available. The National Institute of Mental Health has provided training grants to graduate departments of psychology in the area of clinical psychology, and

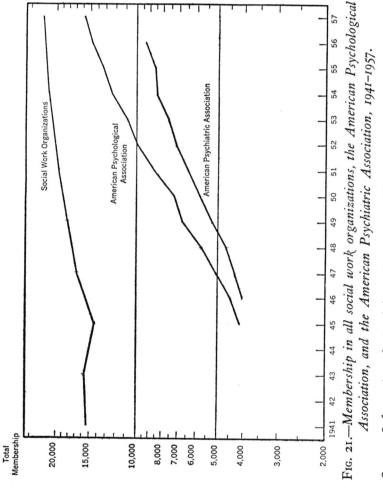

FIG. 21.—*Membership in all social work organizations, the American Psychological Association, and the American Psychiatric Association, 1941–1957.*

Source: Information obtained from directories of the various professional organizations.

recently has extended this support to programs in other nonclinical areas. Vestermark (1957) reports support of training in clinical psychology by the USPHS of nine million dollars over the past eleven years. The amount of support for students in clinical psychology provided by the Veterans Administration has been another major source of strength to the field. The influence of the Veterans Administration training program in clinical psychology has been profound. By beginning its support immediately after the war, and by insuring recognition of psychology's competence in diagnosis, therapy, and research, the pattern established by the Veterans Administration has been copied by a number of states and by other agencies. We will have some further things to say later in this report about the close relationship between support of training and research and manpower available in a field.

The distribution of psychologists by state and region is indicated in Table 53. For the United States as a whole, there is one psychologist to each 11,300 people. As the number of psychologists trained promises to continue to increase at a proportionately faster rate than the population increase of the country, these ratios will continue to improve for the foreseeable future.

The increase in the number of psychologists is favorable to the need for improving service in the field of mental illness and mental health. The fields of psychology growing most rapidly are those most directly concerned with mental illness and mental health.

Large numbers of psychologists in recent years have been employed by Federal, State, and local governments, by schools, by private industry, and by hospitals and clinics. One-third to one-half of all psychologists in the United States are employed in clinical psychology. These psychologists work in clinics, hospitals, and other agencies dealing with emotionally disturbed adults and children. The clinical psychologist engages in diagnostic testing, in counseling and psychotherapy, and in research in the field of mental disorder. Generally he works with professional members of other mental health disciplines in settings where the skills of the various groups can be brought to bear in a team approach.

The tradition in the field has been for psychologists to find employment in public and private agencies and institutions. Relatively few have entered independent practice or have been self-employed. There are signs that this situation may change markedly. In many of our larger cities, well-trained psychologists are finding independent practice to be a satisfying and rewarding part-time or even full-time activity. The social demand for this kind of service has created a climate making it possible that large numbers of psychologists will begin to offer their skills independently of the auspices of a social agency or institution. There is strong ambivalence within the field of psychology about this potential change. As we have noted earlier, the private practitioner suffers less from inflation and from the frustrations of formal regulation when he operates independently. If our society continues to underpay its public servants, we are likely to witness increasingly rapid movement of psychologists, and of other professionals, into independent practice.

The basic science side of psychology includes about one-fifth of the members of APA. Most of these are employed in academic settings, although an increasing number are employed by Federal agencies, especially the Department of Defense, in a research capacity. The place of employment of psychologists is indicated in Table 54 and Figure 22. These data, taken from the National Scientific Register, include some psychologists who are not members of APA. Still, it will be noted, the largest single place of employment of psychologists continues to be the higher educational institution (see Hoch, E., 1957).

Education and Experience Requirements.

Advanced training in a graduate school is required for most kinds of professional employment in psychology. Of all of the employed psychologists in the country, fewer than 5 per cent hold less than the master's degree.

The Ph.D. degree has become a prerequisite for most careers in psychology. This must be qualified by the realization that a large number of persons with the master's degree are now employed, sometimes in responsible positions, but usually at the technician

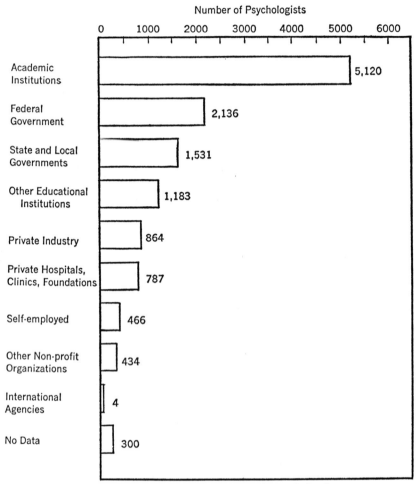

FIG. 22.—*Place of employment of psychologists.*

Source: Letter from Public Information Office, American Psychological Association, February, 1957.

level. Opportunities for professional advancement are much better for persons holding the doctorate and an increasingly large number of jobs are closed to those without the Ph.D.

Many people in the field believe that there will gradually develop two levels of training in psychology, and that the present preoccupation with requiring the extensive training to the doctorate will be recognized as unrealistic for a wide variety of important jobs in applied fields. These trends are not sufficiently clear for any but the most vague predictions. According to the National Scientific Register, slightly more than half of the psychologists in the United States hold the Ph.D. or an equivalent degree. We must note that there probably are additional people working in the field, not part of the Register study, whose training tends to be less thorough.

Three-quarters of psychologists are male. Data on sex, degree level, and specialty within psychology are reported in Table 55.

A kind of identification of professional competence useful to the public, and to any group interested in the identification of competence among applied psychologists, is the status of *diplomate* of the American Board of Examiners in Professional Psychology. This Board, set up shortly after World War II as a certification body, has established procedures for the examination and evaluation of psychologists who meet certain rigorous training and experience requirements. Those who pass the examinations are given a diploma which indicates special competence in an area of applied psychology. At the present time persons are certified in clinical psychology, counseling psychology, and industrial psychology. Since its founding, some 1351 psychologists have been certified.

PRESENT AND FUTURE
PROSPECTS FOR PSYCHOLOGY

We have already seen that the demand for psychologists, as one of the mental health professions, is strong and continuing. Combining estimates from various sources, Albee and Dickey (1957) estimated that the nation could absorb 10,000 well-trained psychologists at once. The need for psychologists in public hospitals and clinics, and in a wide variety of private organizations, continues strong. We already have seen the large number of psychologists that would be required to staff adequately our State mental hospitals. We have seen how many are needed in mental health clinics if we are to keep up with our growing population.

In considering future demands for psychologists, we must also remember that a major source of employment of psychologists is in higher education. With total college enrollments expected to increase enormously over the next couple of decades, and to remain at these high levels indefinitely, the demand for psychologists as teachers in our colleges and universities will provide another important source of demand for people trained in the field.

According to the U.S. Department of Labor (1957, p. 191):

Employment of psychologists will increase substantially during the 1960's; though perhaps at a slower rate than between 1945 and 1955 when the number in the profession tripled. In addition to the country's growing population, the following factors point toward long-term expansion of the profession: Increasing recognition by schools, government agencies, and private industry of the contributions that can be made by this relatively new science; growing concern about mental health needs, resulting in a tremendous increase in State funds available for the treatment of the mentally ill; and the emergence of the Federal Government as a major sponsor of psychological research not only within the Government but also in universities and private industry.

The report continues by suggesting the possibility of marked expansion in the number of psychologists employed by state agencies. It points out what we have reported earlier: that understaffed mental hospitals and mental hygiene clinics in the State systems will need a large number of psychologists to bring them near adequate staffing. The report underscores the need for vocational rehabilitation counselors in State programs and estimates a need for an increase from 1600 employed in 1955 to more than 4500 by the early 1960's. This group largely will be made up of psychologists with the master's degree, trained in rehabilitation. Other sources of growing demands for psychologists according to the Bureau include the fields of school psychology, college faculty in psychology, and the increasing use of psychologists by private industry.

The Department of Labor predicts that the Federal government will continue to be one of the largest employers of psychologists. The increase in employment of psychologists in Federal agencies has been phenomenal. There were some 60 per cent more psychologists in 1954 than in 1951 in Federal employment. The Veterans Administration employs some 700 clinical psychologists and about

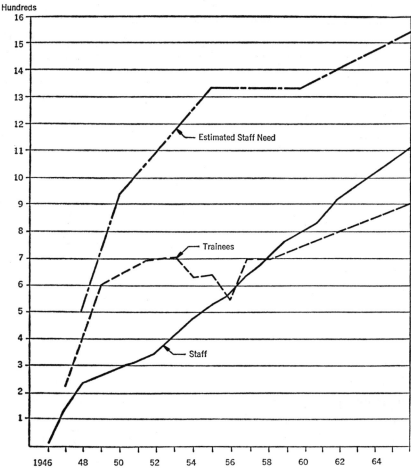

FIG. 23.—*Psychologists employed, trainees employed, and estimates of future manpower needs by the VA.*

Source: Veterans Administration, Department of Medicine and Surgery, Division of Psychiatry, 1953. *Forecast of personnel needs to 1960.* Government Printing Office.

a hundred vocational counseling psychologists, and estimates it will need 1500 clinical psychologists and from 500 to 1000 additional vocational counseling psychologists by the early 1970's. Figure 23 indicates an earlier estimate of needs by the VA that has turned out to be quite realistic. The Department of Defense continues to require research psychologists in large numbers.

Factors Affecting the Supply of Psychologists.

We saw earlier that the number of psychiatrists was closely bound to the number of medical school graduates who might choose to enter residency training in the field. The supply of psychologists is determined by the number of people completing graduate training in the field. The number of students who enter graduate school in psychology and, as we shall see later, social work, is a function of the number of undergraduates receiving the bachelor's degree and the proportion of this number which goes on to graduate or professional school.

We have already noted that during the past several years our graduate and professional schools either have operated at less than capacity or have taken less qualified and less able students to fill their entering classes. The reason for this decline in number, or in quality, of students in graduate and professional schools has been the now familiar shortage of young people of college age which, during the first half of this decade, resulted in the lowest college enrollments and the fewest college graduates since before World War II. This shrunken pool of college graduates has meant that there have been comparatively few students available for recruitment into post-college training in all professional fields, including the mental health professions. In 1956, for the first time in this decade, the number of college graduates increased over the year before. This upturn will continue for the next fifteen years at least, and we can look forward to a gradually increasing pool of college graduates from which advanced students may be recruited. Some of these trends will be evident from Figure 24 and from Table 56.

We have taken several estimates of the number of bachelor's degrees and have attempted to use the highest and lowest of these estimates of the number of future degrees to be granted to show the limits within which we are likely to stay in terms of the number of people completing college. These data will be applicable later to our consideration of trends in social work, and to some extent in nursing.

Increasingly the evidence indicates that the more optimistic esti-

Thousands

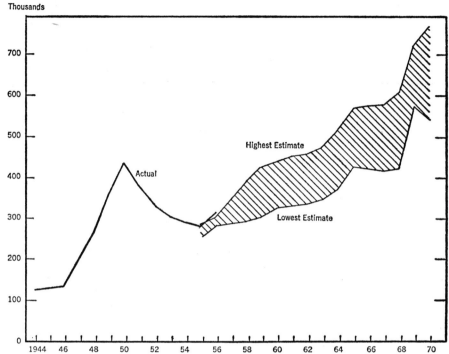

FIG. 24.—*Number of first-level degrees in all fields, 1944–1956, and the highest and lowest estimate of the number of first-level degrees to be awarded, 1955–1970.*

Source: United States Department of Health, Education, and Welfare, Office of Education, yearly. *Earned degrees conferred by higher educational institutions.* Government Printing Office.
Estimates based on data contained in Table 56.

mates of future degree trends are more likely to be right. With the prospect of a larger number of undergraduates available for recruitment into psychology, and because the potential is present for expansion of most graduate departments of psychology, there is likelihood that the number of psychologists to be trained will increase for the foreseeable future. On the other hand, graduate education is expensive, and the limitations of costs, and of competent faculty, will set limits on expansion.

Some interesting data on degree trends are available in psychology.

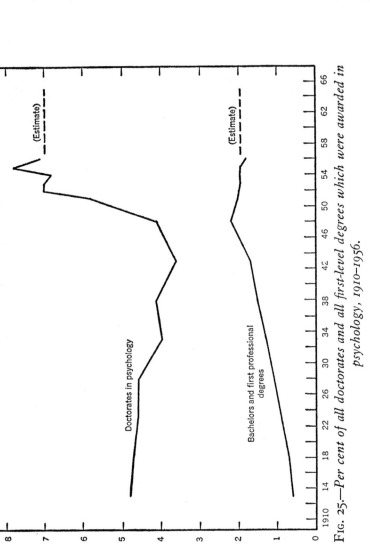

Per cent

FIG. 25.—*Per cent of all doctorates and all first-level degrees which were awarded in psychology, 1910–1956.*

Source: Wolfle, D., 1954. *America's Resources of Specialized Talent.* Harper. U.S. Department of Health, Education, and Welfare, Office of Education, 1957. *Estimates of future degree trends,* mimeographed February 19, 1957. U.S. Department of Health, Education, and Welfare, Office of Education, yearly. *Earned degrees conferred by higher educational institutions.* Government Printing Office.

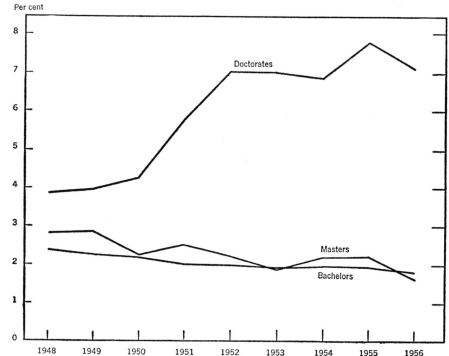

FIG. 26.—*Per cent of all doctor's, master's, and bachelor's degrees which were awarded in psychology, 1948–1956.*

Source: See Table 59.

Early in this century about ½ of 1 per cent of bachelor degrees awarded were in psychology. This percentage increased slowly but steadily through the years to a high point of 2.2 per cent immediately after World War II. During the present decade there has been a moderate decrease to slightly under 2 per cent. Tables 57 and 58 and Figures 25 and 26 indicate these trends. They also illustrate the change in the proportion of doctorates in all fields that are in psychology. Table 59 and Figure 27 compare the growth of psychology with other areas.

Once again we see that there has been a modest increase for psychology over the years. Estimating that 1.95 per cent of bachelors degrees will be in psychology and that 7 per cent of all doctorates will be in psychology (Table 57 and Figures 25 and 26), we have

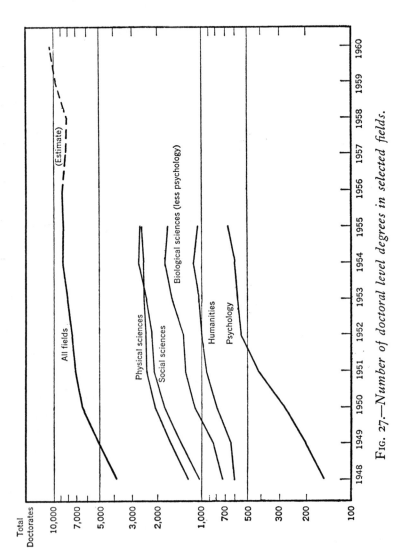

FIG. 27.—Number of doctoral level degrees in selected fields.

Source: See Table 59.

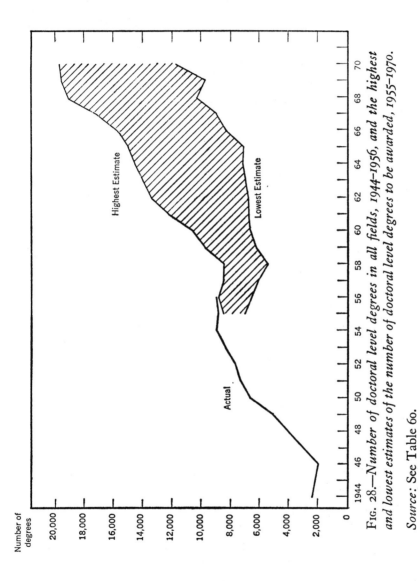

FIG. 28.—Number of doctoral level degrees in all fields, 1944-1956, and the highest and lowest estimates of the number of doctoral level degrees to be awarded, 1955-1970.

Source: See Table 60.

made some predictions about the number of people who will be trained at these levels over the next several years. Basing our predictions on the highest and lowest estimates of total degrees to be awarded we find the limits within which, in all probability, degree trends will occur (Tables 57, 60, and 61 and Figures 25, 28, and 29). Since these calculations were made we have had an opportunity to check them for 1956 and 1957. There is some indication that the percentage of all degrees that are awarded in psychology may drop slightly below our estimates but as the total number of degrees awarded tends to be above the midpoint of our estimates these two factors nearly balance. By 1965 some 700 to 1000 people should be completing their doctorates in psychology each year, and there are good prospects that this number will continue to increase steadily for some time thereafter.

To increase the number of psychologists trained year by year will require that present patterns for support for graduate students be continued and expanded. Training stipends from the National Institute of Mental Health, traineeships in the clinical psychology program of the Veterans Administration, research assistantships on research contracts from Federal, State, and local sources, and direct support of graduate students by universities all must continue and expand if the larger number of students available for training is to be trained.

Support for graduate students in psychology has been good over the last decade. Because support has been available many students have gone on to graduate school who otherwise could not have done so because of the expense and loss of earnings that graduate study involves. If sociology or biology had received the same support as psychology over the past decade, it is quite probable that these sister disciplines of psychology could have grown and expanded at an equally rapid rate.

In addition to the need for increased financial support for students the graduate schools, as we shall see later, face the prospect of faculty shortages, and increased demands on faculty time, from the press of increased enrollment at both the graduate and undergraduate level.

In clinical psychology, departments requesting evaluation of their

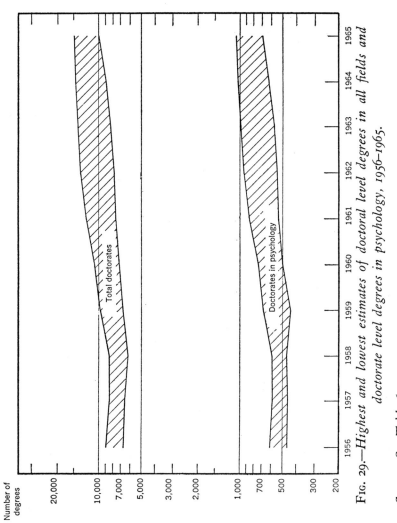

FIG. 29.—*Highest and lowest estimates of doctoral level degrees in all fields and doctorate level degrees in psychology, 1956-1965.*

Source: See Table 61.

graduate program are studied by the Education and Training Board of the American Psychological Association. This Board, among whose duties is the evaluation of graduate programs in clinical psychology, publishes a yearly list of approved programs which has come to be the standard used by many students choosing departments in which to seek training in clinical psychology. Serious faculty shortages and loss of other sources of strength to graduate programs would serve to decrease the number of approved programs available. On the other hand increased support and nurture could bring approval to the number of programs striving to meet the criteria set by this Board.

There are at the present time vacancies in many agency programs providing field work experience for students in approved doctoral programs in clinical psychology. This would indicate that reasonable increase in the number of doctoral students can be accommodated without difficulties, so far as the availability of field work placements is concerned. The most serious limitation in prospect is the problem of expanding graduate school enrollments because of the difficulty in securing enough new and competent faculty. We shall discuss this problem in somewhat more detail later.

Selection of Students in Psychology.

Most psychologists decide to enter the field after they have had one or more courses in psychology in college. This means that nearly all psychologists are people who have changed their minds from other career goals. As psychology is not widely taught in the high schools, the possibility of psychology as a career choice is not brought to the attention of any large number of adolescents. On the other hand, as we have noted earlier, psychology has some advantage over other mental health professions in recruitment. Psychiatry, psychiatric nursing, and, to a lesser extent, social work have few direct teaching obligations in the undergraduate college.

Psychology undergraduates represent a cross section of all undergraduates in intellectual ability, according to Wolfle (1955). He also notes that only 12 per cent of those undergraduates who major in psychology go on for further training and become professional psychologists. This suggests that many students major in psychology as simply a liberal arts subject. Psychology is interesting. A large number of students decide each year to major in the subject even though they have never had previous courses in the field. This would suggest that student interest and motivation are fairly high among those who choose psychology as a major. It is probable that somewhat more than 12 per cent of psychology majors would be potential graduate students if university departments made a more intensive effort to bring information about professional opportunities in the field to the attention of their undergraduate majors and if such guidance were available in the smaller colleges.

Clark (1957) reports that the influence of a particular teacher, and interest in human behavior as a field for scientific investigation, were the two most commonly mentioned reasons for entering a career in psychology.

With respect to intelligence, graduate students in psychology were found by Wolfle (1955) to be significantly above the average of all graduate students and to be among the highest of the various fields of specialization.

According to Clark's study, there has been no substantial change over the years in the social class origin of psychologists. The fathers of two-thirds to three-quarters of those psychologists studied were in professional or managerial occupations. These groups have no monopoly on ability and many potential students probably are lost because of inadequate guidance and insufficient opportunity in other groups.

The Changing Status of Psychology.

A major change of emphasis in psychology, already noted, is the rapid development of the applied areas. Where twenty years ago most psychologists were employed in colleges and universities, now some 60 per cent of psychologists are employed in nonacademic settings. If all the effects of this change are not yet clear, psychology is becoming a more widely known discipline, and this may affect its future by determining what people will be attracted to psychology as a career.

As the activities of psychologists change these changes often are reflected in the course content of the undergraduate level. Twenty years ago most introductory courses in psychology spent a very large proportion of their time discussing sensation and the nervous system. Today much of this content is crowded out of the first course by material on personality, and on theories of abnormal, social, and industrial psychology. Examining introductory textbooks we find that these new and popular topics that have been added have pushed older subjects to one side or have squeezed them into smaller space. Because prospective undergraduate majors in psychology, and therefore prospective psychologists, often are recruited on the basis of their first courses in the field, the change in emphasis may ultimately have marked effects on the characteristics of the students recruited. Much more research needs to be done on this subject, not only for psychology but for the mental health professions in general.

Cost of Training in Psychology.

Most graduate students in psychology earn their own way. There has grown up over the years a system of assistantships, traineeships, and field work placements which enable almost any student who wants a graduate education in psychology to earn his way toward this degree. There is some question about whether all the time the student spends on relatively unimportant activities in these assistantships could not better be used in actual study. Many would argue that field work training and research training are important parts of graduate education, but we wonder what pattern would be established if truly adequate funds were available for the support of graduate students. While the system of financial help that has grown up has been sufficient to take care of most aspiring psychologists, the sharp increase in graduate enrollments that will be possible in the future certainly will require outside financial assistance in greater amount.

V

Manpower Prospects in Social Work

INTRODUCTION

A RECENT DEFINITION of social work by H. S. Maas and M. Wolins (1954) suggests that it is a profession primarily concerned with preventing or alleviating the unfortunate effects of crisis on the individual personality or on groups within society.

Because people identified as social workers engage in such a wide variety of professional activities in such diverse settings, it is difficult to present an orderly analysis of growth and development trends in the field. Joseph W. Eaton (1956) says:

> Social workers are found to be engaged in such diverse activities as budgeting for relief applicants, a study of a couple desiring to adopt a child, supportive psychotherapy, initiation of court action against parents neglecting their children, community organization to pressure the City Council into action to improve a neighborhood, informal education through relationships and play with a group of chronically ill children in a hospital, or helping adolescents to feel socially at ease in the teen-age canteen of a neighborhood settlement house.

With such a variety of roles and functions, it is hard to write a simple and clear-cut definition of who is a social worker and what it is a social worker does. Any effort to define social work is bound to be controversial. The social worker emphasizes methods and techniques in the use of himself as an instrument for effecting better adjustment on the part of the client or the group. Since Flexner (1915) startled social work by pointing to its lack of professional status because of the absence of unique theory and skills, the field has made rapid strides to find its own methods and philosophy.

An examination of social work can focus on the kinds of problems with which social workers deal—the problems of the individual, of identifiable groups, and of the community organization; or it can concentrate on the places in which social workers use their skills—in child welfare agencies, correctional institutions, medical settings, family agencies, settlement houses, agencies serving recreational needs, schools, relief agencies, and other settings.

The caseworker, whose concern largely is with the individual, employs the casework method which, simply stated, is the face-to-face interview based on an understanding of personality dynamics and therapeutic processes. It requires the use of technical skills found effective in dealing with individuals with problems. The casework interview has developed over many years of experience and most social work educators believe that the technique of the casework interview can be taught through careful supervision.

The social worker who deals primarily with groups uses the group experience to nurture and strengthen the healthy components of personality at the expense of the less healthy components. A thorough understanding of group dynamics, and of techniques for fostering group relationships, together with knowledge of the relationship of group processes to individual personality, are among the skills and knowledge required of the trained group worker.

Those social workers concerned with community organization study community structure and learn the skills that have been developed to help various groups come together to work for the betterment of all members of the community. The theory, skills, and techniques of the community organizational specialist are varied, but many involve facilitation of improved communication between groups in the community as well as techniques for interpreting these various forces to each other.

Historical Development.

An analysis of the complex historical origins of social work is beyond the scope of this report. The roots of social work go back hundreds of years. With the concentration of population in the cities during and since the Industrial Revolution, the increasing problems of the poor, the unemployed, the handicapped, and the discriminated-against, have all cried out for the relief from daily crisis that human personality seeks.

The early American colonists brought to the New World the methods and philosophy that had been developed in Europe to meet the needs of the poor and the handicapped. In impoverished and struggling societies, the poor are often blamed for their poverty and a common attitude is that the needy have brought their condition on themselves through ignorance, laziness, or personal defect. Because of this attitude, poor relief had been made as distasteful as possible. Programs devised to meet the needs of the poor were usually palliative and were not concerned with its elimination or the discovery of its causes.

Social work originated in the nineteenth century largely as a protest against the existing methods of dealing with poverty and destitution. There existed hundreds of local charities but their methods were inefficient and inadequate. In the 1880's, Charity Organization Societies came into existence. A part of professional social work traces its origin to this movement. The original aims were to promote the development of improved living, working, and health conditions of the lower economic groups and to organize the relief resources of the community so as to eliminate duplication and fraud. Some of these organizations were transformed into relief-giving agencies in their own right.

Many social workers in the Charity Organization Societies concentrated their major efforts on correcting the external factors in society responsible for poverty—lack of opportunity for the individual and consequent family demoralization. This group devoted its energies to the development of improved employment, housing, health, sanitation, education, leisure-time opportunities. Some social workers made efforts to secure social legislation to effect this improvement.

Influenced by psychiatry and the child guidance movement, some social workers focused attention upon the individual client and on the problem of effecting changes in him that would help him use his own potential to the fullest.

Settlements in impoverished neighborhoods also began to be developed. The settlement focused on the individual as a member of a group and the group often became the unit of service. The settlement houses, and also the character-building agencies, the public recreation agencies, and the adult education agencies all contributed to the development of group work.

The movement together of these various approaches to the alleviation of crisis has been an interesting and complex example of the forces operating to create a professional organization.

The development of theory in social work as to the best methods of effecting changes in the individual client, and in larger social units, has been rapid. Educational programs for the training of social workers moved from a kind of apprenticeship system to the establishment of separate graduate schools and, after much struggle, to the establishment of professional schools within universities. As Hollis and Taylor (1951, p. 10) point out, many of the early vocational schools of social work were filled with misgivings about the movement of training programs into the universities. They feared this type of education would be concerned largely with theory and would be controlled by the social sciences. This concern, of course, reflected a lack of appreciation of the social process involved in the achievement of professional status which, as we have seen, always includes the development and the primacy of theory.

From the beginning of truly professional education in social work, the real and pressing demands of society, and of social agencies serving that society, have had profound influence on the content of social work education. The emphasis on casework, and the growing strength of casework, reflects a strong social need for workers in the field of medical and psychiatric social work, child welfare, and the family agencies.

Most observers agree that one of the most profound influences on the field has been the introduction into social work education of modern psychiatric concepts. Hollis and Taylor (1951, p. 13) say: "These emphasized emotional and social causes and treatment of maladjustments reflected in individual behavior, and tended to divert social work from its earlier focus on environmental factors and need for social reform to correct social injustices."

With the achievement of improved living standards and the elimination of widespread endemic poverty, the focus of social work has tended in the direction of work with individuals and recent years have seen a relative decline in the emphasis on community organization and group work. In recent years, 85 per cent of social work students have specialized in casework; group work, community organization work, and other areas of specialization have been represented by the remaining 15 per cent. Table 62 and Figure 30 indicate the per cent of social work students in different types of field work placements in recent years.

Social Workers in the Field of Mental Illness and Mental Health.

How many social workers should we include in our examination of manpower trends in mental illness and mental health? The specialty within social work most directly concerned is psychiatric social work. But the number of psychiatric social workers is only a very small fraction of the total number of social workers in the country. A good case can be made for the argument that every social worker is crucial to problems of mental illness and mental health. In their concern with alleviating or preventing crisis in human lives social workers are mostly concerned with the alleviation of the very problems we have said define mental health.

Another problem we face is to decide on a definition of the professional social worker. According to Katherine A. Kendall (1954): "It has been estimated that there are approximately 75,000 persons employed in social work positions in the United States, of whom 16 per cent have completed two years or more of graduate study, 11 per cent have had one but less than two years, 13 per cent have had less than one year, and 60 per cent have had no social work education."

Benjamin E. Youngdahl (1951) says: "At present the established norm for professional training consists of two years of graduate professional training in an accredited school of social work." This definition agrees with the one used by the Health Resources Advisory Committee (1956).

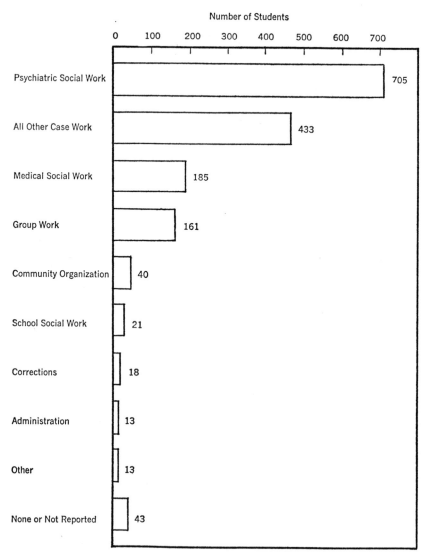

FIG. 30.—*Distribution of 1,632 second-year social work students as to field work placement, November 1, 1956.*

Source: Council on Social Work Education, 1957. *Statistics on Social Work Education,* November 1, 1956 and *Academic Year,* 1955–1956.

The U.S. Department of Labor (1957, p. 193) estimates that there are some 80,000 social workers in the United States. About two-thirds of these people are employees of Federal, State, and local governments. Most of the remainder are employed by voluntary agencies supported by contributions. The Bureau of Labor Statistics reports that in 1956 about three-fourths of the social workers in this country had less than one year of graduate professional education. The lowest proportion of social workers with graduate training was to be found in the field of public assistance, and the highest proportion of trained workers was to be found among workers in private agencies in urban areas.

Psychiatric social workers are the most highly trained group in the field. Louise N. Mumm (1957) points out that while two-thirds of all social workers have college degrees, and half of them have taken some graduate training, social case workers employed in mental hygiene clinics nearly always have had one or more years of graduate training.

There is little question but that graduate training in social work is essential for the most effective work with clients. Here we find one more indication of the curious social imbalance in our society. Perhaps because social workers tend to deal with the less fortunate and less influential members of society, and because the results of social work activities are not recognized to be life and death matters, our society has not demanded that social welfare personnel be adequately trained. We demand that our physicians, our airline pilots, our dentists, and our morticians have the necessary training and qualifications before we let them work. But many social workers arranging adoptions, calculating relief budgets, and dealing with delinquent gangs, do not have the skills and knowledge already available because they have not been properly trained.

With 75,000–80,000 people employed in social work positions, the membership of the National Association of Social Workers includes less than one-third of this number. This Association, which came into existence just two years ago as an amalgamation of the several social work organizations that existed previously, has a membership of some 22,000. Table 63 indicates the membership of the various

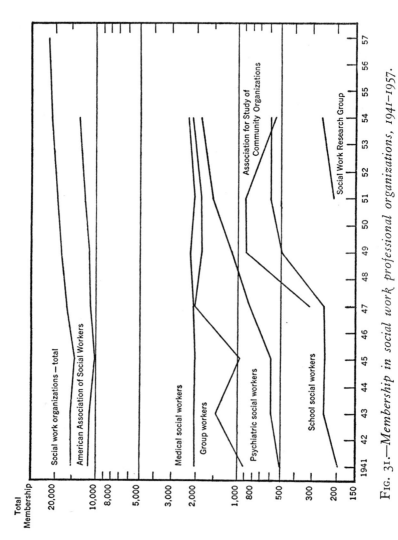

F𝐈𝐆. 31.—*Membership in social work professional organizations, 1941–1957.*

Source: Social Work Yearbook, Volumes 6–13.

social work organizations since 1941. The reader will note that there has been no marked increase in membership in groups other than the psychiatric social workers. In Figure 21 we have shown the growth curve based on the total of these groups. Figure 31 shows the separate curves of membership.

Demand for Social Workers.

We have already seen that serious shortages of social workers exist in our public mental hospitals and clinics and that the prospect is for a growing shortage in the areas we have examined. Because we believe that not only those social workers who work with mental patients or emotionally disturbed people but practically all social workers are essential manpower in the field of mental health, we will indicate some additional indices of shortage in the field.

A recent summary reported by McCurdy (1957) of vacancies and of turnover in member agencies of the Family Service Association of America indicated a continuing need for more personnel in these agencies. At the beginning of 1957 there were 2300 persons employed in these agencies in a casework capacity. Nearly five hundred more professional specialists in noncasework functions were also employed. At the time of the survey 253 positions were vacant, representing approximately ten per cent of the professional casework positions. The high mobility of social workers, in part a reflection of the widespread demand for their services, was indicated by the 630 terminations during the preceding year. More than one-quarter of all the caseworkers left their positions in a single year. The shortage of professional social workers is complicated by the considerable expense of recruitment required by the turnover of personnel accompanying the shortage. New workers in agencies must have time to get acquainted with the changed conditions in the new setting so that turnover is an especially costly manpower problem.

The study also found that the size of the community is related to the number of vacant positions. Smaller communities have many more vacant positions than the larger cities.

According to Hollis and Taylor (1951, p. 82) some 85 per cent of social and welfare workers live in urban areas where only half of the general population lives. The urban concentration of social workers is understandable in view of the historical origins of social work, but we may be sure that social workers are needed in rural areas as well. We have already seen that social workers in smaller communities are likely to have had less formal training. The distribution of members of the National Association of Social Workers by region and state is presented in Table 64. The reader will note the marked variability in the availability of social workers in different areas.

In 1956, more than half of all social work students were from the ten most urbanized states, and only 6 per cent were from the ten least urbanized states.

Every estimate of the need for social workers stresses the divergence between the number of positions and the number of people being trained. The need continues to rise faster than the output of available people. One prediction by the Council on Social Work Education was that an additional 50,000 social workers would be needed by 1960. More than 4000 group workers are needed each year, but the number trained in schools of social work does not exceed 200 a year. Mumm (1957) points out that in 1953, with some 5000 medical and psychiatric social workers employed, there were 2300 vacant positions and some 3600 positions in the offing in the immediate future.

There are wide differences between the states in terms of the numbers of psychiatric social workers in relation to population. For the United States as a whole in 1954 there were 1.3 psychiatric social workers for each 100,000 population. This means that there was one psychiatric social worker for each 78,000 people. Tables 64 and 65 indicate the relationship between the number of psychiatric social workers and population. Also contained in these data is evidence of the importance of the presence of a graduate school with psychiatric social work curricula to the presence of trained psychiatric social workers in a state. In the fifteen states above the national average in ratio of psychiatric social workers to population, there were twenty-three schools of social work with psychiatric training. In the thirty-four states below the national average, there were only fourteen schools of social work.

Another way of illustrating this point is to compare the number of schools with psychiatric social work curricula in the states above the median state to the number of schools in the states below the median state. Here the differences are startling—thirty-one schools to six schools.

Table 64 contains data on the number of psychiatric social workers to population by region and by state. If psychiatric social workers are fulfilling an important function in the states most adequately staffed with members of this discipline, then there is implied a strong need for trained people in those states far below the average.

EDUCATION AND EXPERIENCE
REQUIREMENTS OF SOCIAL WORKERS

We have already pointed out that the profession of social work believes that graduate training is essential for successful practice in the field. The first year of graduate training is quite similar for the specialties within social work; specialization within the various fields of emphasis occurs during the second year, in part as a result of field work placement experience.

There are some fifty approved schools of social work in the United States. Admission to a school of social work generally requires completion of four years of college with preparation in the social and biological sciences. The Bureau of Labor Statistics (1957) estimates that some 200 colleges and universities offer one or more undergraduate introductory courses in social work. At least half of these schools offer ten or more semester hours in a planned sequence of courses in social work. Social work schools do not require such specific undergraduate preparation in the field, although these courses serve a valuable function in orientation and recruitment. One of the problems that social work faces is that so few undergraduate students are acquainted with career opportunities in the field. The students make decisions about their education before information about social work as a career is available to them.

As social work has become more and more professionalized there has been the inexorable movement of training programs into the universities. Apprenticeship training in social agencies has been replaced by a two-year generic curriculum in graduate schools of social work, although field experience under supervision is still an important part of the student's experience.

Following completion of academic curricula, field work placement, and a thesis, the social work student receives a master's degree. Most of the fifty-three accredited schools give the degree of Master of Social Work, although there are a number of other equivalent degrees in the field.

In general, the principle has been accepted that professional social work education should consist of an orderly progression during the last two years of college and through two years of graduate training. This goal is not likely to be realized until much larger numbers of undergraduate students are aware of career opportunities in social work and can plan their educational development accordingly. Until this widespread awareness of career opportunities is available and more students follow this sequence, graduate schools of social work will be required to teach material that students should have covered at the undergraduate level.

The basic social work curriculum attempts to produce social workers with skills based on scientific knowledge about society and about human behavior. The case method of teaching is used and class discussion usually is based on case records. The student receives careful supervision in his field placement and learns to apply in practice what he has learned in theory.

In recent years there has been much discussion, and some actual beginning, of an extension of social work education beyond the master's level. Thirteen graduate schools now have doctoral programs in social work. Increasingly, it is felt that such advanced education is required for those individuals engaged in teaching, administration, research, and other leadership positions in the field.

Degree Trends in Social Work.

The number of graduates of two-year social work programs in the United States increased rapidly in the years immediately after World War II, rising from 1049 in 1946 to 1946 in 1952. In general, the curve of the number of graduates of schools of social work follows, with a two-year lag, the curve of first-level degrees for all fields. This means, of course, there has been a decrease in the number of social work graduates each year since 1952 because of the decrease in the number of bachelor's degrees year by year during this period, as described previously. Table 66 illustrates the trend in numbers of total graduates of schools of social work and shows separate totals for men and women. Figure 32 illustrates these data.

For the past five years the number of social work graduates has varied between the limits of forty-five to fifty-six for each 10,000 first-level degrees granted two years before. This information, together with Office of Education estimates of trends in first-level degrees over the next decade, allows us to make predictions about the number of degrees that will be awarded within social work for the next few years. Table 67 gives an estimate of future degree trends in social work. The lower estimate is based on a projection of fifty graduates in social work for each 10,000 first-level degrees two years before; the higher estimate is based on a rate of fifty-five graduates per 10,000. The total degree trends are based on 1957 estimates of the Office of Education. These predictions suggest that by 1960 something like 2000 students a year will graduate from schools of social work and by 1965 something like 2500 will graduate each year.

Recent reports suggest that our predictions of increased enrollments in schools of social work are reasonable. According to an article in *The New York Times* (March 23, 1958), there has been a recent increase in the number of students enrolling in schools of social work. Current registrations are within 4 per cent of the peak enrollment year of 1950.

This article quotes Witte to the effect that some 1800 students are graduated now each year with degrees in social work in contrast to a need of 12,000 new workers a year that could be employed in public and private social agencies.

In 1957 there were 4165 full-time students in accredited social work schools working toward the master's degree. The year before there were only 3811.

A somewhat more refined prediction of the number of graduates

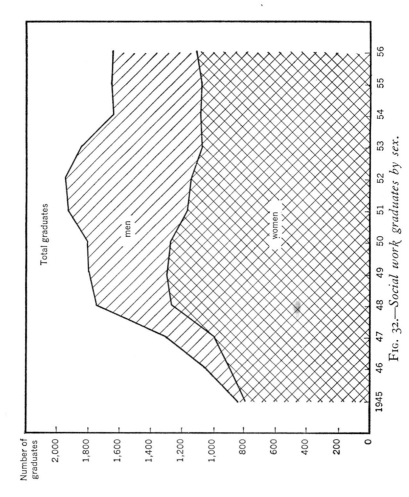

Fig. 32.—*Social work graduates by sex.*

Source: Council on Social Work Education, 1956. *Statistics on Social Work Education,* 1955–1956.

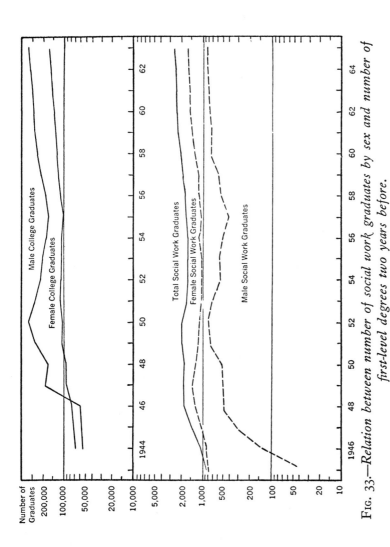

Fig. 33.—*Relation between number of social work graduates by sex and number of first-level degrees two years before.*

Source: Council on Social Work Education, yearly. *Statistics on Social Work Education*, New York. U.S. Department of Health, Education, and Welfare, Office of Education, yearly. *Earned degrees conferred by higher educational institutions*. Government Printing Office.

of schools of social work can be obtained by separating predictions for male and female students. Table 68 indicates the increase, following World War II, in the number of men who enter the field of social work. This proportion now seems fairly stable at about 30 to 35 per cent. If we make separate predictions of the number of male and female graduates of social work programs, based on five-year trends, and using Office of Education predictions of first-level degrees, we find, as indicated in Table 68, that some 2000 social workers a year will complete their education in 1960, and that this will increase slowly to 2500 in 1965. Our two methods of estimate agree.

We have only made predictions for a fairly short time of the number of social workers who will be completing their graduate training. It is fairly safe to assume, however, that this number will continue to increase and that schools of social work will be able to eliminate the vacancies that have characterized their classes for the past several years. This assumption is based on the increase in the number of college graduates, elsewhere described. The prospect is that our schools will be able to operate at what has been considered capacity level. However, this output will be far short of the total number of trained people judged necessary by the various expert estimates of need. Most schools have not been fully utilized for some time. Many schools could be doubled in size if funds were available for additional faculty and student stipends. Ample field work opportunities exist, as was the case in psychology, to accommodate sizable increases in the number of students in training. Again the limiting factor is the number of competent faculty and financial support for the increasing number of potential students who will be available in the swelling manpower pool of college graduates in the years ahead.

Three-quarters of all students in schools of social work receive financial grants of some sort. Of all student grants awarded in 1956, 60 per cent came from public funds, 27 per cent came from private agencies, and 13 per cent came from school funds. About 27 per cent of the students graduating in 1956 had made commitments to work in agencies in exchange for financial support during their schooling. Wittman (1956) found that more than half of the students who were

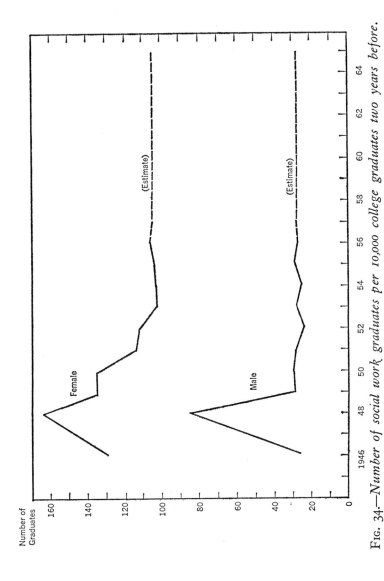

Fig. 34.—*Number of social work graduates per 10,000 college graduates two years before.*

Source: Council on Social Work Education, yearly. *Statistics on Social Work Education.* U.S. Department of Health, Education, and Welfare, Office of Education, yearly. *Earned degrees conferred by higher educational institutions.* Government Printing Office.

receiving aid could not have entered professional training without such financial assistance.

Cost of Training in Social Work.

Professional training in social work schools is expensive. The cost of two years of graduate study in social work is estimated to be something like $4000. This expense, coming after college expenses, finds most social work students dependent on financial assistance of some sort. Most surveys (Wittman, 1956, Witte, 1956) emphasize the inadequate financial support available for social work students. While a majority of students receive support, few receive enough to pay all of their expenses; and the inadequacy of scholarship and other financial resources becomes more apparent when we note that more than a third of social work students are married.

Thus, while over two-thirds of the full-time students receive some form of aid, most of it is in such small amounts that it provides only marginal support. Many social work graduate students manage to meet their educational costs through loans, self-deprivation, or borrowing. Others work part-time. In any event, most of the students in schools of social work cannot devote full time and attention to their studies.

Witte (1956) notes that student aid is of great importance to social work students, perhaps more so than to students in many professions, because social work salaries in the years after graduation are not sufficient to justify incurring a heavy debt which must be repaid on completion of the professional education.

Standards for the Selection of Social Work Students.

The selection of students for professional social work education is based both upon intellectual capacity and upon personal suitability and adaptability.

The academic prerequisites include a bachelor's degree with undergraduate work at a sufficiently high level of performance to indicate intellectual capacity to engage in graduate study and research.

Because so much of the work of social workers requires emotional as well as intellectual involvement, personal maturity and potential for emotional growth are important in the selection of students. Candidates must be sufficiently mature to cope with the emotional changes which they experience as they acquire knowledge of human development and behavior and as they work with clients. They must be able to endure the emotional stress inherent in the development of professional relationships with clients where the focus is on helping people, or enabling people to help themselves, and not on manipulating, controlling, or using people. It has been found that an emotionally immature person is not able to establish and sustain the professional relationship which underlies all social work activity.

Different schools have different descriptions of the personality characteristics they look for in prospective students. In general, social work schools seek warmth and sensitivity in students tempered with the objectivity necessary to be helpful to people in trouble.

Schools of social work base their assessment of potential students on academic records, personal references, the applicant's autobiography, and the admission interview. Although all these different sources are important and necessary in obtaining an overview of the student's qualifications, the Committee on Admissions of the Council on Social Work Education believes that the admission interview is the most useful and most reliable tool for personality assessment in the selection of students. In 1954, a National Roster of Interviewers was established which makes available to accredited schools of social work a nationwide list of persons with special training in interviewing and personality assessment. These people may be used by any accredited school to interview candidates.

While most schools of social work follow careful admissions procedures, the method of selection is, of course, not perfect. In many instances, the student's potential can only be known through his reaction to the learning situation. Not all who begin their social work training are permitted to complete it. There is much more individual faculty attention to the student's emotional qualifications for practice than there is in many other types of professional education. However, the selective devices are sufficiently satisfactory that the rate of attrition is low.

PRESENT AND FUTURE PROSPECTS
FOR SOCIAL WORK

We have already indicated estimates of degree trends in social
work and have seen that despite the prospect of a substantial increase
in the number of people completing their graduate training in this
field the demand for trained social workers far exceeds any prospective increase in the field. The prospect is that many social work positions will continue to be filled by people with training judged insufficient by informed observers. Once again we see that one of our
indices of shortage is clearly present in a mental health profession.

Thousands of vacancies in child welfare and public assistance,
hundreds of positions in Federal agencies, positions in clinics, hospitals, the Red Cross, in probation and parole, and in dozens of other
settings, will continue to be unfilled or will be filled with inadequately trained people.

Because two out of every three social workers are women, there
is a somewhat higher turnover rate in social work than is the case
in psychiatry or psychology. Women social workers marry and
leave the field. A shortage of male social workers is most evident in
positions in probation and parole, and in certain areas of group
work and community organization, and especially in administrative
positions. According to the Bureau of Labor Statistics, 86 per cent of
male social workers are married, and 20 per cent of women working
in the field are married.

The field of specialization in social work that has increased most
rapidly in the past decade is the one in which there has been the
most outside financial support. Psychiatric social work has increased,
or at least held its own, while other areas of social work have declined
with the decline in student enrollment. There is every indication that
psychiatric social work will continue to be the most glamorous and
most popular specialty.

Several additional factors need to be considered in our concern
with prospects in social work. Fauri (1955) has called attention to the
fact that while preparation for professional responsibility in social

work requires, in general, six years of college and graduate education —roughly equivalent to the amount of preparation required for lawyers and dentists—salaries of social workers have lagged appreciably behind other professional groups with comparable educational prerequisites.

This comparison would be somewhat less clear-cut if Fauri had chosen certain alternative salaried professional groups employed, as are social workers, by public and private agencies and institutions. The tradition, as we have noted, has been for self-employed professionals to have larger incomes than those who work for organizations. Despite this qualification, it is still true that salaries in social work are a major handicap in recruiting sufficient numbers of people to the field.

Eaton (1956), in reviewing the evidence about the status of the social worker, concludes that it is a middle-range status profession. Social workers have somewhat less prestige than members of the top professional groups, but they definitely are as respected as those in a wide range of middle-level professions. Eaton points to the evidence that the social worker suffers from some feeling of insecurity due to the difficulties he has in finding a secure status position in society. Coming often from middle-class homes, supported by upper-class contributions, and working with lower-class clients, the social worker is never quite certain of his sympathies or his identifications although his broad experience makes him empathic to a wide variety of people. It is probable that in our culture there is a fairly finite number of potential social work recruits, largely because satisfactions in social work tend not to emphasize the economic and prestige rewards that are so important to large numbers of young people in our society.

Social work grew up as an attempt to alleviate and to remedy inequitable social conditions leading to widespread human distress. As time has passed, and as social work has tended more and more to be an organized profession, it has been subjected to a problem characteristic of any group aspiring to be a profession. As we have noted, it has needed theory.

Rudiments of good theory grew up within social work itself, but the parallel development of psychoanalysis, with its rich and varied theoretical fabric, was a great temptation. Social work, and especially psychiatric social work, has taken psychoanalytic theory as its own in many centers throughout the country.

The adoption of psychoanalytic theory by much of social work has led to a sharply changed direction and flavor of professional activities, especially of the caseworker. The emphasis in casework, which involves dealing with clients or patients in an office, requires different skills and theoretical approaches than did earlier social work. The emphasis in social work on alleviating and eliminating social conditions leading to distress has declined, and social workers now attempt to alleviate distress by enabling clients to work through and understand their emotional problems.

One critic has said (Wertham, 1950):

Social problems are social problems, and you cannot psychoanalyze them out of existence. Psychiatric social service, with which I have had daily contact for many years, is indispensable. But psychiatric social service is increasingly becoming psychoanalytic social service, and more and more even the "social" is being left out until only psychoanalytic service remains. That doesn't help people with real social and family problems.

From quite a different source (Committee on Mental Health Services, Montreal, Canada, 1956) comes the observation:

It was pointed out that there is somewhat of an anomaly in professional relationships in so far as the social worker, ostensibly concerned with the social environment, is actually closest to that branch of psychiatry and those psychiatrists most exclusively concerned with the individual relationship and psychotherapy—the psychoanalyst. At the same time, the social worker was also most distant from those psychiatrists who, one would have thought, were concerned with the professional interests of the social worker—those in social psychiatry.

The point here is that the public image of social work, as in the case of psychology, changes as a result of the kind of activities in which people in the field engage. Whereas in bygone days social work probably recruited students interested in social action, the emphasis now on personality dynamics cannot help but affect the field by affecting the kind of students attracted to it.

It should be pointed out, in fairness to social work, that the social needs with which social work originally concerned itself have changed a great deal in the past half century. With the overwhelming flow of goods from our productive machines and, in recent years, with our high level of employment, poverty as a widespread and uncontrolled social evil has assumed relatively less importance. Poverty has become what Galbraith (1958, pp. 325-327) calls (1) case-poverty or (2) insular poverty. In the former there frequently are intrinsic reasons—alcoholism, mental retardation, emotional disturbance—that may explain the difficulty, and, in the second, the pockets of poverty endemic to certain rural regions or to certain areas of cities are due to complex causes, not the least being the reluctance of members of the local population to leave the place they were born.

So it is true to a much greater extent now than during the early decades of the present century that responsibility may be found within the individual personality for social difficulty. Still, there are many social wrongs that the social worker could help right, and the criticism that social work is less interested in social action than in case work still needs to be considered as it affects recruitment to the field.

VI

Manpower Prospects in Psychiatric Nursing

INTRODUCTION

Psychiatric nursing is the specialty within nursing that is primarily concerned with mental illness and mental health. But for the same reasons that manpower resources in medicine were judged important to the mental health of the nation, so are our resources in all of nursing of crucial interest. As we indicated earlier, illness of any kind is a threat to human mental equilibrium.

In the succeeding discussion we will focus our attention on psychiatric nursing, but we will also look at some of the manpower trends in the whole field of nursing.

Probably no other profession enjoys as much widespread affection and approval as nursing. Nursing is the largest health occupation by far. The image of the nurse as a person who brings reassurance, comfort, and relief to the suffering patient makes recruitment for the field relatively favorable. In a nationwide survey by the University of Michigan Survey Research Center (1956) of a representative sample of girls between eleven and eighteen, it was found that 11 per cent of this age group expected to enter the field of nursing. Although there is a downward trend with increasing age (under fourteen years of age, 14 per cent expect to enter nursing; over sixteen years of age about 5 per cent have this expectation) the number of girls who aspire to a career in nursing is most impressive.

As we shall see later, one of the factors responsible for the shortage in the field of psychiatric nursing is likely to be found in the public image of the nurse. Nursing students working with mental patients do not do many of the things that are part of the image of nursing duties popularly held. It may be that the fundamental reason for the shortage of psychiatric nurses is to be found in the very different nature of nursing activities in this field.

Historical Development.

Psychiatric nursing is a relatively new field of specialization. We have seen that changes in attitudes toward the mentally disordered are a recent development still in process. So long as mental institutions were viewed as simply custodial, there was no need for nursing care for patients. As the concept that the deranged person is suffering from an illness has gained increasing acceptance, asylums have become hospitals. Hospitals are places where nurses work. The belief that the mental hospital should be an active therapeutic setting is still not universal, and psychiatric nursing is still struggling with the definition of its proper role and function and with distorted and prejudiced public images of mental disorder.

Psychiatric nursing looks to England for some of its important historical roots. In the middle of the last century nurses were first employed in the wards of the Gloucester Asylum. Other English hospitals began to be concerned with the education of the mental nurse, and toward the end of the century mental nurses were certified by the Medico-Psychological Association of Great Britain and Ireland.

In the United States courses for psychiatric nurses were given at McLean Hospital in Boston in 1882. By 1885, the hospital at Norristown, Pennsylvania, began hiring trained nurses. By the turn of the century, many mental hospitals had undertaken to train nurses, largely recruiting their students from attendant personnel already employed.

By 1916, a committee of the American Nurses' Association found training schools for nurses in forty-one mental institutions. As a rule, the quality of training was below that for general hospital schools of nursing.

The number of nurses in the United States employed in mental hospitals has grown very slowly, and even today something less than 5 per cent of all professional nurses are employed in our mental hospitals. As we have seen, they contain more than half of the hospital beds in the country.

Because of the complex trends and influences in the field, a definition of psychiatric nursing to which everyone in the field will subscribe is difficult. A recent conference at the University of Minnesota (1950) suggested that psychiatric nursing is "a branch of the art and science of nursing, is concerned with the total nursing care of the psychiatric patient through the development and guidance of interpersonal relations, the creation of therapeutic situations and the application of the nursing skills in psychiatric treatment, and with the prevention of mental illness and the promotion of mental health."

The United States Employment Service's job description (1949) defines a psychiatric nurse as:

Applying psychiatric, psychological, and sociological principles of therapy in attending persons suffering from mental and nervous disorders. Participates in giving special and corrective treatments such as electroshock, insulin shock, and artificial fever. Assists psychiatrists in helping patients adjust themselves and control their thoughts and emotions. (Practices as clinical bedside specialist, prevention specialist, instructor, professor, consultant, or supervisor in institutional nursing, public health nursing, nursing education, or private practice nursing.)

The report of the Expert Committee on Psychiatric Nursing of the World Health Organization (1956, pp. 41, 42) lists some of the issues with which psychiatric nursing is struggling. The report states:

The contribution of the psychiatric nurse to the care of the mentally ill throughout the world raises broad and difficult problems. . . . The role of the psychiatric nurse is always directly affected by the progress in the development of psychiatry and this in turn is a reflection of the concurrent cultural concepts regarding mental illness. The education of the psychiatric nurse has altered and extended with the change in her role and new understandings in psychiatry. This has not been a steadily evolving process, with smooth transitions for which the profession is prepared. Instead, psychiatric nursing has developed in an uneven, erratic manner, leaving gaps in the care of the mentally ill and in programmes of mental health, even in the most highly organized countries. These gaps present many of the central problems in the field today.

Psychiatric Training for all Nurses.

With the increasing realization that there are large emotional components in many health problems and that physical illness is a severe stress affecting the personality of the patient, and with the increasing awareness of the huge size of the problem of mental illness, the training of nurses has gradually come to include the requirement that student nurses have experience with mental patients on psychiatric wards or in mental hospitals.

Twenty years ago half of the State approved schools of nursing included psychiatric nursing experience in their basic program. The number of schools requiring psychiatric nursing experience increased steadily. Just after World War II, two-thirds of all the State approved schools of nursing included this experience. By 1950, 90 per cent did so; and today State boards of nursing in all the states require this experience as part of their curricula, although in actual fact the nurses often do not receive it.

Leaders in nursing education are inclined to the view that the psychiatric experience for student nurses enriches and broadens the educational experience of the fledgling nurse and gives her perspective and sensitivity to emotional components of all illnesses. Few argue that the three-month placement in a mental hospital or on a psychiatric ward adequately prepares the nurse for later work, without further training, in psychiatric nursing. In reality, however, the psychiatric field placement during training *is* the preparation of a majority of psychiatric nurses. Many mental hospitals offer additional training for staff nurses, but such additional training is not especially intensive or widespread.

The psychiatric experience of the student nurse is necessarily the mechanism for recruitment of nurses into this field. Most hospital schools of nursing send their students to a psychiatric hospital for this clinical experience. Too often the psychiatric field placement is in a large State hospital with relatively poor facilities for nursing care, and with varied and uneven supervision and instruction. Recently a careful study by Long (1958) attempted to determine the effect of psychiatric field experience on the attitudes of student nurses toward psychiatric nursing as a career. He found no consistent change in attitudes among student nurses, many of whom changed from unfavorable to favorable attitudes and vice versa as a result of their experience working in a mental hospital.

Training Requirements in Nursing.

There are several kinds of educational patterns that lead to a career in nursing. One of the most important numerically is the hospital school where the student nurse spends three years in training following graduation from high school. Upon completion of these three years the student nurse receives a diploma in nursing; upon satisfactory performance on a qualifying examination the nurse is registered by the State. Of the 1118 schools of nursing approved by State agencies, 82 per cent are represented by hospital schools. According to the National League for Nursing, 85 per cent of all student nurses who completed their training in 1957 received diplomas from hospital schools.

A second pattern of education leading to a career in nursing is the bachelor's degree program found in some colleges. These programs require four or five years of training which combine academic work in the classroom with clinical training in the hospital. There are 202 of these degree programs in the United States and, in 1957, they accounted for some 18,640 students.

In recent years, another kind of educational pattern in nursing has appeared, and many leaders in the field are hopeful that it will assume increasing importance as a career pattern. This new program is the associate degree program in a junior college or community college. In general it involves two years of study, largely basic science study in the classroom, with field work placements in the clinical services of community hospitals. In 1957, some 1360 student nurses were enrolled in this kind of program. It leads to certification in nursing, and also includes the degree of Associate in Arts or Sciences, upon completion of the two-year curriculum.

Graduate training leading to the master's degree in nursing is offered by a number of universities. These advanced programs re-

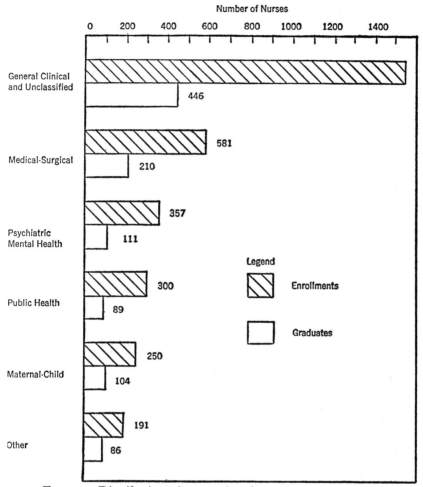

FIG. 35.—*Distribution of nurses in advanced programs, 1955.*

Source: National League for Nursing, 1956. Preparation of nursing leaders. *Nursing Outlook, 4* (no. 9) :517.

quire graduate academic study, often with emphasis on a specific area of specialization. Table 69 and Figure 35 indicate the distribution of nurses in advanced programs by specialty.

Graduate training in psychiatric nursing, while not numerically a major emphasis, is increasing, and support for this training is now available from a number of sources.

Nurses who become teachers, supervisors, administrators, and consultants to large programs should have, according to current thinking in the profession, the advanced training obtainable only at the graduate level. There is some discussion in the field about graduate training at the doctoral level for nurses, although the question is not resolved as to whether the doctoral training should be in nursing or in some related scientific specialty.

The professional nurse giving direct care under medical supervision to patients is usually a graduate of a diploma or an associate degree program. Nurses holding positions as head nurse in the hospital, staff public health nurse, school nurse, and a variety of other responsible positions, are believed to need at least baccalaureate program training.

We have already suggested that teachers and other leaders of the nursing profession are most likely to be found in the group which receives advanced nursing education at the graduate level. One of the serious shortages in the field of nursing in general, and in psychiatric nursing in particular, is the limited number of students and graduates from these advanced programs.

Nursing spokesmen estimate that by 1960 the nation will need annually at least 4000 nurses trained by the advanced programs for leadership positions in all clinical nursing. At present the output of our advanced training programs is only about 725 per year. In psychiatric nursing the need is especially acute: ". . . Much of the nursing care available to the 750,000 patients in mental disease hospitals is given by psychiatric aides whose only preparation is that which they receive on the job. How can professional guidance and supervision be provided for these aides, about 90,000 in number, when the annual increment of psychiatric nursing supervisors or supervisor-instructors amounts to a total of less than thirty?" (National League for Nursing, 1956)

It is estimated that two-thirds of nurses pursuing specialized degrees in nursing are only part-time students. In psychiatric nursing there is the highest proportion of full-time students, largely because of support for training programs and scholarships provided by the National Institute of Mental Health. Even in psychiatric nursing, however, one-fifth of all students are part-time.

Figure 36 illustrates the increasing importance of the master's degree program in preparing nurses for advanced positions. When we look at Figure 37, however, we see how far there is to go. At the 1956 level of enrollment some 725 nurses finished their graduate training yearly. If our programs were operating at capacity, 1,400 would be the yearly total. To reach the goal of 5,200 annual grad-

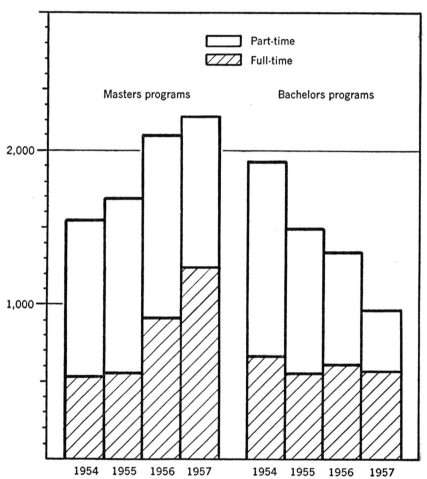

FIG. 36.—*Enrollments in masters and bachelors programs in nursing which prepare for advanced positions in nursing.*

Source: Educational resources for the preparation of nurses. *Nursing Outlook,* 6, February, 1958.

Annual
graduations

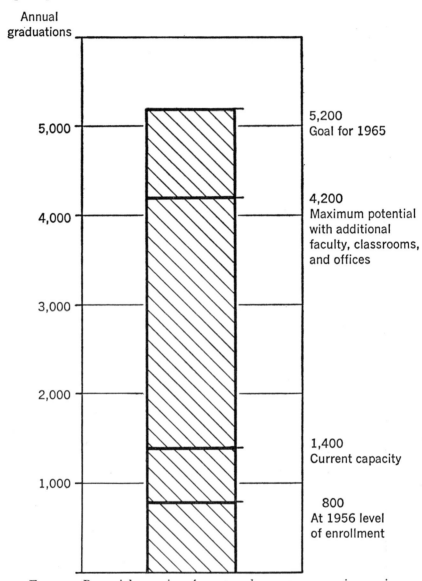

5,000 —

5,200
Goal for 1965

4,000 —

4,200
Maximum potential
with additional
faculty, classrooms,
and offices

3,000 —

2,000 —

1,400
Current capacity

1,000 —

800
At 1956 level
of enrollment

FIG. 37.—*Potential capacity of masters degree programs in nursing.*

Source: Educational resources for the preparation of nurses. *Nursing Outlook, 6,* February, 1958.

uations by 1965 (assuming 300 professional nurses per 100,000 population and the current ratio of 13 per cent of the profession in leadership positions) programs would have to expand beyond any presently contemplated maximum.

Other Indications of Shortage.

In an earlier chapter we found that the shortage of nurses in mental hospitals is so great as to be almost completely discouraging. According to *Facts about Nursing,* published by the American Nurses' Association, 1957, there is one nurse to every fifty-three beds in psychiatric hospitals in contrast to one nurse to every three beds in general hospitals. The situation is worse when we look at the figures for general duty nurses separately. There is one general duty nurse to every four beds in general hospitals and one to every 141 beds in psychiatric hospitals.

The report goes on to describe a survey of 326 psychiatric hospitals in 1956. It reported over 3000 vacancies for full-time professional nurses. Some 31 per cent of full-time positions were reported vacant in State or local government hospitals. It should be kept in mind that reported vacancies bear little relation to need. States with active programs often report more vacancies than states with little apparent concern for staffing problems.

The actual amount of care given to mental patients by professional nurses is further limited by the fact that one of every four nurses in mental hospitals devotes a major share of her time to administration, teaching, and supervision. Also, one of every three nurses in mental hospitals is a head nurse, or an assistant head nurse, whose time with patients is also limited. Only about two-fifths of the professional nurses in mental hospitals can devote the major share of their working hours to patient care. The number of nurses available for patient care is somewhat higher in the Federal public mental hospitals (almost all of which are Veterans Administration hospitals); 56 per cent as compared with 31 per cent.

Other Trends in Nursing.

We cannot fail to be impressed with the sharp discrepancy between the ratio of nurses to patients in psychiatric hospitals as contrasted with other hospitals. Yet we must bear in mind that there is a steady and increasing demand for general duty nurses in general hospitals and for specialists in the various areas of nursing, in nursing education and research.

The number of nurses in proportion to the population has continued to increase throughout the present century. Figure 38 indicates the growing supply of professional nurses. A long-term goal of the nursing profession is to achieve a ratio of 300 nurses per 100,000 population. This goal now seems within the realm of possibility for the near future. Figure 39 indicates the need for professional nurses to reach this goal, and to reach the more ambitious goal of 350 per 100,000. Figure 40 suggests growth curves necessary to achieve these various aspirations.

The increased number of nurses trained, and in prospect, has not alleviated the shortage of nurses. Although the number of nurses trained has increased significantly over the past several decades, the shortage of nurses is more severe than ever. One reason for this paradoxical situation is the very high rate at which nurses leave the field. The Bureau of Labor Statistics reports that 5 per cent of all professional nurses leave the field each year. Most nursing school graduates are young, unmarried women. A sizable proportion of them marry either before they have completed their training or within the next few years thereafter. It is estimated that two-thirds of inactive nurses are under forty years of age.

An important reason for the sharp increase in demand for nurses is our increased hospitalization requirements. In the past fifteen years the number of our citizens covered by hospital insurance has leaped from slightly over 10,000,000 to slightly under 110,000,000. Comparable increases in insurance coverage have been true for surgical care and for regular medical care. This means that medical and hospital care are now available to a much broader base in the population, with increased demand for services of the health professions.

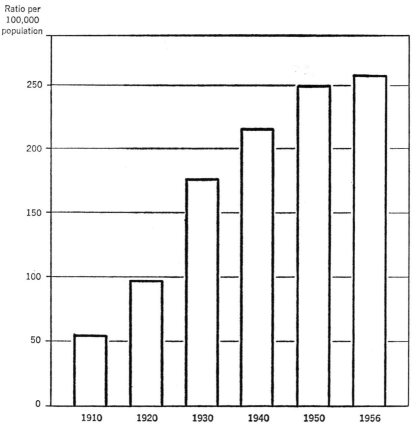

FIG. 38.—*The increasing supply of professional nurses.*

Source: Nurses for a growing nation, 1957. Pamphlet published by the
National League for Nursing. This figure based on material contained
in American Nurses' Association, *Facts about Nursing,* 1955–1956.

Hardin, C. A. Supply of professional nurses in 1955, *Am. J. Nursing,*
56 (no. 12) :1545.

Other significant factors in the increased demand for nursing
service, already noted, are the booming birth rate and the increasing
number of older people in the population. Man's healthiest years
are after childhood and before old age. With increases in the number
of people outside each of these limits there is increased demand for
health service.

With increased competition among hospitals for nurses, working

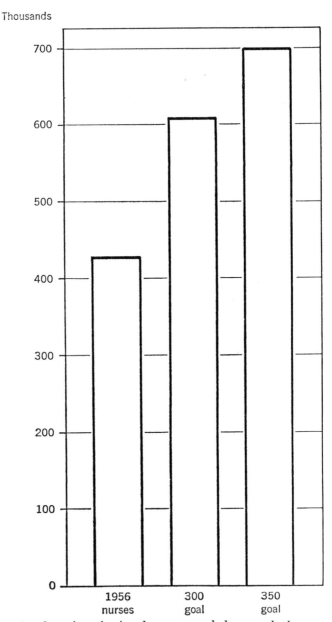

Fɪɢ. 39.—*Number of professional nurses needed to reach the 1970 goal of 300 for 100,000 population and 350 for 100,000 population.*

Source: Nurses for a growing nation, 1957. Pamphlet published by the National League for Nursing. This figure based on material contained in American Nurses' Association, *Facts about nursing, 1955-1956.*

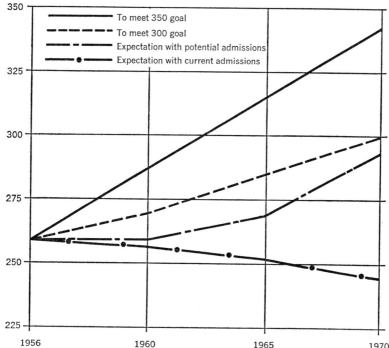

Ratio per
100,000
population

FIG. 40.—*Growth curves necessary to reach various goals in professional nursing.*

Source: Nurses for a growing nation, 1957. Pamphlet published by the National League for Nursing. This figure based on material contained in American Nurses' Association, *Facts about nursing, 1955-1956.*

conditions in the field have tended to improve. The pattern now is for a forty-hour week with additional compensation for evening or night shifts. Salaries in nursing, however, have tended to lag behind other professional occupations requiring comparable education. While there is wide variability in nursing salaries in different parts of the country, one of the major sources of dissatisfaction among nurses has been low salaries. Once again we see the example of salaried professional people being at an economic disadvantage.

The number of new students in schools of nursing has been quite steady during this decade. The prospect now is for increased enrollments. We know accurately the number of seventeen-year-old

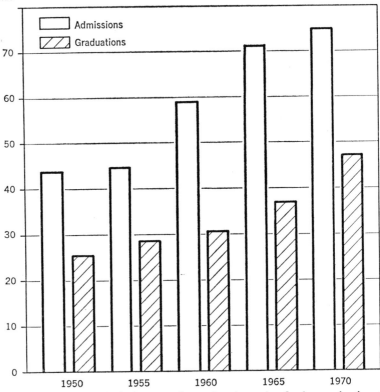

Thousands

FIG. 41.—*Trends in admissions and graduations in basic professional nursing programs.*

Source: Nurses for a growing nation, 1957. Pamphlet published by the National League for Nursing. This figure based on material contained in American Nurses' Association, *Facts about nursing, 1955–1956.*

girls there will be in the population year by year. Estimating the number of seventeen-year-old girls per 1000 who enter nursing training, predictions have been made (West and Crosby, 1956) of the number of girls who will enter training year by year through 1965. Table 70 indicates these numbers. Figure 41 illustrates the anticipated increase in admissions and graduations through 1970.

With the relatively optimistic numerical outlook for nursing we must remember that a very small percentage of new nurses enter psychiatric nursing. As noted earlier, less than 5 per cent of professional nurses employed in hospitals are in psychiatric hospitals. Table 71 illustrates this fact.

The reader will also remember that a not very high percentage of nurses in graduate training are specializing in psychiatric nursing. Not only is there in prospect a continuing shortage of psychiatric nurses but also a shortage of teachers and leaders in the field.

TRAINING STANDARDS AND TRAINING PROGRAMS IN NURSING

Student nurses receive training in a variety of clinical areas—placement in the services of medicine, surgery, obstetrics, gynecology, psychiatry, and other clinical specialties is part of the regular educational pattern.

There is no specific certification of nurses as psychiatric nurses although many centers in the country offer graduate training in this clinical area. For the most part, however, nurses who have completed hospital programs are recruited as psychiatric nurses, and become psychiatric nurses without further additional specialized training.

Since 1923, each state has given legal recognition to the practice of nursing. Most of the state laws restrict the use of the title "registered nurse" to those persons who have met the requirements specified in the law, including a state examination, but most states do not prohibit the practice of nursing by individuals who do not claim to be "registered" nurses.

Requirements for licensing are set by the individual states, and a great deal of variability exists in these requirements. All states require the licensing examination prepared by the National League for Nursing, although the passing score set by states varies considerably.

Every school of nursing must meet standards that have been set by a State Board of Nurse Examiners if its graduates are to be eligible for State licensing examinations. Because the State requirements must be met by every school, they turn out to be minimum standards which are exceeded by many of the schools in the State.

National accrediting of nursing education has developed out of the need for higher standards than those required by the various State Boards. National accreditation does not replace State Board approval, is voluntary, and gives recognition to schools already approved by the states.

The National Nursing Accrediting Service was established in 1949 through the merger of three agencies, which had previously been accrediting nursing schools on a national basis. In 1952, six national organizations of graduate registered nurses merged to form the present two major cooperating organizations—the American Nurses' Association, and the National League for Nursing. The national accreditation of all educational programs for professional nurses became a function of the National League for Nursing.

Accreditation involves a careful study of the curriculum and program of the school together with an evaluation of the instructional program, the general atmosphere, the physical facilities, and the over-all pattern of training at the school. Although certain fundamental principles are used as criteria in accreditation, flexibility is permitted so that the accredited programs need not conform to any rigid pattern. Full accreditation of a program does not continue indefinitely. To insure the maintenance of standards, accredited programs are resurveyed every six years and interim reports are required three years after each survey.

Student Recruitment and Student Selection.

Nursing offers a nearly ideal career for many young women. Nurses' training is an ideal way for a girl finishing high school at seventeen to prepare for the security of fairly certain employment throughout her lifetime; nursing offers excellent preparation for marriage and homemaking responsibilities, and, for many, improved status and prestige. While nursing continues to be a more common career choice for girls from farms and smaller communities, increasing numbers of girls from larger communities are entering the field, perhaps because of the movement of our population to urban centers.

Admission to any of the major programs in nursing education requires graduation from high school, usually with a college preparatory course. Because the nursing curriculum emphasizes science, and often biological science, some familiarity with laboratory work and with the sciences is important. Most schools set age limits at eighteen to thirty-five for students.

For the past ten years the number of student nurses enrolled in basic diploma schools has remained fairly constant, but the number who have entered degree programs has more than doubled. In 1947, 6 per cent of all nursing students were in programs leading to an academic degree in nursing. By 1957, this percentage had increased to 16 per cent. Professional nursing spokesmen anticipate that the college nursing program will continue to gain in popularity. This means, very probably, an increase in the educational and ability requirements for successful completion of the nursing curriculum. Students in college programs must, on the average, complete more formal academic requirements and therefore must have better preparation.

In a study by Harry W. Martin and Ida H. Simpson (1956) (and this finding is reported frequently in other studies), it was found that a very large proportion of girls who became nurses had chosen nursing as their goal relatively early in life. Nearly half of their sample had made the decision to study nursing before the age of sixteen, and more than a quarter had made the decision before the age of thirteen. This would suggest that recruitment for professional nursing must start quite early.

Recruitment for psychiatric nursing, as we have indicated, presents many special problems. Two-thirds of the psychiatric nurses interviewed by Martin and Simpson had not applied for a position in the psychiatric field when they sought their first job. Nearly 40 per cent reported that they considered leaving psychiatric nursing at one time or another. Many of them felt that their family and friends disapproved of their working in this field.

A number of studies suggest that the average nursing student has relatively unfavorable attitudes toward psychiatric nursing. Actually, Long (1958) found that negative attitudes among student nurses were not limited to psychiatric nursing, but were characteristic of nursing services dealing with chronic patients of whatever diagnosis.

Geriatric nursing, tuberculosis nursing, and nursing in other chronic diseases were seen as equally unfavorable.

Cost of Training.

There is a great deal of variability in the cost of training for nurses. In general, costs are somewhat less than ordinary college training because often a portion of the student nurse's expenses is borne by the hospital providing her clinical experience. Many hospitals arrange to pay a part, or all, of the costs of training in exchange for an agreement from the student nurse to accept her first position in the hospital providing the support.

In collegiate programs, and especially in graduate programs, fellowships and student stipends are often available. Many nursing leaders would favor arrangements throughout nursing education that would leave the educational institution free to arrange clinical experience for the student nurse in a manner judged by the nursing educators to be most proper. There is a feeling in some quarters that student nurses are sometimes exploited and that many of the duties they are asked to perform are not strictly demanded as part of an ideal training program.

PRESENT AND FUTURE PROSPECTS
IN PSYCHIATRIC NURSING

We have already indicated, in the course of our discussion, some of the most serious problems in psychiatric nursing. All the evidence suggests that our nation is faced with continuing shortages of professional nursing personnel in those facilities responsible for the care and treatment of mental patients. Despite the prospect of increasing numbers of nurses being trained in the next decade or two, if psychiatric nursing continues to attract less than 5 per cent of hospital nurses there is no hope that shortages will be eased. Indeed, with the anticipated increase in demand for professional personnel in the field of mental illness and mental health we are not likely to be able to maintain our present inadequate ratios.

It is easy to speculate about the reasons for this situation. What is needed urgently is research of the kind begun by Long (1958) into the interests, values, and sources of job satisfaction of student nurses and the relationship between these variables and attraction or rejection of careers in psychiatric nursing.

One important study was conducted by the National League of Nursing Education (now National League for Nursing). Over 9000 nurses, employed in some 600 different centers concerned with the care and treatment of the mentally ill, completed a questionnaire. Nearly half of the respondents were employed in State and local public psychiatric hospitals with an additional quarter being employed in Federal hospitals. Among the findings was the fact that a significantly higher proportion of male nurses were working in psychiatric settings (7 per cent in contrast to less than 1 per cent of active professional nurses in general). Three-quarters of the nurses in psychiatric settings had received their basic training in general hospital schools of nursing and 25 per cent had received their training in a school connected with a mental hospital. A large proportion of the group had had no basic psychiatric nursing (Nowakowski, Aurelie J., 1950).

A number of interesting questions are raised by this and similar studies. It has been suggested that adolescents who are attracted to a career in nursing are attracted by a public image of nursing differing markedly from the experience the student nurse gets in the mental hospital field placement. Schools of nursing in psychiatric hospitals have declined in number and importance in recent years. Yet some evidence indicates that a significantly higher proportion of student nurses trained in a school centered in a mental hospital elect psychiatric nursing as a career. It may be that self-selection operates here too, in that adolescents who elect to undertake training in nursing in a mental hospital are less likely to be threatened or repelled by work with mental patients. While no nursing leader has suggested a return to the practice of training nurses in schools located in mental hospitals, research on this subject might give clues about factors responsible for the choice of psychiatric nursing as a career.

There is also evidence that a high proportion of student nurses trained in small psychiatric units, or in psychiatric hospitals that are intensive research and treatment centers, are likely to elect psychiatric nursing as a career. Research is needed to determine whether changes in locus and program of the psychiatric affiliation, on an experimental basis, would result in increases in the number of student nurses recruited to the psychiatric field.

A number of investigations have reported that the duties of the psychiatric nurse are less clearly defined, and involve much less actual patient care than do other areas of nursing. Careful studies of job duties and responsibilities are needed before we can define clearly the problems interfering with satisfactory recruitment of psychiatric nurses.

VII

Manpower Prospects in Other Professions Related to Mental Health

INTRODUCTION

W<small>E HAVE ATTEMPTED</small> to bring together information from existing sources which would give a picture of our present and future prospects in the professional fields most directly concerned with the care and treatment of mental patients, with the prevention of mental illness, and with the discovery of causes of these disorders.

It is important to recognize that the groups of interest to us are by no means the only professional disciplines important to this field. There are a large number of other professions vitally concerned.

To discuss every profession involved in the role of mental health would make this book overlong. The major professional groups concerned serve as ample illustrations of our point. We would add one precautionary measure, however, which has previously been mentioned. To increase the numbers in one professional group without increasing the total pool of young persons eligible for, and entering, professional training solves no problem at all but merely shifts the shortage from one area to another. There is the possibility that developing opportunities for professional services in new areas may induce persons into professional training who would have no interest or emotional investment in training in the presently constituted fields.

In recent years new groups have developed, and some have achieved virtually professional status, such as the rehabilitation workers. Approximately thirty colleges and universities now offer specific courses of training for this group. To date, no definite body of theoretical knowledge has been added, but it appears that in a matter of time rehabilitation will emerge as a full-blown, independent, professional group of vast importance to the health field and particularly to the mental health field. In addition, groups such as music therapists, bibliotherapists, and a variety of other groups now contributing significantly to the care of mentally ill persons, particularly those in hospitals, and to mental health promotion, particularly through recreational and occupational pursuits, will emerge significantly onto the scene. In addition to a long list of professional groups and new groups moving toward independent professional status are two professional groups that have long worked in the field of mental health and the treatment of the mentally ill. Occupational therapists, as a professional group, occupy an important place in the field of mental health.

We have selected the field of occupational therapy as an example of a professional group that has come to occupy a potentially important place in this field. Not only can the occupational therapists make an important contribution to efforts at rehabilitation of patients in mental institutions, but by their skills and knowledge of rehabilitation in general they can do much to improve the adjustment and mental health of people suffering from a wide variety of chronic disorders and physical handicaps.

We will also discuss briefly the manpower situation in the clergy. Every assessment of resources available to deal with the problem of mental disorder immediately encounters evidence of the importance of religion. Not only do clergymen make an important contribution as chaplains in our mental hospitals, but as a resource for counseling, reassurance, and the strength that comes from religious belief, religious leaders are a vital influence.

Many other professional groups belong in this survey. The importance of teachers to the mental health of the nation is incalculable. We will have some things to say about manpower deficits in our educational system later in this report. Another project of the Joint Commission on Mental Illness and Health is preparing a study of mental health in the classroom. The reader is referred to that report for more detailed consideration of the importance of teachers.

We must recognize, too, that the mental health of our people is influenced by the stability of our laws and by those persons trained to interpret and enforce them. Discoveries in a broad range of research areas have vital consequences for mental illness and health. The architects who help plan our mental institutions, the accountants and personnel workers who keep them running, and the administrators concerned with policies and planning, all represent important professions contributing to mental health.

Research scientists in chemistry and biology, in sociology and anthropology, to name but a few areas of knowledge, have made some of the most important contributions to the understanding and control of mental illness and to the maximization of mental health. Later we will examine briefly some of the indices of manpower shortage in the natural and social sciences.

OCCUPATIONAL THERAPY

Historical Background.

The first training programs in occupational therapy were located in hospitals although a few were actually begun in art institutes. These early courses, inaugurated shortly after the turn of the present century, were primarily designed for nursing personnel engaged in work with the chronically ill or the physically incapacitated. Probably the first training course in occupational therapy was at the Adams Nervine Hospital in Boston in 1906, closely followed by the Savill School in Chicago in 1908. The first college course, entitled "invalid occupations," appeared shortly before World War I.

It was during the First World War that occupational therapy as a separate profession received its first sharp impetus. A three-month training program was ordered to prepare some 200 persons as the "reconstruction aides" requested by General Pershing for employment in army hospitals in Europe. Since that time the profession has enjoyed a steady growth. While its early beginnings were very frequently centered in work with mental patients, the concept of the rehabilitation of the physically handicapped has broadened the field markedly. For a number of reasons occupational therapy schools did not remain in the hospitals, as has been the case with many schools of nursing, but followed the typical pattern of professional development and moved into academic institutions. After 1923 all new occupational therapy programs were established in accredited colleges and universities and in 1944 the last of the hospital schools disappeared.

Present Function.

The work of the occupational therapist is clear in the abstract but varies widely in practice. The occupational therapist is concerned with organizing a variety of activities that will assist in the rehabilitation of persons with physical handicaps or mental conditions usually involving long-term disability. Occupational therapists also supervise the rehabilitation programs designed to improve the morale, skills, education, and psychological organization of people suffering from a wide variety of physical and mental disabilities. They work in hospitals, rehabilitation centers, sanitaria, orthopedic schools, in the patients' homes, and in sheltered workshops. The patients helped most frequently by occupational therapists are those with tuberculosis, mental disorder, rheumatic fever, cerebral palsy, injuries due to accident or war, and with cardiovascular and metabolic disturbances. In recent years, occupational therapists have begun to specialize in working with particular conditions so that some now work exclusively with physically disabled groups, others with mental patients, others with the palsied.

Occupational therapists work primarily in hospitals, and this is the source of greatest demand. The Federal government, particularly the Veterans Administration and the Armed Services, is the largest employer of occupational therapists.

Patterns of Training.

Admission requirements for the student interested in training in occupational therapy depend on his background. High school graduates are required to complete four years of college together with a nine-month in-service supervised practice program in a setting providing this type of therapy. Upon completion of this program, the student receives a B.S. degree in occupational therapy. Many of the schools also accept college graduates who may qualify for certification in occupational therapy by completing eight months of additional training. There is some sentiment for the requirement of graduate study in the training of occupational therapists. There are now three programs at the graduate level, all leading to the master's degree.

Facilities Available for Training.

The present capacity of approved occupational therapy schools is 3500 students, although in the year 1955–56 only 2600 students were enrolled and the number of graduates amounted to approximately 500. It seems very probable that within the next few years existing schools will be up to capacity, although all estimates of future need for occupational therapists suggest that present schools will be insufficient to provide the number of trained persons who will be required in a growing population with an increasing number of aged, disabled, and mentally disordered.

In 1935, at the request of the American Occupational Therapy Association, the *Council on Medical Education and Hospitals* of the American Medical Association assumed responsibility for the inspection and accreditation of occupational therapy programs. Students graduating from approved schools take the National Registration Examination and, upon satisfactory completion of this examination, are entitled to call themselves registered occupational therapists (OTR). This examination is recognized by Federal and most State agencies in the employment of occupational therapists. There are no State licensing laws in this field.

Numerical Trends.

Early in 1957 there were approximately 5500 occupational therapists who were registered with the American Occupational Therapy Association. A large proportion of occupational therapists are women, although according to the Bureau of Labor Statistics an increasing number of men are entering the field and increasing numbers of opportunities for male occupational therapists are appearing.

The Health Resources Advisory Committee points out that in the United States today there are nearly 2,000,000 people of employable age who require rehabilitation, and these, together with the many hundreds of thousands of handicapped and chronically ill children, represent a tremendous social demand for the skills of a variety of professional workers including especially occupational therapists.

"Interest in these people springs from more than humanitarian motives. It is strengthened by the knowledge that our nation can gain immeasurably from the fullest use of our human resources. We know that people with handicaps can be trained with singular success—and they do more than repay the costs of rehabilitation—through the goods they produce, taxes they pay, the public social services they no longer need" (Rusk and Switzer, 1953).

Salaries and Working Conditions.

According to the Bureau of Labor Statistics salaries of occupational therapists ranged from $3500 upward in 1956. New graduates employed by the Federal government could expect to earn $3670 a year and those with a year's experience began at $4525. State institutions offered approximately $4000 a year in 1956 for beginning occupational therapists.

Salaries paid to rehabilitation workers, including occupational therapists, are reported to compare unfavorably with professionals in similar fields.

"In the future our nation will be forced to use rehabilitation techniques and personnel to a much greater extent than ever before. . . . But if rehabilitation is to meet its own manpower needs, it will have to compete with other industries, other occupations, other professions, other competing demands for able, competent people" (Tickton, S., 1957, p. 12).

THE CLERGY

One of the important groups to be considered in any discussion of mental illness and mental health in our society is the professional group responsible for religious leadership and religious education. There are more than three hundred thousand clergymen in the United States. From the founding of our country down to the present time religious leaders have had tremendous influence on the developing pattern of national character, and they have been a bulwark against the effects of stress and crisis.

There are several levels of involvement in the relationships between the clergy and the field of mental illness and mental health. Most directly, the presence of mental hospital chaplains in our mental institutions illustrates an important concern of religion for those people with mental disorder. At the next level, the role clergymen serve as a first line of defense in mental health by counseling and by offering spiritual support to people in emotional trouble is clearly established. As an example of concern at still another level, we find increased awareness among religious leaders of the need for bringing to clergymen in training the latest information on research findings in the field of mental disorder and on principles of counseling for good mental health; there is also a concern with developing an understanding of those social and cultural factors which organized religion can support, or criticize, as they affect the mental health and spiritual welfare of the lay membership of religious groups.

In all cultures, and throughout the ages, religious leaders have been a source of support and guidance for people in the intimate crises of their daily living. Recently, in the United States, there has been a sharp increase in church membership and participation. Although some social critics have attributed this increase to other factors than an upsurge in interest in religion itself, we have nonetheless witnessed a sharp increase in the demand for guidance of people in emotional difficulties.

During World War II, the chaplains attached to military units earned the respect and gratitude of innumerable servicemen, and, despite the good humored references to the chaplain in the military culture, the general reaction was favorable. After World War II, former military chaplains returned to theological schools in large numbers to take intensive training in pastoral counseling, frequently

exceeding in numbers the resources of the schools in this subject
area.

A recent national survey reported by Ernest E. Bruder (1957) revealed that about 40 per cent of all people seeking help for emotional
problems turned first to their clergymen for guidance. As the
first resource for people in emotional trouble, the clergyman is in a
unique position to provide help, or to refer people for other professional help. Frequently the clergyman is on the scene at the earliest
stages of emotional problems. As a welcome visitor in his parishioners' homes and as a socially acceptable source of advice, he often
can detect, and even smooth over, personal problems when they
are first manifest. Immediately one sees the need for training and
experience for the clergy in these areas. (The nationwide sampling
survey of people's mental health made for the Joint Commission
by the Survey Research Center will furnish further documentation on this subject.)

Because the clergy are often the first to be consulted in the emotional crises in people's lives, they play a very important role in the
mental health of the nation. In recognition of this role the National
Academy of Religion and Mental Health was established in 1956.
The aim of this organization is to foster education and research
in the relationships between religion and health, particularly mental health. The Academy sponsors scientific research, holds con-
ferences to which are invited theologians, psychiatrists, and other
professional persons in the field of mental health, obtains fellowships, scholarships, and grants-in-aid for clergymen of all faiths who
desire graduate and clinical training in pastoral psychology. It in-
terprets theological doctrines to mental health workers and serves
as a center of information with respect to relations between religion
and mental health. From its beginning, the National Academy of
Religion and Mental Health has had the support of leading clergymen and psychiatrists. Today the membership in this organization
includes some fourteen hundred psychiatrists, six hundred ministers, and two hundred organizations (seminaries, medical schools,

convents, monasteries, and mental health agencies). Recently it dropped the name "National" from its title and became international in scope.

Mental Hospital Chaplains.

Nearly everyone agrees that mentally ill persons may benefit from contact with sympathetic and informed members of the clergy. The first clergyman to be employed as a full-time chaplain in a mental hospital was Anton T. Boisen who in 1925 began his chaplaincy at Worcester State Hospital. By 1943 the movement had grown so slowly that only thirteen of 184 hospitals replying to a questionnaire from the National Committee for Mental Hygiene reported full-time Protestant chaplains, although an additional fifty-three had part-time chaplains. By 1948 the number had increased to forty-one full-time Protestant chaplains.

In 1948, there was formed a National Association of Mental Hospital Chaplains. The 1957 membership of this Association was about 300.

The training of the chaplain is generally believed to require additional clinical experience and academic course work beyond the regular training program for a particular religious affiliation. Hospital chaplains have found a wide variety of ways to minister to the spiritual and emotional needs of patients. Conducting religious services and Bible study groups, visiting and working with patients' families, and reassuring and praying with patients have turned out to be useful and helpful roles unique to the clergyman.

The American Hospital Association (1955) reports a survey of chaplains available in all types of hospitals. Eighty-seven per cent of all hospitals responded to the request for information. Two-thirds of all hospitals responding reported that chaplain services were available. This includes full-time chaplains, part-time chaplains, and chaplains who are simply on call. Of 461 hospitals primarily concerned with mental patients, 88 per cent reported the availability of chaplains. Of 3575 nonmental hospitals, 65 per cent reported chaplains available. It is difficult to know what significance to attribute to this data without further information about the amount of time chaplains spend with patients.

Training in Pastoral Psychology.

There has been a sharp increase in recent years in the demand for and availability of training in pastoral psychology. This growing field of emphasis stresses the clergyman's role as a counselor and as an important first resource for people with problems. There is an increasing awareness of the need for special training for the clergyman in the recognition of mental disorders, in the mechanics of referral, and in the effective counseling of the disturbed individual and his family.

In 1947, there were twenty training centers offering special training in pastoral psychology (Protestant denominations). By 1958, more than 300 centers offered this training.

The training available varies widely. In some instances short courses, seminars, and lecture series are the rule. Some sixty offerings are reported available of this type (National Council of Churches, 1958). At the other extreme we find sixty-four training centers that offer at least six weeks of carefully supervised resident full-time training in an accredited agency.

The Roman Catholic Church and various Jewish centers also offer pastoral psychology training.

Detailed descriptions of this growing area of emphasis are to be found in the January 1958 issue of *Pastoral Psychology*.

Shortages of Clergymen.

It is difficult to find recent evidences of the adequacy of the number and training of clergymen in the United States.

A survey of the member denominations of the National Council of Churches (Million, 1957) found that serious shortages of clergymen existed in 1956 (some 25,000) and revealed that estimates of need by member churches were based on the most unrealistic estimates of length of service from members of the clergy.

Million estimated that nearly 169,000 clergymen would be needed *in addition* to the regular replacement needs of the member churches by 1975. When all needs were taken into account, he arrived at the figure of 618,750 Protestant ministers needed in the next eighteen years! He also examined in some detail the training of ministers and suggested that sizable numbers of those now ordained are inadequately prepared academically.

While the above material is based on the information available from the sources in various Protestant churches, it is used merely to illustrate a point and was selected because of the ready availability of this material. The clergy in both the Catholic and Jewish religions participate equally in the chaplaincy programs in the mental hospitals in practically all areas of the country. Except for the religious services for their communicants, there is little important difference in the chaplain's role as played by the clergy from the three major religious groups in this country. Similarly, the Catholic and Jewish groups participate extensively in spiritual guidance and in counseling activities with patients in mental hospitals and with their own parishioners, either in the religious setting or in more formally organized counseling services. Documentation as to possible shortages in the clergy for the Catholic and Jewish groups was not available to us, but interviews with the leaders in their groups suggest that shortages are of about the same extent as in the Protestant clergy.

VIII

Manpower Prospects in Other Occupations Concerned with Mental Illness and Mental Health

INTRODUCTION

There are many people employed in occupations having direct relevance to the care and treatment of mental patients in other than professional capacities. Indeed, the observation is frequently made that a very large proportion of employee time devoted to patient care is made by relatively untrained workers.

Let us look briefly at the manpower situation in some of the nonprofessional occupations most directly concerned with the field of mental illness.

PRACTICAL NURSES AND ATTENDANTS

There is a steadily growing demand for all kinds of nursing care. There has been an increase in opportunities for people, mostly older women, to find employment as practical nurses. Figure 42 indicates the increase in the proportion of the hospital nursing team that is made up of practical nurses and auxiliary workers.

Significant numbers of practical nurses and auxiliary workers have been employed in our mental hospitals. Table 72 indicates the number of practical nurses and auxiliary workers employed in all types of hospitals and the number employed in mental hospitals. The reader will note that there has been a slight, but con-

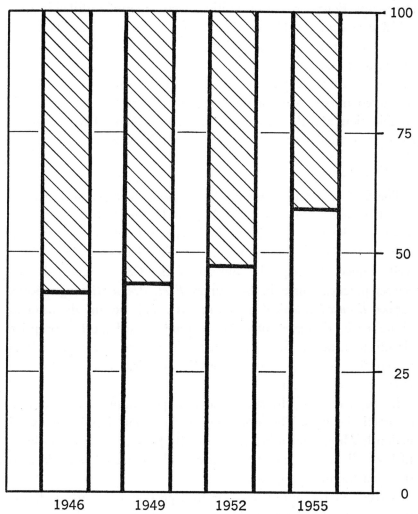

FIG. 42.—*The hospital nursing team.*

Source: Nurses for a growing nation, 1957. Pamphlet published by the
National League for Nursing. This figure based on material contained in
American Nurses' Association, *Facts about nursing,* 1955–1956.

tinuing, decrease in the proportion of these people who are employed in mental hospitals during the early years of this present decade.

In our earlier discussion of shortages we found that the number of vacancies was somewhat less severe for nonregistered nurses and attendants. Four per cent of positions were reported unfilled in 1956.

Table 11 contains data on the distribution of attendants and non-registered nurses by region and state, and also contains information on unfilled positions reported for these occupations. A very high proportion of these positions are for attendants, rather than non-registered nurses. Most manpower data report the two groups in combination, and this practice is rather misleading. Let us examine these occupational groups separately for the moment.

Practical Nurses.

The field of practical nursing has gradually become an organized and definable group. Since World War II, the skills and duties of this group have become increasingly clarified and the standards of training leading to employment in this field have been increasingly well defined. In 1940 the Bureau of the Census reported some 200,000 practical nurses in the country. *Facts About Nursing* reported 125,000 *licensed* practical nurses in 1954. This decline does not indicate a true decrease but rather a trend toward more appropriate classification and definition. In 1954, there were 13,233 people who passed the licensing examinations in practical nursing. In 1955, 12,672 passed the exams.

By 1956, most of the states had laws pertaining to the licensure of practical nurses. The proportion of the group licensed by examination has been increasing each year. By January 1956, more than a fifth of all licensed practical nurses had completed some kind of specified training program.

A study of the graduates of trainee programs recently indicated that only about 1 per cent were employed by mental hospitals.

In 1938, the nonprofessional nursing personnel in all United States hospitals amounted to sixty-two per 1000 patients. In 1956 this ratio was more than 200 per 1000 patients. During this same period the number of professional nurses also increased sharply.

Although the figures may not be strictly accurate, two trends are apparent—a large increase in the number of total nursing personnel per unit of population, and a more rapid increase among the nonprofessionals than among the professionals. Other data suggest that both of these trends will continue for some years.

Data on salaries of practical nurses, like data on salaries of all occupational groups, are so rapidly outdated as to become meaningless in absolute figures. A study in 1953 found that the salary of practical nurses employed in general hospitals was approximately 70 per cent of the salary of professional staff nurses in these same hospitals.

As mentioned above, the use of practical nurses has had its greatest development since World War II. In 1947, there were about fifty schools of practical nursing; in 1957, the total was about 400 schools. The number of graduates has increased from about 1000 in 1947 to more than 7000 in 1955. During this time, a fairly well organized educational program has been formulated and a system of State and national approval of schools has been established. About a quarter of the schools are operated by hospitals. The remainder are run by vocational schools. Programs are typically one year in length and generally include three months of classroom and laboratory instruction and nine months of supervised experience in the care of patients.

A study by the United States Office of Education in 1954 indicated that approximately half of the practical nurses were high school graduates while a third had had some high school but did not graduate. Ten per cent had had no high school and 7 per cent had had some education beyond high school. More than 99 per cent were women and more than half were married.

Practical nursing students mainly seek training near their homes. Many of them are older women with personal and family ties in the community. The average age in the study mentioned above was thirty-five. Graduates tend to seek employment in the hospitals where they received their clinical experience.

Communities that have never had a practical nursing school are likely to have a reservoir of older women who are eager for this kind of training. As this reservoir may be fairly rapidly exhausted with the inauguration of a training program, it has been suggested that a rotating system of training be considered.

The major problems in the field are concerned with the improved utilization of the practical nurse, the preparation for the practical nurse in the field of chronic and mental diseases, and increasing the supply of practical nurses by reaching those who are willing to enter the field but for whom no training program is easily available.

A very low percentage of licensed practical nurses are employed in mental hospitals. Even if we include attendants in our figures, less than one-third of all practical nurses and auxiliary workers are employed in mental hospitals (Table 72).

There are many reasons for this situation. We have noted that practical nurses are older and, frequently, married women with family responsibilities who tend to seek work close to their established homes. There is also a tendency for them to work in the hospital where they receive their clinical training. Most of the training programs for practical nurses are either located in general hospitals or use general hospitals as the clinical setting for the student's experience. There is relatively little likelihood of these people receiving much experience in working with mental patients (Leone, Lucile P., 1956).

The group of potential practical nurses described previously does represent one possible source of additional manpower for our mental hospitals. If practical nurse programs were established with field work placements in mental hospitals, training programs might include satisfactory work experience with mental patients. Temporary or permanent training centers for practical nurses established in communities with easy access to large mental hospitals might provide a continuing source of personnel for these hospitals.

It might be reasonable to consider looking to the pool of girls in junior high school who are considering leaving school to seek employment as possible recruits to the field.

Attendants and Psychiatric Aides.

Between 80,000 and 90,000 people are employed in our mental institutions as attendants and psychiatric aides. In recent years, attention has gradually been focused on this occupational group.

Numerous studies of the characteristics of good attendants, factors involved in attendant turnover, and problems in the establishment and evaluation of training programs for attendants have found their way into the literature. This concern is certainly justified when we realize that it is this group which has the most daily and continuing contact with the patients.

The shortage of attendants, if we consider reported vacancies, is not especially serious. The survey by the Council of State Governments, some of the data of which we have reported earlier, found only 4 per cent of attendant jobs unfilled. This still turns out to be a sizable number of jobs; and we have no way of knowing the relationship between reported vacancies and aspirations of states for adequate staffing.

On the qualitative side, most observers are concerned with the kind of personnel attracted to these positions. Traditionally, the position of attendant in a mental hospital has been a haven for the inadequate. Sadistic persons, alcoholics, and even vagrants have all too commonly been employed in these jobs. Often former mental patients obtain employment as attendants, and, in many cases, they represent a more sympathetic and understanding group. Again, traditionally, the pay has been poor and the status of the position negligible.

In recent years, the position of the attendant has been improved considerably in many states. Training programs have been instituted and improved salaries and working conditions have occurred. The National Institute of Mental Health has sponsored valuable training institutes and studies concerned with the in-service training of attendants, and with the training of practical nurses as well. Several of the states have begun experimental programs using junior colleges and community colleges together with State hospitals in setting up psychiatric aide and practical nurse training schools.

No recent and accurate data are available on the actual extent and permanence of the improvements. Because of the importance of the attendants in patient care and treatment, a study of the emeging patterns and practices with respect to this occupational group is badly needed.

IX
_____

The Crisis in Education

INTRODUCTION

MOST OF THE ESTIMATES of the availability of professional manpower in the field of mental illness and mental health indicate that the years ahead are likely to be years of continued shortage. Our estimates of this shortage are based on a number of factors, any one of which could change drastically, with the consequent invalidation of many of our predictions.

For example, a major research breakthrough in the biochemistry of schizophrenia, or in the treatment of arteriosclerosis, could reduce the demand for professional services in our large State institutions. Such a research breakthrough would seem less likely to be achieved than it might be, because of the serious shortage of research personnel in the field. Another project of the Joint Commission on Mental Illness and Health is studying the research resources. We refer the reader to that study for further information on the pattern of ongoing research and its support.

Another factor which, if changed, could change the manpower picture is the social pattern of patient care. It may be that a century from now our huge State mental hospitals will have passed into history and will represent just one more stage of evolution in patient care. Another project of the Joint Commission on Mental Illness and Health is preparing a report on care of the mentally ill in our society. The trends found in that study cannot help but give insights into future manpower needs.

We would be unrealistic to pin our hopes on research breakthroughs in the future, or on rapid changes in the patterns of patient care, as the mechanisms through which manpower shortages in the mental health professions are likely soon to be eased. New treatment techniques discovered, and more effective patterns of patient care, usually require more trained personnel rather than fewer. Much more possible, though as we shall see not likely, is an improvement in the manpower situation resulting from a sharp increase in the number of competent personnel trained.

Shortages in the mental health professions do not exist in isolation. We have already described the widespread shortage of highly trained people in a variety of technical and professional areas. There seems to be a pervasive resistance to an all-out educational effort by our country.

Professional manpower trends depend on the strength of our educational system and on the number of students enrolled and completing their training. As we have seen, the longer the training that is required for a professional field, the greater is the present shortage.

We have also seen that a shortage of eligible students sometimes has led to the acceptance into educational programs of students of poor ability.

Resistant attitudes toward lengthy and difficult educational programs certainly affect recruitment into the mental health professions, as they affect the recruitment to many other fields.

Let us take a hard look at trends in education to see if we can discover some of the factors responsible for our present and prospective manpower shortages.

OVERVIEW

During the past few years, a number of studies have been made under both Federal and professional auspices; these have attempted to assess the dimensions of the educational problems besetting the United States. Among the areas of concern in the studies are the following: First, the problem of the number of able students who do not go on for college education because of lack of money, or motivation, or both; second, the deterioration of the quality of our educational plant and our failure to attract competent teachers and faculty members to our educational institutions; and, third, the rising costs of education, promising to be a further barrier to able students who have not the financial ability to pay for college and professional education.

These problems are all aspects of a more basic and fundamental problem, according to many educators. The fundamental problem, they say, is a lack of appreciation or interest in intellectual achievement and the acquisition of knowledge which has grown up over a long period of time and is reflected in our pervasive neglect of educational plant, the low repute in which teaching is held, and a lack of a ground swell of support for education in the face of crisis.

Now suddenly we have been forced to the realization that the quality of our educational system has been on the downgrade for a number of years. Three-fourths of all American high school students study no physics. In the Soviet Union, every Russian high school graduate has the equivalent of five years of physics. Only slightly more than one-third of our own high school students study geometry and less than two-thirds of our students even study algebra. Every Russian high school student, on the other hand, takes mathematics through trigonometry.

A major trend in our educational system has been to emphasize courses leading to better personal adjustment, or to focus on the acquisition of skills which have immediate vocational applicability. In the process, we have had a strong tendency to neglect more difficult subjects and especially those most suited to the preparation of scientists.

At the same time we have been extremely wasteful in our utilization of the brain power of our young people. By limiting college admissions to those who could afford to pay the costs of education, or who could find ways of earning their own support, we lost a large number of young people each year who have the intellectual qualifications to succeed in higher education. At the same time, because of inadequate or complete lack of preparation in certain subjects, our college students have tended to drift toward those subjects which do not require extensive preliminary preparation in mathematics and the sciences. We are now witnessing, as a result, a severe shortage of people trained in the sciences and technology.

A recent study by the Educational Testing Service (1957) points out that many of the students now attending college are less intelligent than others not attending college and that in general we are losing a very large number of high ability students because of a lack of financial support for their education.

What does it cost to go to college? There are all sorts of estimates, and the dollar value changes with inflation, but in 1957 the cost was somewhere between $1500 and $2000 a year although many of our top schools are considerably above this figure.

It is essential to recognize that despite this apparently high cost, tuition represents only a small fraction of the total cost of education, and income from tuition represents less than half of the operating expenses of most colleges and universities. It has been estimated that tuition supplies some 15 to 35 per cent of the total cost to the college or university of a college education (Table 73). The balance must be made up in income from endowments, grants, or other forms of direct aid. Many educators point to the fact that tuition is one of the last remaining goods or services that is paid for in cash. A number have suggested that a college education be paid for over a period of years, on the installment plan, just like houses and other major capital investment. As studies have shown that a college education increases one's earning power over a working lifetime upwards of $100,000, the suggestion seems quite reasonable.

A recent report by The President's Committee on Education Beyond the High School (1957) has emphasized the need for finding ways for providing increased income to higher educational institutions. Among the suggestions of this group was an increase in tuition, with student loans as one possible source of meeting the increased tuition. The President's Committee emphasized that the most important need in higher education at the present time is for well trained and competent faculty members. It suggests that one of the first tasks facing society is to find ways of raising faculty salaries at least 50 per cent during the next five years. Because the salaries of college faculty members have been and are so low, these people are really subsidizing part of the college education of their students.

Many faculty members, of course, eventually tire of being unappreciated contributors to our educational charity system and leave the universities for more remunerative jobs elsewhere. The President's Committee points out that in those colleges where top quality faculty members are paid high salaries, there is a much smaller drop-out rate on the part of students. It is always possible to fill academic jobs with someone willing to teach for the salaries offered, but if the United States is to maintain its leadership in the educational field it will be necessary to make a massive effort to recruit more able faculty.

At the present time we are spending some three billion dollars each year for higher education. Between now and 1970, it will be necessary to double this yearly expenditure and during this intervening period an additional eighteen billion dollars will have to be found for increased physical plant and other facilities.

It is difficult to state forcefully enough the dimensions of the educational crisis our nation faces. The wave of young people of college age that is about to break over our institutions of higher education threatens to swamp our facilities. Faculty members at present are being lost because of the immediate demands for personnel in government and industry and because of pitifully inadequate academic salaries. The production of new doctorates is at a low level partly because of the "thin generation" of the thirties now in graduate school and partly because of the lack of incentive for education. And finally, and perhaps most important, the quality of our high school teaching is often low and promises to worsen.

Here are some of the grim facts compiled by the Fund for the Advancement of Education (1956):

Enrollments in elementary and secondary schools will continue to rise. In the secondary schools, already seriously crowded, there will be a 71 per cent rise over 1954 enrollments by 1970.

College enrollments will double, and could possibly triple, over the next fifteen years. (Claims that colleges and universities will limit admissions and raise entrance requirements fail to take into account the tremendous social demand for higher education, and the equally great, but largely unrecognized, social need for highly trained people.)

In the next ten years, three new teachers will have to be found for every two we now have in our schools. The demand for college teachers will be even greater. Over the next fifteen years we will need from sixteen to twenty-five new faculty members for every ten now teaching. This is only the quantitative problem. The problem of finding these people at a level of ability commensurate with our needs is even more serious, as we shall discuss in detail below.

In recent years about one-fifth of all college graduates have entered the teaching profession. To staff adequately our elementary and secondary schools we would need *more than half* of all college graduates every year for ten years! Obviously this is impossible of realization. Something has to yield. Class sizes will continue to increase and more "emergency" teachers will be hired, though some feel we have nearly exhausted the pool of potential emergency teachers.

By 1965, the problem of recruiting college teachers will make present difficulties seem mild. Present estimates foresee a decline in the proportion of college teachers with the Ph.D. degree from the present 40 per cent to about 20 per cent by 1970, despite the most strenuous efforts to encourage new Ph.D.'s to enter the teaching field.

From 1950 to 1955, our output of high school teachers in several important subject areas sharply declined. The greatest decline was in science (57 per cent) and mathematics (51 per cent), and, of the small number of qualified science teachers produced, more than half decided against entering teaching. Prospects for the future are not much better, as we shall see.

A sort of vicious circle is in operation. The growing shortage of college faculty will make the anticipated expansion of college enrollments difficult to accommodate. And yet, expanded enrollments aside, we are losing many more potential college graduates than we are training. Of the top 25 per cent of our young people in ability, 40 per cent do not go on to college after finishing high school.

As we have noted there have been a succession of studies and reports detailing the dimensions of our education crisis. The reports all seem to suffer the same fate. Their life in the public eye is brief. Note is taken of them in the mass media, heads are shaken, and the reports are buried.

A Committee on Scientists and Engineers headed by Howard L. Bevis reported in December, 1957, to the President:

> The Committee is equally concerned about the failure of the American public generally to recognize the long-term implications of the inadequacy of science and mathematics education and by its inclination to regard temporary improvements in the manpower supply as permanent panaceas. The long-term demand for scientists, engineers, technicians, in fact for trained brain power of all types, is so great as to make temporary, localized variations in supply of merely passing interest.

Awareness of the inadequacies of our whole educational system evidently is reaching a very wide range of public spokesmen. In the short space of two weeks, former President Herbert Hoover and Steelworkers' Union Chief David McDonald spoke out with much the same eloquent message. Herbert Hoover (1957) emphasized the fundamental weakness of the laissez-faire high school system that permits students to choose their own courses of study.

"The trouble is," he said, "that we are turning out annually from our institutions of higher education perhaps fewer than half as many scientists and engineers as we did seven years ago."

McDonald (1957), in a letter to Senator Lister Hill, said: "As matters stand right at this moment, by 1960 America will . . . have 500,000 too few teachers."

Another passionate spokesman for better education, and critic of the inadequacies of our educational system is Admiral Hyman Rickover, who has waged a campaign to set up a few topnotch high schools that he would designate as Class A and which might then serve to make all other schools automatically Class B. The Class A schools would be a target for the other schools to emulate.

Says Rickover (1957):

> In no other Western country are educational institutions so precariously placed financially, so dependent on local politicians, on the whim of small communities where few have ever had a higher education. Half of our colleges are continuously threatened with bankruptcy. The future looks bleak unless in

some way Federal assistance can be made acceptable and some sort of national standard can be established to which diploma and degree-giving institutions must conform.

There are those who foresee the oncoming tide of college students as the final blow to our system of higher education, already reeling from financial problems and inadequate teaching staffs. The argument is as follows: doubled student enrollment will have the same effect on our colleges and universities as it is having presently on our high schools. Students in great numbers will arrive at our college campuses poorly prepared because of their overcrowded high school classes with inadequately prepared and demoralized teachers. There will be a greater emphasis on vocational and adjustment courses in the colleges because of the necessity to revise the college curriculum downward to the level of the training of the students. As the quality of preparation of students (not necessarily the *ability* of students) declines, the demand will be for mediocre teachers with larger classes. Standardized outlines, texts, and punchcard evaluation systems will be the rule as a solution to the overcrowding and the general decline of standards.

Just as the prestige of high school teaching has declined in the past half century, the argument goes, so will there be a decline in the prestige of college teaching. Scholars and scientists who stay in the academic field will move exclusively into the graduate and professional schools, and, as these are engulfed, on to new postgraduate schools.

Arthur A. Ekirch, Jr. (1956) warns: "Like his confreres in the high schools, . . . the professor will have become a technician. But because of the limited amount of technical skill needed to impart rote learning to large numbers of dull and indifferent students, the professor will again be poorly paid."

It is important to note that an increase in the number of students enrolled in high school or college does not necessarily mean a decline in the average ability of the population of students in these secondary or higher educational institutions. Wolfle (1954, p. 173) reports on studies which show that increases in enrollment have not resulted in a decline in the average level of students' ability. What has happened, apparently, is that the small enrollments of half a century ago were not drawn from the top ability group exclusively, and that today more and more students of a wide range of ability are going on for more education. Because of the great reservoir of high level ability in our population, increasing enrollments do not mean a loss of quality, so long as admission standards are high.

On the other hand it is important, too, for us to realize that, while there is an increasing percentage of high school graduates who are going on to college, these young people are not being drawn only from the graduates with the highest levels of ability. Wolfle has shown that the average ability of the beginning college student is not appreciably greater than that of the average high school graduate. This means that other factors than intelligence determine who goes on to college, with a consequent loss to the nation of many high school graduates with outstanding ability who for other reasons decide not to continue their education.

WHY IS EDUCATION IN SUCH DIRE STRAITS?

It was Plato who observed that man cultivates that which he most values. As education is a largely uncultivated field in the United States in recent decades we begin to suspect that it is not highly valued. We know that there are other than purely logical and objective reasons for any massive social movement or social inertia. We must be prepared to find that simple and forthright expositions of the enormousness of the need for improved financial and psychological support of education will not bring society galloping to the rescue.

There are a number of paradoxes in the complex problems of present-day American education. In the distorted and murky picture that social scientists are able to develop from their technical Brownies we begin to see that as production problems have largely been solved, with the resultant abundant increase in consumer goods for the large majority of our people, there has been a corresponding decrease in the urgency of intellectual pursuits and a corresponding rise in the importance of the specialist in distribution and sales.

There is no great need for intense and specialized education for a majority of people in a consumer's world.

But the picture is not so clear as this. The solution of the problems of production remains valid only so long as new products are created for which a demand can be synthesized and so long as the mechanized and automated productive machine runs smoothly. This means that while education is not too important for most citizens, it is crucial for the maintenance of the technological aspects of our consumer society. But with our system of universal education, the casual and haphazard intellectual demands made of the majority also have tended to implant bad habits in the highly able pupils who might better have served society had they received more rigorous intellectual discipline. Now we are faced with increasingly serious shortages of highly trained minds and, worse still, with the deeply entrenched patterns of an educational system with a relatively minor intellectual function.

Our schools and colleges have become a safe and antiseptic place where, with some relief, we deposit our children from the age of six until they are ready to find gainful employment and strike out on their own. Little real concern has been devoted to the curriculum by anyone except the professional educators. This profession has not been one to attract large numbers of thoughtful social philosophers or exceptionally able scientists. Rather, the field of education has become, in too many cases, the redoubt of unimaginative minds poorly trained in knowledge but ritualistically drilled in the catechism of life adjustment. The educators have taken over by no plot or revolution, but often have been allowed and encouraged to build their underpaid empires in school systems no longer especially important to a country devoted to the leisurely enjoyment of the fruits of production.

Our children have been safe in the educational system. Many of the educators into whose care we have entrusted them have been sincere, God-fearing, kindly people, without guile and without knowledge. We have underpaid them, but we haven't bothered telling them what to do, and many of them have been willing to trade freedom not to teach subjects they did not understand for security, responsibility, and a very modest income. Nor should our college faculties be held blameless. While they point scornfully to the teachers and educators who are sending them poorly trained freshmen, the college professors largely continue a lecture system that was outmoded by the printing press.

Part of the responsibility for this state of affairs must be laid to the businessman and his organizations. For a long time the businessman has been in the status saddle. In a nation that worships production, and the endless flow of new and ever more colorful goods from the production lines, we have been satisfied to turn over much of our government and most of the decisions affecting our future to the businessman with "know-how."

Most knowledgeable students of the problems of our present-day educational system know that the only solution likely to come soon enough to be effective is Federal aid. But the businessman and his national organizations have argued very effectively that, for obscure patriotic reasons, financing of the schools should be left to the State and local government. These forces dismiss as a disenchanted view the observation that State and local districts are much less able to raise tax funds and are much more prone to yield to local pressure groups.

Galbraith (1958, p. 185) emphasizes the long-standing hostility between the businessman and the intellectual. The businessman, practical and worldly, concerned with getting things done, with producing goods, has long had to share the spotlight of public acclaim with the intellectual. The intellectual has fought for status with the subtleties of a mentality sharpened by years of the necessity of living by his wits. The businessman, with conventional but effective strategy, has fought the intellectual by first reducing his number through starvation, and then seducing most of the remainder with the delights of goods, followed by the threat of their removal. The intellectual largely has been driven from the educational system, particularly at the elementary and high school levels, and to a large measure from the colleges and universities as well. He has been replaced by a tamed breed of conformists representing a generally new social group of status-seeking mover-uppers.

Cornog (1958), principal of a first-rate secondary school, warns that there is no magic solution to our problems in education:

Certainly the upgrading of teachers is a tremendous problem and unfortunately it is one which cannot be solved by a "crash" program of increased teachers' salaries. What is called for is a complete reversal of the values in American life. The teacher will be respected and given status when things of the intellect and spirit are given status and respect in our country. In a country still bemused by gadgets and beguiled by slogans and with only most casual commitments to interests in art, music, literature, and the life of the mind, it is to be expected that teachers whose chief obligation in teaching is to train the mind and to pass on the cultural heritage of the nation have always been working against the dynamics of a materialistic culture.

Arthur Bestor (1958) continues his long-time criticism of the inadequacies of American education in an interview with the *U.S. News and World Report* (Jan. 24, 1958, p. 70) with these words:

An educational system that refuses to single out for high and exceptional honors those who demonstrate in fair competition their brilliance and their willingness to work is not a democratic school system at all. It is simply an anti-intellectual school system. And it is no excuse to say that society as a whole has relatively little respect for intellectual achievement. In this matter the school has got to be the leader. If schools, whose business is intellectual training, do not really respect it, how can one expect society as a whole to do so?

FACTORS AFFECTING THE POOL OF COLLEGE GRADUATES FROM WHICH ARE RECRUITED STUDENTS IN THE SEVERAL MENTAL HEALTH PROFESSIONS

Numerical Trends.

Most of the mental health professions depend on the pool of college graduates as a source of applicants to graduate and professional schools. The size of this pool of college graduates therefore affects the supply of applicants.

(These and succeeding figures are calculated from Wolfle, 1954.)

Of 10,000 youngsters in an age group, 7880 enter high school, 5755 graduate from high school, 2016 enter college, 1190 graduate from college.

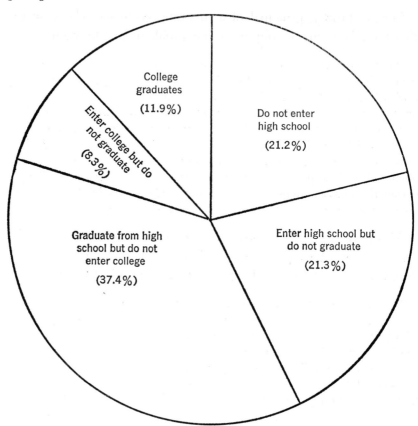

FIG. 43.—*Expected educational attainment of youngsters.*

Source: Calculated from Wolfle, D., 1954. *America's Resources of Specialized Talent.* Harper.

Contrary to widespread opinion, students who enter college are *not* largely drawn from the highest end of the intelligence curve of high school graduates. While some 35 per cent of high school graduates go on to college, it is not just the top group in ability which goes on. The average intelligence of college entrants is only five points above the average of high school graduates (AGCT score).

The unfortunate aspect of this situation is that, of the top 20 per cent of our young people in terms of ability, only one-third finish college. What becomes of this most able 20 per cent?

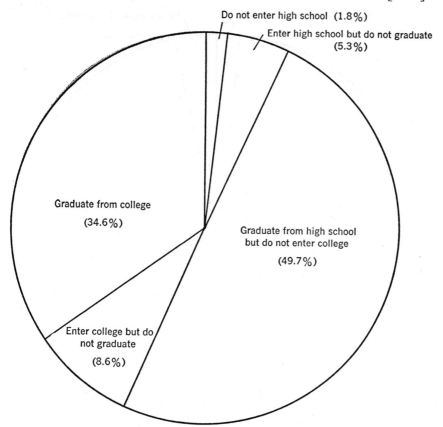

Do not enter high school (1.8%)

Enter high school but do not graduate
(5.3%)

Graduate from college
(34.6%)

Graduate from high school
but do not enter college
(49.7%)

Enter college but do
not graduate
(8.6%)

FIG. 44.—*Expected educational attainment of the most able 20 per cent of
youngsters.*

Source: Wolfle, D., 1954.

Of 10,000 youngsters in an age group, 2000 are in the top fifth
with respect to intelligence, 1963 of them enter high school, 1857
graduate from high school, 864 enter college, 692 graduate from
college.

In short, of our brightest youth (those in the top fifth of intelligence) who finish high school, more than half fail to enter college
and only 35 per cent of these bright young people graduate from
college.

What about the educational achievement of our young people
who have the ability to succeed at the highest educational levels?

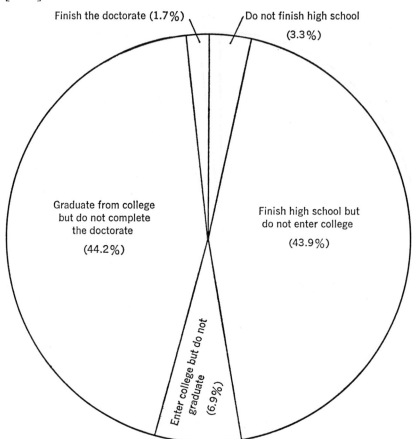

FIG. 45.—*Expected educational attainment of youngsters with at least the ability of the average recipient of a doctorate.*

Source: Wolfle, D., 1954.

Studies show that the average student receiving the doctorate has mental ability equivalent to an AGCT score of 130. How many of our young people with this level of ability, or higher, actually achieve this educational level? Note that we are only concerned here with those who have ability equal to the *upper half* of the group of students now completing the doctorate.

Of 10,000 youngsters in an age group, 691 have *at least* the ability of the average recipient of a doctorate, 670 of them finish high school, 366 enter college, 318 graduate from college, 12 finish the doctorate.

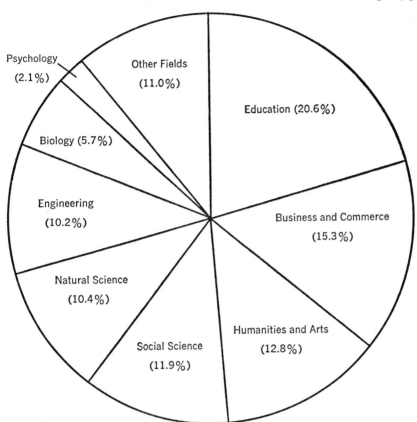

FIG. 46.—*Major fields of emphasis of college students (except health fields).*
Source: Wolfle, D., 1954.

We see that only slightly more than half of this total group enter college, less than half finish college, and fewer than two in a hundred go on to the doctorate.

What is the present distribution of fields of specialization of students in higher education, and how many of each group go on to the doctorate?

Of 10,000 college graduates (bachelors and first professional degrees), 980 will receive their degrees in natural science, and 74 of these will complete the doctorate, 200 will receive their degrees in psychology, and 12 of these will complete the doctorate, 1120 will receive their degrees in social science, and 24 of these will complete the doctorate, 1200 will receive their degrees in humanities and arts,

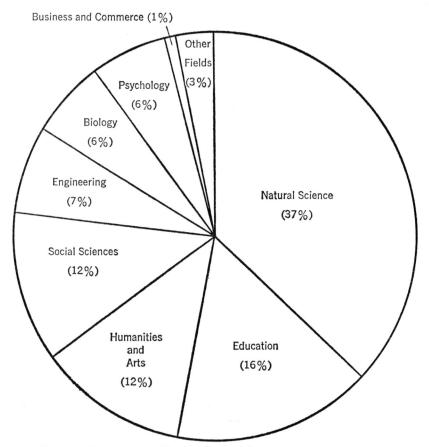

Fig. 47.—*Percentage distribution of doctorates by major fields.*

Source: Wolfle, D., 1954.

and 24 of these will complete the doctorate, 960 will receive their degrees in engineering, and 14 of these will complete the doctorate, 530 will receive their degrees in applied biology, and 12 of these will complete the doctorate, 1440 will receive their degrees in business and commerce, and 2 of these will complete the doctorate, 1940 will receive their degrees in education, and 32 of these will complete the doctorate, 1030 will receive their degrees in all other fields, and 6 of these will complete the doctorate, 600 will receive their degrees in health fields (most of which are doctorates).

Over the years since the turn of the century, there have been

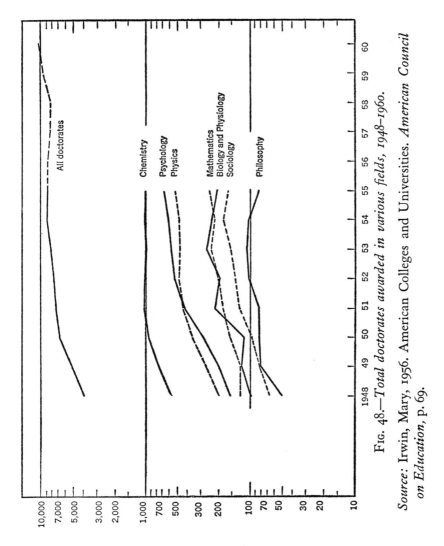

FIG. 48.—*Total doctorates awarded in various fields, 1948–1960.*

Source: Irwin, Mary, 1956. American Colleges and Universities. *American Council on Education,* p. 69.

changes in the proportion of doctorates awarded in various fields of specialization. The largest decline has been in the humanities and arts; smaller declines have occurred in the proportions in social and natural sciences. All other fields have increased, with education leading the way. Recent years have seen a marked increase in the proportion of doctorates awarded in psychology, though this specialty still includes less than 8 per cent of all doctorates. Note that these are all proportional changes—all fields have increased enormously in absolute numbers. Table 74 illustrates the growth of selected natural and social sciences in recent years.

According to the U.S. Office of Education (Iffert, 1958), one-fourth of all college students leave school before the beginning of their second year. About 40 per cent of students who begin college fail to graduate. If along with this fact we consider that less than half of the brighter 50 per cent of high school students even enter college we begin to see some of the dimensions of the waste of potential in the United States. The highest drop-out rate is from technological institutions and the lowest from teachers colleges.

Causes of the Numerical Trends.

What are the factors which determine who goes to college? Wolfle (1954) divides them into essential factors and important but not essential factors. The essential ones include intelligence, satisfactory scholastic achievement, adequate financial resources, and motivation. All of these are necessary, beyond some easily identified minimum.

The important, but nonessential, variables include sex, geographic location, and cultural, religious, and ethnic background. These variables affect the statistical chances of securing a college education, but are not essential ones.

Wolfle shows clearly the relationship between intelligence in combination with high school grades, and college entrance and college graduation. At the extremes of the curve, 4 per cent of the bottom group in both grades and intelligence begins college and 66 per cent of those at the top in both grades and intelligence begins college. Few of the college group that is low on both variables graduate and

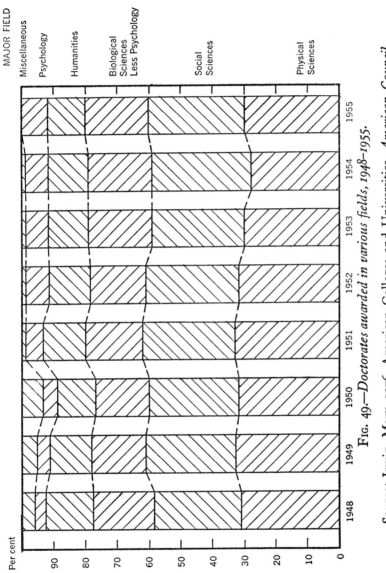

FIG. 49.—*Doctorates awarded in various fields, 1948–1955.*

Source: Irwin, Mary, 1956. American Colleges and Universities, *American Council on Education.*

most of the college group that is high on both graduate (Table 75).

With respect to cost, John D. Millett (1952) has estimated that in 1950 a family income of at least $5000 a year was needed to finance the higher education of one child in the family. About 30 per cent of American families had an income as high as this or higher in 1950. Living costs and income have both increased since 1950 but the percentage of the population that has enough income to finance the higher education of at least one child has very probably remained at about one-third of U.S. families. Public and private sources of scholarships and student loans extend to other able students the opportunity for higher education although there remain a sizable number of students who probably would go to college but are blocked because of financial handicap.

The fourth essential factor listed is motivation. This is crucial in the sense that probably everyone with ability, who has enough motivation, can get through college, while anyone with ability, who does not have the desire, is likely to fail. Motivational factors are complex and probably are related to attitudes in the home and community and to attitudes among the peer group of the adolescent's culture.

Among the nonessential factors, research and census studies have shown that, while more girls than boys graduate from high school, the opposite ratio holds for college entrance. Also, more boys than girls finish college, once enrolled. While there are exceptions, in general more students enter college from states with the highest quality school systems as measured by indices such as teachers' salaries, value of school property per classroom unit, and similar indicators of strong support of education. Socio-economic and other factors related to father's occupation also have an influence on the chances of going to college; for example, two-thirds of the children of professionals and semiprofessionals enter college after high school, and only 10 to 15 per cent of the children of farmers and blue collar workers go on from high school. Also, children of farmers have a hard time once in college and the rate of drop-out is high. This is not the case in other groups where all have about the same chance of graduating, once enrolled. Finally, factors such as membership in a minority group generally tend to decrease the chances of college attendance.

According to the President's Committee on Education Beyond the High School (1957), there are identifiable reasons why many intellectually able young people stop their education with high school graduation and are therefore lost so far as the need of the nation for more highly educated people is concerned.

As the Committee points out, "The percentages of able high school graduates not continuing their education beyond high school are especially high among children of nonprofessional parents, minority groups, girls, and rural and low-income families. This suggests that important answers to the problem of promoting individual development may lie in actions concentrating upon young people in these groups."

The Committee points out that, while 92 per cent of the high-ability sons of professional people are planning to attend college, only 69 per cent of the high-ability sons of factory workers have these plans; and, further, that four-fifths of all the sons of professional people plan to attend college in contrast to less than a third of all of the sons of factory workers.

More girls than boys are apt to quit school after high school. One reason is financial. Studies have shown that girls tend to need more financial support from their families and are less able to find employment or scholarships to finance their college careers.

"Educational opportunities throughout the nation are not always fully accessible to minority group members," according to the President's Committee. "Not only are there cases of overt discrimination in admission and after admission in access to curricular and extra-curricular opportunities, but—perhaps more widely important—there are discriminatory employment practices which discourage some of these young people from seeking an advanced education."

Young people who live in isolated regions of the country, educationally speaking, are much less likely to go to college. The presence of an educational institution nearby is a constant reminder of the availability of further education and tends to attract students by its accessibility and because of the fact that its graduates, both as examples and more directly, tend to encourage able young people. Where it is possible to live at home and go to college, of course the financial burden is eased.

The President's Committee on Education Beyond the High School also points to the financial realities of higher education as a discouraging factor for many bright young people who are lost to higher education. They quote one study which points out that it is two and one-half times as likely for a child to go to college if its parents' income is over $9000 than if it is less than $5000.

"Further, the striking fact was revealed that a youth who is academically in the lower half of his graduating class, and whose family income is $9000 or more, is more likely to go to college than a youth in the upper fourth of his class and in a family with income of less than $5000."

A preliminary study by John Darley, reported by the Carnegie Corporation (1957), found in one midwestern state indication that there is no necessary relation between mental ability level and attendance in higher educational institutions. With something over 30,000 students graduating from the high schools of that state in June, the following September found approximately one-quarter of this group enrolled in colleges and universities in the state. Of this college student group, 43 per cent were from the top quarter of high school graduates in terms of ability, but 28 per cent were from the lower half of their classes in ability. Forty-one per cent of the upper half of the high school classes were not in colleges in the state (some may have gone out of the state).

If these findings are extrapolated to the country as a whole (a national study is now under way), it would mean that more than a quarter of our present college students come from the lower half of the ability range as reflected in high school standings. Many students go to college if they can afford it, not if they can profit by the experience. The presence of these less able students pulls down the whole level of instruction.

The Educational Testing Service has taken a long, hard look at current statements to the effect that the U.S. is "wasting" thousands of "gifted" students a year because of their failure to continue their education. The study points out the fact that many kinds of talent do not require extensive academic achievement—music and politics are two obvious examples. It also takes a hard look at the definition of giftedness.

Taking these factors into consideration, two cut-off points were selected for definition of gifted students. When the top 30 per cent of students according to intellectual ability is used to define the group with high academic promise, and yet broad representation, the study found that 100,000 high school students a year at this ability level did not plan to attend college.

A second, and more rigorous, cut-off point included only the most able 10 per cent. This group would be expected to have academic aptitude of such a high order as to almost require advanced education to realize its full potential. Yet about one-fifth of this very able group does not plan to enter college.

Further, the study found, contrary to expectations from past studies, that high ability students could be induced not only to go to college, but also to consider a particular course of study, if scholarship help were made available. When those able high school students who had expressed no interest in college were asked if they would accept a scholarship to a good college if it were offered, eight out of ten reported an interest in considering the possibility. The average student in this high ability group would have considered a scholarship in three of ten areas described.

FACTORS AFFECTING THE QUALITY OF
TRAINING OF STUDENTS RECRUITED
TO THE MENTAL HEALTH PROFESSIONS

Shortages and Inadequacies of Public School Teachers.

In a report that focuses its attention on professional personnel and the manpower output of professional schools, it seems strange to be concerned with the teacher shortage in the public schools. On reflection, however, it will be apparent that the future recruits to higher education, including professional education, are profoundly affected by their experience in the elementary and secondary schools, and by the quality of the instruction they received there.

Repeatedly, critics have scored the mediocre quality of elementary school and secondary school curricula aimed at the average child, and have described the unfortunate effects those curricula have on the study habits and attitudes toward education of exceptionally bright children. For the most part, professional people are former bright children. A shortage of teachers in the elementary schools today, with the consequent overcrowding of classrooms, double shifts, and the presence of numbers of poorly-trained, half-trained, and hastily re-treaded teachers, means that the basic educational foundations are not firmly laid, nor are positive attitudes and good study habits secured with respect to the acquisition of knowledge.

A report of the Fund for the Advancement of Education (1956) pointed out that in the ten years from 1956 to 1965, 1,900,000 teachers would be needed and only 3,700,000 college students would be completing their training in *all* fields. Obviously we will not attract this large proportion into teaching. As the nation has about exhausted its supply of reserves, substitutes, and emergency teachers, there seems to be no immediate solution to the problem of overcrowding, double shifts, and slipping standards.

In 1955 about 30 per cent of college graduates were qualified for teaching (40 per cent of the women and 12 per cent of the men). From 1950 to 1955 the total number of college graduates prepared to teach in high schools declined by 40 per cent; those prepared to teach science and mathematics declined by more than 50 per cent.

In recent years, new graduates have accounted for less than half of all new teachers. The other new teachers have been recruited from former teachers, former graduates, nongraduates, or substandard licensees. More than a fifth of all teachers added during the past few years have held substandard certificates in their states.

What is the latest information about the adequacy of our public schools?

The Research Division of the National Education Association (1958) has made a careful study of the need for teachers in September, 1958, as measured against the probable supply. The results are most discouraging.

Too few teachers are being trained, and a sizable proportion of those who are trained choose not to enter the field. In general we need more elementary school teachers than high school teachers, but we are training more high school teachers than elementary school teachers. Further, the fields of concentration of the high school teachers do not match the needs of the high schools in many respects. Nearly a third of all new high school teachers are trained either in social studies or physical education. Only 8 per cent are trained in any of the sciences, only 5 per cent are trained in mathematics, and only 2.5 per cent are trained in foreign languages.

What determines the need for new teachers? One of the most important determinants is the steadily rising enrollments in the schools. For the past several years the increase in enrollment in the elementary schools has averaged three-quarters of a million each year and in the high schools almost a half million each year. Twenty-five thousand new teachers each year are required to handle the additional enrollments.

Some 95,000 teachers each year leave the field of education and must be replaced.

If we add these two absolutely essential demands for teachers we find that 120,000 new teachers are required each year. Figure 50 illustrates the steady increase in school enrollments.

But there are other demands for new teachers as well. If we wish to relieve the overcrowding in many schools—it results in double shifts and little education—more new teachers are needed. If we were simply to reduce the size of classes to thirty pupils per teacher (a very modest aspiration to be sure when we learn that the Russians have only seventeen pupils per teacher), we would need something more than another 30,000 new teachers. If we were to add the needed additional teachers to provide educational services judged essential, but not now provided, another 10,000 would be required. Finally, if we aspired to replace the teachers now in service who are not college graduates (30 per cent of all elementary school teachers) an additional 60,000 teachers would be required.

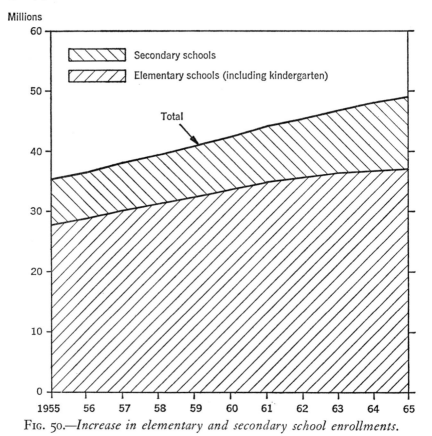

FIG. 50.—*Increase in elementary and secondary school enrollments.*

Source: U.S. Department of Labor, Bureau of Labor Statistics, 1957. *Occupational outlook handbook,* p. 58.

If we add all of these demands together, we reach the frightening total of 220,000 teachers who would have had to be found by September, 1958, to have provided an even reasonably competent public school system.

The Class of 1958 included 116,000 qualified teachers. But only some 75 per cent (or even less) of this group will enter the teaching field, if previous years' experience may be used as a guide. This means that there were some 85,000 new teachers accepting teaching jobs in 1958. It was shown above that there was a firm need for

120,000, and a very reasonable need for 220,000 teachers. We are short, tragically short.

What happens to all those students who are qualified and prepared to be teachers? The Research Division of the National Education Association (1958) studied the members of the Class of 1957 who were prepared to be teachers. About 83 per cent of the elementary school teachers actually entered the teaching field but, of the 65,000 new high school teachers trained, only 66 per cent entered teaching. Relatively few (about 4 per cent) continued their education. Most of the losses to education were to business and commerce, and to home-making.

The estimated demand for new teachers provided by the Bureau of Labor Statistics is indicated in Figure 51.

As we have noted, the shortage is worst for teachers in certain fields. According to the National Education Association the United States is falling farther and farther behind the demand for competent science teachers. The Association points out that in 1956–1957 colleges in the United States trained only 2892 mathematics teachers and 5044 science teachers. By contrast 10,566 teachers were trained in social studies, 8463 in English, 6118 in commerce, 5277 in physical education for men, and 6911 in physical education for women.

More than 12,000 physical education teachers and less than 3000 mathematics teachers trained in one year! Who is going to teach mathematics ten years from now?

A study conducted by the American Association of University Women (Dolan, Eleanor F., 1957), under the sponsorship of the National Science Foundation, discovered an estimated 13,000 women college graduates who expressed an interest in teaching. These women may possibly represent a pool of potential additional teachers still available for recruitment. Unfortunately, a very small percentage of the group was found to be interested in teaching mathematics or natural science. Something less than 2000 expressed an interest in these critical subjects.

The National Science Foundation has encouraged explorations to find other people who might take up some of the desperate need

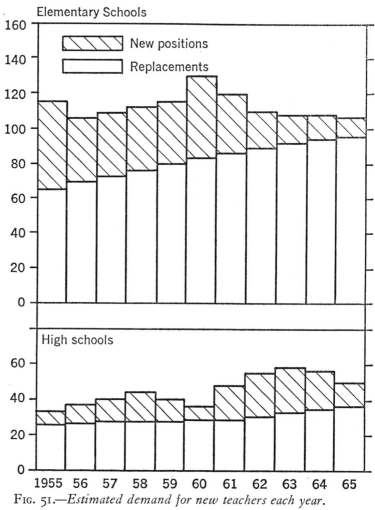

FIG. 51.—*Estimated demand for new teachers each year.*

Source: U.S. Department of Labor, Bureau of Labor Statistics, 1957. *Occupational outlook handbook,* p. 58.

for mathematics and science teachers. One of the places being explored is among the ranks of retired military officers. Several universities are offering, under National Science Foundation auspices, retread courses for retired officers who may then be called on for a second career as mathematics teachers.

The point to be understood from these trends is that students arrive at college poorly prepared, especially in science and mathematics. In addition, they bring with them attitudes about these fields of study that have been distorted and soured by inadequate and incompetent teachers. Indeed, their attitudes toward learning in general are likely to be most unsympathetic as a result of their educational experience.

The nation needs scientists, but it needs scholars in all fields. The mental health professions need their share. But we are likely to find that scholarship is increasingly rare because it is not nurtured in the schools society has provided.

James B. Conant, former president of Harvard, has taken a long and searching look at our high schools. He has suggested some changes that may help the picture.

The most important change recommended by Conant is the elimination of the high school which graduates less than 100 students each year. Small high schools, with their demand for teachers, do not adapt well to the necessary grouping of students by ability and career planning.

Among his other recommendations, Conant advocates a dual marking system for the able and the less able students, with much tougher courses outlined for the able students. For this group he suggests four years each of English, mathematics, and a single language, and three years each of social science and science for a total of 18 academic credits. The less able students would follow a somewhat less demanding program intellectually with more emphasis on vocational training.

The Deteriorating Quality of College Faculties.

The effectiveness of professional personnel in the field of mental health, as in other fields, is largely dependent on the quality of the training programs preparing new members of the various professional fields. Nearly everyone will agree that effective preparation is dependent on the training and competence of teachers whose job it is to instruct the young people who are preparing for future work in the various disciplines.

There are two important indices of the quality of the instruction we can look forward to in our universities in the foreseeable future. One index is the academic training of the college faculties. Another index is an assessment of the supply of replacements for faculty members who die, retire, or leave the field. While academic degrees are not all-important, they do represent one of our best indications of superior ability and achievement.

A recent study of the Research Division of the National Education Association (1958) brings to a focus the deteriorating quality of the preparation of college faculties and the gloomy prospects of continuing deterioration. As the report points out, our nation is only now beginning to realize the dimensions of these tragic facts. Indeed, the realization of these facts is still not sufficiently widespread and a climate of indifference, denial, and resistance to the facts is much too prevalent. Teaching staffs are deteriorating in our higher educational institutions, at the moment when they should be strengthened, for the prospect of doubled college enrollments just around the corner makes the situation even more desperate in prospect. More and more of our fledgling professionals are receiving, and will receive, a second-rate, or a third-rate education.

Let us look at the evidence. The NEA study obtained information from 829 degree-granting institutions in every part of the United States. It determined the educational qualifications of every new full-time faculty member, not previously employed in a college or university, with respect to educational attainment. This group of new full-time faculty members was taken as an estimate of the demand for faculty being satisfied by persons coming into higher education. How many of these new full-time faculty members have completed the doctorate and how does this number compare with previous years? The following figures are revealing:

Year	Per Cent Holding the Doctorate
1953–54	31.4
1954–55	28.4
1955–56	26.7
1956–57	23.5

In 1953–1954, 40.5 per cent of the total staff of these colleges and universities had the doctor's degree. As will be seen from the above figures, each year has witnessed a progressive decline in the percentage of new faculty members with the doctorate (Figure 52). Now let us look at the other side of the coin. What percentage of the new faculty members are at the minimal level of training as represented by their having less than the master's degree?

Year	Per Cent with Less Than the Master's Degree
1953–54	18.2
1954–55	19.3
1955–56	20.1
1956–57	23.1

In 1953–1954, 10.4 per cent of the total staff of these higher educational institutions had less than a master's degree. In each succeeding year more and more of the new full-time faculty members were at this minimal level of training (Figure 52).

The import of these data can hardly be overlooked. There is a steady deterioration in the academic preparation of new faculty members in our nation's higher educational institutions.

In looking at separate fields we find that some subject areas have suffered more than others. The biological sciences dropped slightly from 54.5 per cent holding the doctorate in 1953–1954 to 51.2 per cent in 1956–1957. In mathematics the decline was from 34.2 per cent to 20.5 per cent. In engineering the decline was from 15.9 per cent to 11.1 per cent, and in the physical sciences from 53.0 per cent to 43.7 per cent; in psychology the decline was from 68.4 per cent to 55.3 per cent, and in the social sciences from 42.4 per cent to 33.7 per cent.

One argument used to explain away these figures is that the drop in quality is limited to the small liberal arts colleges and teachers colleges. This cynical view, which in itself is revealing, does not reflect the facts. The decline in new full-time faculty members holding the doctorate in our large State universities was to 25 per cent in contrast to 48 per cent of the total faculty at this level in 1953–1954.

In our nonpublic universities, 33 per cent of the new faculty members employed in 1956–1957 had the doctorate in contrast to 52 per cent of the full-time staff at this level in 1953–1954.

Meanwhile the increases in underprepared new faculty members

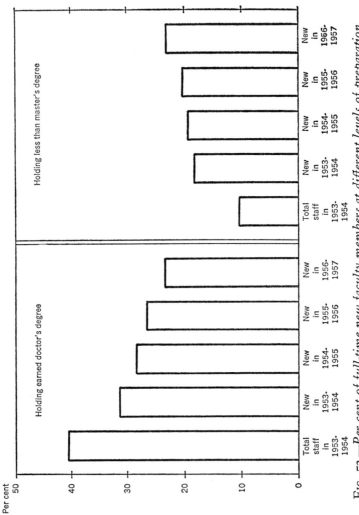

FIG. 52.—*Per cent of full-time new faculty members at different levels of preparation.*

Source: National Education Association, Research Division, 1957. *Teacher supply and demand in colleges and universities,* 1955-1956 and 1956-1957, p. 17.

are just as dramatic. In the State universities, 28 per cent of the new faculty members had less than the master's degree in 1956–1957 in contrast to 11 per cent of the full-time staff in 1953–1954. For the nonpublic universities the increase was to 19 per cent from 12 per cent.

These data, when understood, cannot be blinked away.

What are the sources of the new full-time faculty members? Traditionally, of course, the graduate schools have been the source of faculty. But there is evidence that our graduate schools are not training enough people to provide replacements, requiring higher educational institutions to look elsewhere for faculty recruits. Further, to darken an already gloomy picture, a sizable proportion of the new doctorates leaving the graduate schools go into other occupations than teaching and particularly those in the areas of the most critical need.

Of the new faculty members employed in 1955–1956 and 1956–1957, some 45 per cent were obtained from the graduate schools. Nearly 14 per cent were recruited from the high schools. An additional 14 per cent were recruited from business. There has been a small but significant decline in the proportion of new faculty members recruited from the graduate schools in the last three or four years. As the other sources of faculty (the high schools, business, home-making) run dry, the shortage of willing persons completing their graduate training will become more apparent.

The fields in shortest supply—engineering, physical science, and mathematics—report the largest number of unfilled positions in our colleges.

A study by the National Education Association's Research Division attempted to determine what happened to the 8840 doctoral-level graduates of 1955 and the 8903 doctoral graduates of 1956. First of all, a third of these new doctorates were already committed to the jobs they were in. This means that only some 6000 each year represent a potential supply of college faculty. Of this reduced group, one-third goes into some noneducational occupation reducing the supply of new potential teachers to 4000. Of this latter group, about 10 per cent goes into some educational endeavor other than in the colleges and universities. This reduces our original 9000 recipients of the doctorate to 3500 who enter higher educational service.

Unfortunately, the proportion of recipients of doctor's degrees entering the field of higher education is lowest in the fields where teaching shortages are greatest. Nearly three-quarters of the recipients of the doctorate in engineering go into noneducational pursuits. The same is true of the chemists. Sixty per cent of the physicists enter other fields, and 70 per cent of the other physical scientists do likewise. Sixty-one per cent of the psychologists do not enter the academic world. Little wonder that the quality of education in these fields is threatened.

Are there other possible sources than the graduate schools, of teaching prospects for our higher educational institutions? Those who deny or minimize the problem often suggest that women who have left the field be urged to return. The fact is that relatively few women complete the doctorate and particularly in those fields in shortest supply. In 1956 there were ten female recipients of the doctor's degree in mathematics. There were sixty-eight in the physical sciences and eighty-six in psychology. Of 470 graduates in physics, eight were women.

The foregoing facts should make it clear that unless a massive effort is made to expand the output of our graduate schools and, further, unless our higher educational institutions are able to attract a higher percentage of the people completing their graduate education, particularly in the fields of the most critical shortage, the prospect for the future of higher education is bleak indeed. Our graduate schools are like a group of starving women repeatedly giving birth. Without nourishment and support, each year's crop of children is weaker and more undernourished and the prospects for the next year are worse for mother and child.

Many other assessments of this situation are in essential agreement. Dean Dayton D. McKean (1958) of the Graduate School, University of Colorado, in testifying before Congress, pointed out that the national shortage of college teachers will run to 270,000 in twelve years. He goes on to say: "No one knows where they will be found, but any fellowship program that will help any students stay in graduate schools or will speed their progress by letting them study instead of working part-time at tending bar or scrubbing floors will provide the nation with that many more trained people that much sooner."

According to the President's Committee, there are some 225,000 full-time and part-time faculty members in the nation's 1900 colleges and universities. Using the most conservative estimates the Committee points out that something between 180,000 and 270,000 new college teachers will have to be found in the next twelve years— 15,000 to 22,500 annually.

The alarming fact is that our graduate schools are currently awarding some 9000 doctor's degrees annually and, as we have seen, not half of these people enter college teaching. Further, many of this latter group are already engaged in teaching and so do not represent a real increase in the field.

"The cumulative deficit at the doctoral level," says the Committee, "is an alarming prospect."

The teachers colleges steal faculty from the high schools, the liberal arts colleges steal from the teachers colleges, and the universities steal from everyone, including each other. The big fish eat the little fish and the little fish eat mud.

The President's Committee points out that more than a third of our present college teachers are already forty-five years or older so that the reduction in faculties by death and retirement will accelerate at a time when there is a tremendous expansion of undergraduate enrollments.

"The most critical bottleneck to the expansion and improvement of education in the United States is the mounting shortage of excellent teachers. Unless enough of the Nation's ablest manpower is reinvested in the educational enterprise, its human resources will remain underdeveloped and specialized manpower shortages in every field will compound. Unwittingly the United States right now is pursuing precisely the opposite course. . . . Our nation, like the prodigal farmer, is consuming the seed corn needed for future harvests." (President's Committee, 1957)

Increasingly we hear the suggestion that improved audio-visual aids, and even closed-circuit television, may solve the problem of faculty shortages in the future. Students will be assembled by marshals in their proper classrooms where they will be permitted to watch a large screen on which a capable faculty member will appear simultaneously to several sections of the course. Proponents of this procedure argue that the obvious advantages outweigh the absence of spontaneity and class discussion, and even suggest that periods may be set aside for discussion.

Robert L. Johnson, Jr. (1957) mocks this proposal by carrying it to its ridiculous extreme. He suggests that the television course could be put on film and projected from some central geographic location, say Kansas City, so that college students all over the country could see the program simultaneously. This would permit the use of a really outstanding professor, who would not need to be paid after his first performance as a permanent film record could be used indefinitely. The use of a film would also permit an accurate record to be kept, Johnson notes, so that there never would be any question about what the students had heard in classes. It might even be possible to have films approved by various groups concerned with public morals and welfare. We do not recommend this—nor does he.

College Faculty Salaries.

Salaries of college faculty members have lagged behind most other fields. A number of observers have pointed out that it is the college faculty that is providing steady and heavy donations to higher education. By working for salaries that represent successively smaller amounts of purchasing power because of continued inflation, college faculties have postponed the necessity for our educational system to find more income and have in effect contributed their missing purchasing power to the students in institutions.

According to Seymour E. Harris (1957): "In 1955–1956, the average for physicians (net) was $16,000 against the $5200 median income of college teachers. Whereas the top 2 per cent earned $10,000 or more in college teaching, the top 2 per cent in medicine earned $50,000 or more. Whereas 0.4 per cent received $14,000 or more in college teaching, 57 per cent of the physicians earned $15,000 or more."

Harris goes on to say:

Yet the Harvard full professor (average age about 50) with an income of $14,000, which is the top one-half of one per cent in the profession, earns less than the *average* doctor at a much lower median age. The comparison is not with the top two per cent of the doctors, who earn more than $50,000, but with all doctors—incompetent, average, and successful.

In 1953, the professors in large state universities, with incomes of $7,000, were earning less than railroad engineers; associate professors in these institutions, less than railroad firemen; assistant professors and instructors, 24–30 per cent less than railroad conductors and switch tenders, respectively.

Expenditures for Higher Education.

It is estimated that in 1953–1954 about 3.4 billion dollars were spent on higher education. This represented 0.95 per cent of the gross national product. At no time in recent history have we spent as much as 1 per cent of our gross national product on higher education.

Total faculty salaries for higher educational institutions in 1953–1954 were approximately 1.1 billion. If faculties were to have the same competitive position in the professional labor market that they enjoyed before World War II, this amount would have to be raised by 75 per cent. There has been an increase in the real personal income for each member of the labor force in the United States of some 78 per cent since 1939–1940. There has been no similar increase in faculty salaries. One estimate, carefully prepared, suggests that "no less than a 125 per cent increase in present real faculty salaries by 1970 is needed to recover and retain the profession's pre-World War II position in the labor market" (Louis, Pinnell, and Wells, 1958).

According to the President's Committee:

A recent study found that from 1940 to 1956 real income (measured in buying power after taxes) increased twenty-nine per cent for lawyers, sixty-four per cent for industrial workers, ninety-six per cent for physicians, but only twelve per cent for college teachers as a whole. A modest increase for college teachers was entirely in the lower rank; full professors suffered a net decrease.

In a competitive society the most talented are quick to observe that teaching is not so highly valued as other occupations. Too many who might become fine teachers are choosing other, more favored careers. There are also many excellent former teachers, who left the profession for economic reasons, who might be brought back into teaching. Intensified efforts with respect to salaries, particularly for the higher ranks, may thus bring really significant results in recruiting.

The Committee went on to recommend:

That boards of trustees, legislatures, and all others responsible for academic budgets give the absolute highest priority to raising the salaries of college and university teachers as substantially as may be necessary to reach and then to maintain levels which, together with other advantages, will provide the teaching profession with an equitable share of our best talent and abolish the faculties' hidden subsidy to education. In the light of both necessity and equity the Committee suggests that the goal be set at no less than double the present average level on an over-all national basis within five to ten years, although it recognizes that there are and will be substantial differences by region and by institution. . . .

That institutions strengthen the economic status and drawing power of the teaching profession by the provision of such additional inducements as moderate-cost faculty housing where not locally available, health benefits, group insurance, retirement programs, and educational opportunities for the children of faculty members.

The report goes on to recommend that the faculty of every higher eductional institution join in the search for highly talented young people who may be recruited into college teaching. Overwhelmed by the prospects of shortages in college faculty, the Committee recommended that every possible source of college teachers be explored—including more women, more retired people from a variety of fields, and other sources not named.

The Committee recommended strengthening of the graduate schools' programs at both the master's and doctoral level, and at the same time searching for more effective aids to teaching, especially in electronics and television.

The Committee further recommended that: "vigorous efforts [be made] throughout our American society to remove barriers to the pursuit of education by all talented youth. The Committee particularly recommends that educational institutions abolish discriminatory policies and practices based on race, creed, color, sex, or national origin, where they exist."

The Committee recommended expanded counseling programs, expanded public and private support for college students, and expanded research on educational problems such as school drop-out.

After wrestling with the question of the propriety of Federal scholarships and recommending "that private, local, and State sources increase their support of scholarship funds to several times the present amount and number of scholarships," and stating that "assistance by the Federal Government . . . should not at the present time. . . . undertake to provide new scholarships (other than single 'work-study') for undergraduate students," the Committee then qualified its recommendation by saying that if this series of sources should not turn out to be effective then it would suggest a Federal scholarship program.

Finally, the Committee pointed out the ineffectiveness of occasional temporary study committees and suggested that the Federal Office of Education be strengthened so as to be the source of information and recommendations on these kinds of educational policy.

Counterinfluences to the Depressing Educational Picture.

One bright side of the educational situation involves admissions standards. Many universities will be raising rather than lowering their admissions standards, as applications for freshman classes increase. Indeed, a number of university presidents confess ruefully that many of the old grads would not have been admitted had standards been as high in the past as they are now.

For those higher educational institutions which hold the line on admission standards, quality of students and demands on faculty will go up, not down. This is especially true for private institutions and for professional and scientific institutions.

The tide of college applicants may have the effect of broadening the gap in quality between schools which restrict admissions and those which, by law, must admit all comers, such as many State universities.

In many parts of the country there is a trend for more and more parents to send their children to private schools at the secondary level rather than to the public schools because of the fall in quality of instruction in the latter. The unfortunate aspect of this situation is that the cost of good quality schooling becomes prohibitive to the great majority of the population. The nation loses the intellectual potential of bright students who cannot afford the better, and therefore more expensive, schools.

A *New York Times* survey (Buder, 1957) reports a major rise in tuition costs in a representative sample of universities across the country. Twenty-nine of thirty-five universities covered in the survey have increased tuition in the past year and a half and ten more plan increases this year or next. Others are considering even further increases. Most university spokesmen agreed that tuition costs were eliminating students of limited financial resources from considering college, or else were sending them to the lower-cost public institutions.

Alternatives to Federal Aid to Education.

A favorite argument for the editorial writer is that our American industry is supporting heavily the costs of education through scholarships and contributions and that Federal aid would endanger this support as well as bring on the horrors of bureaucratic control.

The problem of the relationship between higher education and American industry is exceedingly complex. A fundamental question, rarely considered in all of its implications, is whether American education does, and should, exist primarily for the benefit of our industrial organization. A sizable proportion of the graduates of American educational institutions study subjects preparing them for employment in industry, or for employment in other educational institutions which in turn train students for industry. The increase in vocational, practical, and technical courses in our educational institutions reflects the tremendous need for people so trained by our industrial plant.

Few students study shorthand and typing in order to work for themselves; bookkeepers, accountants, engineers, chemists, physicists, and technicians of every description, are prepared by our educational institutions for future employment in business and industry.

Most reports on the crisis in education feature, or at least include, the urgent recommendation that educational institutions seek, or be presented with, additional funds from private sources, individual and industrial.

As a matter of fact, private gifts and grants represent only 6 per cent of the sources of current income of colleges and universities in the United States. Privately-controlled institutions have to depend on student fees as their largest source of income while State governments provide the largest share of support for publicly-controlled colleges and universities. Private institutions receive less than 2 per cent of their support from State governments. Endowment earnings, largely based on prior gifts, bring all institutions only 4 per cent of their current income, and even the privately-controlled institutions, often believed to be largely dependent on endowment income, derive only 8 per cent from this source.

While corporate giving to educational institutions has increased somewhat in recent years (the total in 1956 being almost $100,000,-000) this amount represents less than ¼ of 1 per cent of total corporation income in 1956.

Corporate giving to higher educational institutions is often, understandably, based on "enlightened self-interest." Corporations which give money to establish specialized laboratories are really insuring the future supply of research and other trained personnel in areas of their specialized needs.

Resistance to Federal aid to education means that the Federal power to tax incomes and earnings will not have to be used to increase educational expenditures. State and local taxes are less likely to be used for higher educational expenditures. At least this has been the case in the past.

John K. Norton (1958) has criticized the special interest organizations who first go to Washington to argue that state and local groups should provide the massive financial support necessary to meet growing enrollments and shortages of facilities in education, and then go back home to throw roadblocks in front of state support with the argument that such massive expenditures would bankrupt the states. At the local level these same people fight against increases in the school budget.

"Federal support to underpin state and local support for education is as inevitable as were the local and then state support for schools at an earlier time in our history. The overwhelming majority of people want it, as repeated opinion polls clearly demonstrate. It remains only to galvanize this desire into practical action" (Norton).

A Federal aid to education act was passed by Congress in August, 1958. The act can be criticized for being little and late, or it can be viewed as a first step in the right direction on a track where we have noted that the Soviet Union is already in full gallop. At the last minute a provision for Federal scholarships was struck from the bill, though it does provide for low-interest loans to college students.

Other features of the act are designed to encourage guidance and counseling of students entering high school; to improve equipment for instruction in science, math, and languages; to strengthen or establish language programs; to help states set up supervisory departments to help local schools improve math, science, and language instruction; and to foster research into the educational use of TV.

The new bill is not a cure for the sickness of our educational system. But it is an encouraging hint that at long last we have noticed that there is a patient in the house who is critically ill.

X

Implications for the Future

INTRODUCTION

ONE OF MAN's unique capacities is his ability to anticipate and plan his future. The ability to use trends in the present to predict and control reality in the future is a major source of security to human beings.

Unfortunately we do not always use this ability. Too often, securing the future for one group means mortgaging the future of another, or, worse still, it means sacrifices for groups which do not enjoy sacrifice.

Looking ahead, we can be sure that our nation will be faced with serious problems in the field of mental illness and mental health for a long time to come. We can also foresee a continuation of the shortages of professional manpower already outlined in this report. Our mental hospitals will continue to be overcrowded, and our mental patients will receive little treatment.

Much has been made of the fact that in the last year more patients have been discharged from our mental hospitals than were admitted. The reality is less optimistic. The new tranquilizing drugs have enabled us to discharge, as improved, sizable numbers of patients who would not otherwise have left our institutions. But the rapid growth in our population, and the increasing numbers of older people in the age groups where mental illness is most common, promise to keep our institutions filled and overcrowded.

From whatever viewpoint we look—humanitarian, economic, or scientific—mental disorder is our nation's most serious health problem. Everyone concerned agrees that our professional personnel prospects are grim and promise to get worse.

Blain (1958) says:

> The problems of personnel shortages in psychiatric services are so over-whelming, so well known, and so frustrating that they seem to threaten the very possibility of progress. For lack of manpower, whole programs lie in abeyance, clinical facilities are hopelessly overtaxed, and some perforce are closed to new admissions. Waiting lists are static. Key positions, such as state commissionerships, superintendencies of mental hospitals, directorships of psychiatric clinics, and professorships, stand vacant for months and even years. Research, crying to be done, awaits the scientists to carry it out. Teaching and supervision, the key ingredients of programs which will vastly expand our human resources, are only sparsely available. The actual carrying out of preventive technics is virtually a dream. Broad-scale planning for the nation, state, and community takes on an Alice-in-Wonderland atmosphere for there are no real people to fill the slots in the neat organization charts that we conjure. So much is done by so few and our efforts are so thinly spread that total efficiency is inevitably of a low order. The herculean nature of the task and the paucity of our forces to attack it remind us of Don Quixote charging at his windmills.

The stark reality is that in mental health we are not likely to keep up our present number of professional personnel in ratio to population. No optimistic voices have been heard. And we recognize that something more than a crash program, with supporting publicity and fanfare, is needed. If shortage existed only in the mental health professions our problem would be much simpler. But, as we have seen, our nation is suffering from a pervasive shortage of highly trained personnel in all categories.

What possible solutions or sources of even moderate relief are available? There are several logical answers to our problem. We will explore a few of these briefly in a moment.

To effect some relief of the shortage of professional manpower in the field of mental illness and mental health we can (1) train more personnel, (2) redistribute existing and anticipated personnel to achieve a more equitable balance between supply and demand, (3) change our patterns of patient care so as to achieve a better utilization of available professional manpower, (4) use new or different methods of treatment, either involving less highly trained personnel who are in greater supply or techniques which enable us to reach large numbers of patients per professional person, (5) make an all-out research effort to discover ways of preventing or curing larger numbers of cases of mental disorder.

Let us take a look at each of these possibilities. They do not exhaust the logical solutions, but they are the ones most frequently proposed.

WE MUST TRAIN MORE PERSONNEL

No matter where we choose to look at the manpower problem we are led back inevitably to the same source of our difficulties. The source is to be found in the climate of opinion which has resulted in insufficient space, insufficient funds, inadequate staffs, and public apathy to a massive educational effort. Manpower shortages, as we have shown, are not limited to the mental health professions. They are part of a pervasive decline in the attractions of education in most fields. We are not training enough people to help those in our mental hospitals, or to solve our problems of urban degeneration, or to offer help to our handicapped, or to be concerned with our intellectually exceptional children, all for the same reasons that we are not keeping up in scientific competition. Too many of our intellectually capable young people are dropping out of school all along the line without achieving the maximum of their intellectual capacity through training. Too many more of our young people who do stay in school are receiving less, many times less, than the best instruction and guidance possible.

Recent months have witnessed a parade of reports and recommendations concerned with the deterioration of our educational system. Perhaps the weight of all these voices will be sufficient to produce action.

We have already seen that those states where training programs flourish are in the best personnel position. Training programs attract students and, because training for the mental health professions usually requires a fairly lengthy commitment in time, students tend to develop roots in the communities in which they are trained. Our data show over and over again the importance of training programs in attracting and keeping personnel. Not only do students who finish their training tend to stay in areas where they have been trained, but the excitement and ferment that training programs engender are crucial to attracting top-flight personnel.

The value of training programs is not limited to single programs in single areas. One of the best examples of the success of a training program as a source of personnel to fill professional vacancies is the experience of the Veterans Administration Clinical Psychology Training Program. Established in 1946, and in continuous operation ever since, the program provides for the part-time employment by the VA of graduate students enrolled in approved university programs in clinical psychology. The graduate students are placed in Veterans Administration mental hygiene clinics and hospitals where, under competent supervision, they learn to apply the psychological techniques that they are studying in the graduate schools. At the same time they provide needed diagnostic, therapeutic, and research service to the Veterans Administration. The financial support that this program has provided has enabled many graduate students in psychology to complete their graduate training. The advantage to the Veterans Administration, in addition to the service that the students render, is to be found in the very large proportion of staff clinical psychologists now employed by the Veterans Administration that have come through the training program. Houtchens (1958) estimates that 67 per cent of the 700 clinical psychologists now employed by the Veterans Administration have come through the training program.

Another excellent example of the value of financial assistance to students in the mental health professions with respect to later availability for public service is to be found in the United States Public Health Service training stipend program. In the years from 1948 to 1956, nearly 4,000 students received training stipends in the mental health professions. In a recent study of the current employment status of these people, it was found that significant numbers of them were engaged in public service, in teaching, and in research. Some 43 per cent of the psychiatrists, 67 per cent of the psychologists, 79 per cent of the psychiatric nurses, and 87 per cent of the psychiatric social workers who were covered in the study were found to be engaged in one of these three activities. Looking at the group as a whole, nearly half of the former training stipend recipients were in public service, 16 per cent of the total were in teaching, and 6 per cent were engaged in research activities. An additional 13 per cent were still in training. Figures 53 through 57 illustrate these trends.

The concern sometimes expressed that students subsidized will later be lost to public health employment because they will be attracted to private practice, thereby representing no major improvement in the manpower needs of public agencies and educational programs, has not been justified by the findings. Over-all, only 10 per cent of the recipients of stipends were found to be engaged in private practice. The largest group, those in psychiatry, was represented by 35 per cent of its numbers in private practice, but this proportion is surprisingly small in view of the very large percentage of younger psychiatrists finishing their training who enter private practice.

There are many other examples of the importance of training programs to availability of personnel. Nearly 90 per cent of all psychoanalysts in the United States are to be found in the twelve states with psychoanalytic institutes or training centers. Only 10 per cent of the psychoanalysts practice in the thirty-seven states without training centers or institutes. We have already seen that the presence of residency programs in psychiatry is an important determiner of the availability of psychiatric service.

In the nine states above the United States average of psychiatrists to population there are more psychiatric residency programs than are to be found in the forty states below the United States average of psychiatrists to population. Table 76 and Figure 58 illustrate this fact. We have already seen that there are many more social workers in those states where there are schools of social work, and many more psychiatric social workers in those states with social work schools including psychiatric social work in their curricula, than in the states without these training programs.

In the years ahead the pool of college graduates serving as the

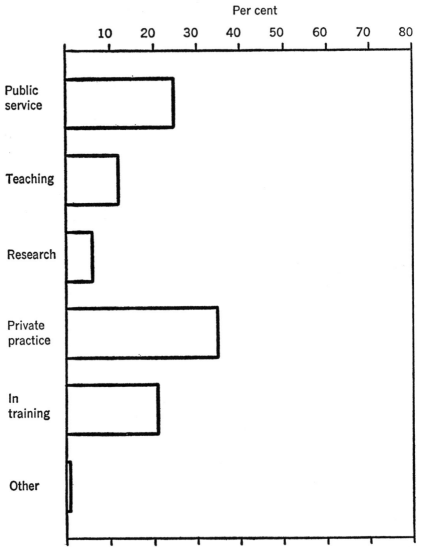

FIG. 53.—*Current employment status of psychiatrists who received USPHS training stipends.*

Source: U.S. Department of Health, Education, and Welfare, Public Health Service, National Institutes of Health, March, 1958. *The training program of the National Institute of Mental Health,* 1947–1957, p. 28. Government Printing Office.

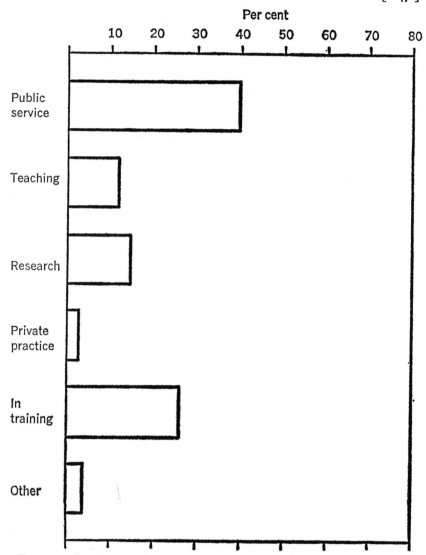

FIG. 54.—*Current employment status of psychologists who received USPHS training stipends.*

Source: U.S. Department of Health, Education, and Welfare, Public Health Service, National Institutes of Health, March, 1958. *The training program of the National Institute of Mental Health,* 1947–1957, p. 28. Government Printing Office.

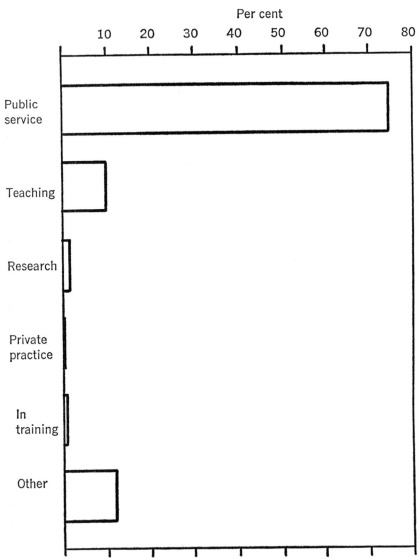

Fɪɢ. 55.—*Current employment status of psychiatric social workers who received USPHS training stipends.*

Source: U.S. Department of Health, Education, and Welfare, Public Health Service, National Institutes of Health, March, 1958. *The training program of the National Institute of Mental Health,* 1947–1957, p. 28. Government Printing Office.

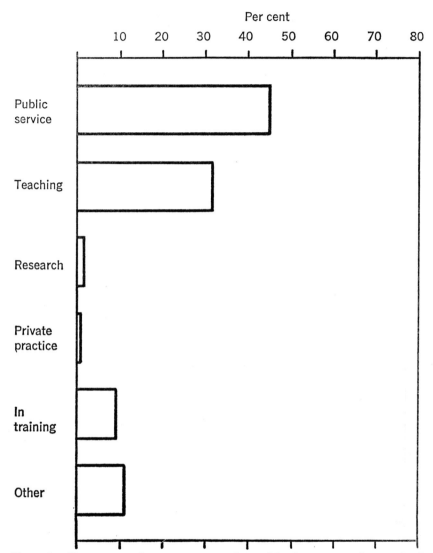

FIG. 56.—*Current employment status of psychiatric nurses who received USPHS training stipends.*

Source: U.S. Department of Health, Education, and Welfare, Public Health Service, National Institutes of Health, March, 1958. *The training program of the National Institute of Mental Health,* 1947–1957, p. 28. Government Printing Office.

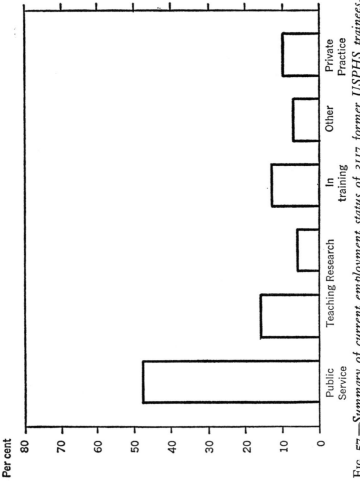

FIG. 57.—*Summary of current employment status of 3117 former USPHS trainees.*

Source: U.S. Department of Health, Education, and Welfare, Public Health Service, National Institutes of Health, March, 1958. *The training program of the National Institute of Mental Health, 1947–1957,* p. 29. Government Printing Office.

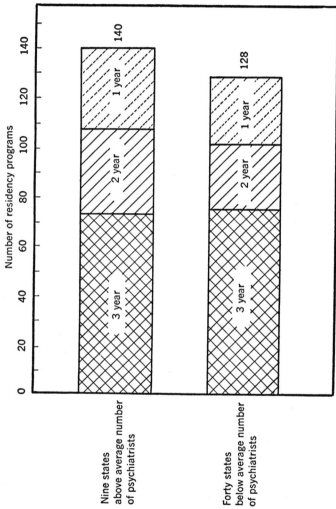

FIG. 58.—*Number of residency programs in psychiatry in nine states above the national average of psychiatrists to population compared with the states below average.*

Source: Journal of the American Medical Association, yearly. Annual residency issue. Population figures supplied by U.S. Bureau of the Census.

source for our professional mental health students will increase enormously. With an all-out educational effort, this enormous increase could be further doubled or tripled. The number of professionals we train will be dependent on decisions society will make about the level of support of education. Strengthening of present programs, establishment of new programs, especially in those areas and regions with the greatest need, and attracting large enough numbers of able and well-prepared students to these programs all depend on whether our society decides to make a massive educational effort in order to achieve these ends.

There are strong adversaries to the suggestion that we turn our attention to the cultivation of the intellect. As Freud pointed out, the voice of the intellect is soft, and though it is frequently drowned out by our passions, it persists. Let us hope that its persistence is effective in time to make a difference.

REDISTRIBUTION OF PERSONNEL

In our democratic society we much prefer to move the donkey with a carrot instead of a stick. One of the problems involved in the availability of professional mental health personnel is their poor distribution with respect to need. We have seen that professionally trained people tend to stay in areas where training programs exist. It is not unreasonable to expect that improvements in the distribution of professional people might be achieved if the rewards were increased in areas where professionals are in short supply. Unfortunately, as a general rule, the areas in which the greatest shortages exist are the same areas that are least able to improve the rewards attractive to professional personnel.

Our society needs to give serious thought to this problem. We have found ways, many of them not too painful, to keep the rich from getting richer and the poor from getting poorer. Some thought must be given as to how a social balance can be achieved in the distribution of professional personnel. Certain states and regions have already begun to explore with their neighbors ways of sharing costs and responsibilities. It is wasteful for every state to establish its own training program in every professional discipline. Regional cooperation, with the different states coordinating their training policies, has been found effective. Studies of the most effective distribution of personnel need to be made. If one state offers good service and good training in one subject area, mental retardation for example, perhaps a neighboring state can cooperate by specializing in another subject area. Ways may be found for states to share facilities and professional manpower available. This approach involves a redistribution of patients rather than just personnel, but it has many advantages to recommend it.

When state systems begin to compete in pay and prestige with private practice larger numbers of professional personnel now lost to our public systems will be attracted to them. We have already emphasized the problem of inflation as it threatens the stability of civil service systems. If we can stabilize our economy, then gains achieved in the financial inducements offered to young professionals to enter public service can be expected to have greater effect.

CHANGES IN THE PATTERNS OF
PATIENT CARE AND IN THE
UTILIZATION OF PERSONNEL

Superficially, the answer is easy to the question of manpower utilization. Every professional person should do those things most helpful to the largest number of people who need help. But at once problems arise. No one knows for sure who needs help the most, and professionals disagree on what techniques are most effective and efficient. In both cases, there is a real need for research.

There are other problems as well. Professional people are human. They respond to the dominant values of their culture and play other roles than their professional ones. Certain activities, certain roles are more fashionable and have greater prestige than others. For these reasons we find that both interprofessional rivalry and jockeying for position within professional groups often interfere with the most efficient utilization of time.

At first thought it would seem that when there are periods of serious personnel shortages there would be increased teamwork and collaboration. In many ways this is true. But the periods of manpower shortage are also times when it is possible for professions to make gains and to consolidate their positions.

When there is not time enough to do everything there is always a temptation to choose those things to do that either are most enjoyable or are most satisfying to professional self-images. There is a great deal of talk about how important it is to turn over certain jobs to less highly trained personnel, and in many cases this is certainly necessary. But sometimes the important tasks turned over are those less eagerly sought after by those relinquishing them.

Periods of shortage tend to be periods when the requirements of professional training are raised rather than lowered. This is a very natural consequence of the concern over the use of poorly trained personnel. We need to be very careful, in defining the requirements of training in the field of mental health, not to set nonfunctional requirements. We must remember that there is a very direct relationship between degree of shortages in a field and the length of the training period required.

What we need are techniques and methods enabling far more people to be reached per professional person. If we do not at present have such techniques, then we should spend time looking for them. The logic of the manpower situation in which we find ourselves makes other solutions unrealistic.

Any efficient utilization of mental health personnel probably is going to involve something other than time-consuming, face-to-face relationships between a single professional person and a single patient. The number of people who need help and the number of people prepared to give help are so out of proportion that time and arithmetic will not permit such individual face-to-face approaches to be meaningful from a logistics point of view. Perhaps experience in the epidemiology of other disorders will suggest solutions. Just as typhoid fever was never brought under control by treating individual cases of the disease but rather by discovering and taking steps to remove the source of the disease, so we may find that time might be spent much more effectively in prevention, in research, or in public health approaches to mental disorder.

Other problems in the utilization of professional personnel are important. A comparison of a list of the priority of the needs for professional services in the mental health field against a list of present professional activities reveals many discrepancies. The outstanding example here is the disproportionate amount of time professional people spend with middle-aged neurotics as against the relatively little time they spend with disturbed children.

We know enough to be able to say with some certainty that it is both economically and morally sound to spend on children most of what little professional time is available, where often some real progress can be made and where future disorders can be prevented or modified. Yet the facts show that the greatest shortage of professional people is to be found in work with children. Once again it appears that there is no necessary relation between the prestige of an activity and its usefulness to society. For many and complex reasons, work with children and work in public agencies serving children have carried less prestige than many other activities. We need to find ways to change this situation, perhaps by increasing the material rewards, but more likely by finding ways of influencing the climate of opinion within the professions.

Similar discrepancies exist in such areas as crime and delinquency, alcoholism, and mental retardation.

Society's institutions tend to have a vitality keeping them alive beyond the time when conditions responsible for their development have undergone drastic changes.

The large State mental hospitals, responsible for the care and treatment of thousands of patients, represent an institution that developed during the last century out of conditions prevalent at that time. Most informed observers believe that our care and treatment of mental patients would be much more efficient if small treatment units were built and located much closer to centers for the treatment of other diseases. There is a trend toward the establishment of psychiatric wards and clinics in general hospitals and for the construction of smaller psychiatric units as part of medical centers.

Professional isolation is often mentioned as one of the limiting factors in recruitment of professional personnel for State mental hospitals. In the Western Regional Survey, State hospital employees themselves complained of isolation from their professional colleagues, lack of opportunities for continued or advanced education, and lack of intellectual stimulation. As the Western Survey pointed out, buildings cannot be moved, but more liberal policies with regard to financing the travel of professional workers to meetings of their professional groups, scheduling of seminars at the State institutions, and a variety of similar activities can go part way toward alleviating the feeling of professional isolation. These suggested methods of dealing with the isolation are, of course, merely symptomatic treatment. It is probable that in the long run we will have to relocate and redefine the function of the mental hospital.

Should elderly senile and arteriosclerotic patients be housed in the large State institutions? Perhaps we will have to find new ways of taking care of the anticipated increase in the number of our aged who will require care because of mental infirmity.

Another project of the Joint Commission on Mental Illness and Health is studying this whole problem, and the reader is referred to their report for further discussion.

Another proposed change in patient care has received some discussion. The lengthy educational preparation of professional personnel in the field of mental illness and mental health makes pessimistic the prospect that their number can be increased sufficiently to meet social needs. A fairly radical proposal has been made by Donald W. Hastings (1955), who notes that others have also recommended the same solution. Hastings suggests the creation of a new professional group, with careful training in psychotherapy, but not required to master all the knowledge at present contained in any of the various professional curricula.

The idea is an intriguing one. Is there any chance that we could train mental health therapists in four years of college? Many would argue that we are not able now to teach therapists all that is known to be effective in a much longer time. Another profession on the scene might increase present shortages in the established professions by attracting some of the prospective recruits now entering the latter fields. Also the deliberate and conscious creation of a profession is a fairly radical departure from the usual procedure in which a profession evolves over a long period of time.

But probably the most telling argument against this proposal is that it holds little promise for eventual relief from the pressure of increasing numbers of the mentally ill. Individual psychotherapy is costly and time-consuming. The hope of psychotherapy lies in the use of discoveries made by competent therapists. This information may in part be translated into public health measures devoted to the prevention or alleviation of future disorders. More mediocre therapists will not contribute to this end.

Daniel Blain and Robert L. Robinson (1957) have devoted a great deal of time and thought to the problem of shortages of psychiatric services. They suggest that we need to redefine the groups that really require psychiatric service in such a way that more realistic dimensions of demand are outlined. They suggest the crucial importance of nonpsychiatric community resources (see the report of the Project on Nonpsychiatric Community Resources of the Joint Commission on Mental Illness and Health) in serving as a major resource to people in emotional trouble and temporary stress, and as a bulwark against the unrealistically excessive demands for psychiatric time.

To be useful, Blain and Robinson's proposal would have to be tried out in a place or region with fully adequate community resources, and, as we have seen, shortages of personnel in salaried positions and especially in public agencies are even more serious there than elsewhere.

These suggestions are open to objections and criticism, but they do represent attempts to come to grips with the appalling manpower problems in mental health. We desperately need (along with personnel, facilities, money, and knowledge) good ideas that can be debated and that can lead ultimately to effective action.

THE NEED FOR RESEARCH

In the last couple of years there has been a wave of enthusiasm for the chemical approach to mental disorder. The tranquilizing drugs are showing real promise as an aid to speedier and more effective therapy. These early reports are encouraging indications that research can be productive even at the present low rate of expenditure.

The memory of previous enthusiasms for new treatment methods that failed to fulfill their promise bids us be cautious in this matter. Still, if the new approaches to treatment fulfill a sizable proportion of their promise we will continue to be in trouble manpower-wise, because nearly everyone agrees that the new drugs are effective only in combination with increased attention and psychotherapy. We are faced with the prospect of larger numbers of hospitalized patients, who formerly did not see a psychiatrist for a long period, now lining up outside his door.

The field desperately needs research into causes, cures, and prevention. What are our prospects for mental health research leading to prevention or to more effective cures? As Hastings (1955) says: "Without more basic knowledge than we have today or are now accumulating, the people who follow us fifty years hence will still be struggling with the same problems that we are. The almost limitless future for the psychological sciences in the years ahead lies along the avenue of well-planned research activity done by many disciplines."

Research personnel in the mental health professions are in desperately short supply. Research in psychiatry requires further training and experience beyond the already overly long training period. The Group for the Advancement of Psychiatry (1955, p. 2) notes that: "Despite increased facilities and sums available for research in psychiatry, the present trend of psychiatric trainees is to enter into the practice of psychiatry, with emphasis upon psychotherapy and the shock therapies, rather than to undertake research."

Probably training in psychology involves the acquisition of more formal research skills than does training in any of the other mental health professions. But it is our general impression that there is an inverse relationship between the amount of time psychologists spend on basic research and their involvement with the field of mental illness and mental health. The clinical psychologist is needed for service responsibilities. When he does research, if he can find the time for it, he is likely to be concerned with the evaluation or improvement of his skills and techniques rather than with more basic attacks on etiology or pathology.

Increasingly the social worker has received research training, but social work is still a service profession and despite the growing emphasis on a research orientation in the social work curriculum, few social workers are deeply committed to full-time research.

Research in the genetics, biology, chemistry, and sociology of mental disorder holds exciting promise for the understanding and control of these problems. But a handful of researchers are at work where an army should be laboring and facilities are woefully inadequate.

CONCLUDING STATEMENT

We must conclude this survey with the prediction that our country will continue to be faced with serious personnel shortages in all fields related to mental illness and mental health for many years to come. Barring the possibility of a massive national effort in all areas of education, with all of the social changes such an effort would imply, or the possibility of a sharp breakthrough in mental health research, the prospects are pessimistic for significant improvements in the quantity or quality of professional services in these fields.

Appendixes

Appendix I

Statistical Tables

Table 1 [a]—Rehabilitation Salaries Compared with Certain Railroad and Industry Salaries, 1956

RAILROAD AND INDUSTRIAL OCCUPATIONS		REHABILITATION OCCUPATION	
Position	Average Salary	Position	Average Salary
Railroad Positions		Social Workers (U.S. Govt.)	$5,447
Engineers	$8,218		
Conductors	7,681	Psychological Counselors (Other)	5,185
Baggagemen	6,814	Rehabilitation Counselors (Other)	5,150
Brakemen	6,239		
		Physical Therapists (U.S. Govt.)	4,962
Industrial Positions			
Plant Jobs:		Occupational Therapists (U.S. Govt.)	4,948
Tool and Die Makers	5,574		
Draftsmen, Senior	5,425	Speech Therapists, Advanced (Other)	4,900
Electricians, Maintenance	5,262	Special Rehabilitation Personnel for the Blind (Other)	4,661
Pipefitters, Maintenance	5,200		
Averages for Entire Industry		Social Workers (Other)	4,600
Water Transportation	6,100		
Pipe Line Transportation	5,700	Special Teachers for Disabled (Other)	4,500
Petroleum and Coal Products Manufacturing	5,700	Physical Therapists (Other)	4,425
Automobile Manufacturing	5,400		
Highway Freight Transportation	5,200	Occupational Therapists (Other)	4,340
Professional Jobs:		Speech Therapists, Basic (Other)	4,200
Lawyers, Salaried	8,442		
Engineers, Industrial	7,750	Home Teachers for the Blind (Other)	3,593
Chemists			
Industrial research	7,656		
Industrial production	7,008		

[a] We have relied heavily, in the present study, on existing data prepared by a number of individuals and agencies concerned with manpower. In many cases their data were derived, in turn, from a variety of sources. The reader is urged to consult the original sources. Many of them contain qualifications, special cautions, and additional information which relate in an important way to interpretation of these data. The Task Force on Manpower is grateful to the large number of individuals and agencies that have responded so willingly to our request for assistance. Sources from which our Figures and Tables are borrowed or derived are given at the foot of each page.

Source: Tickton, S. T., 1957. *Rebuilding Human Lives,* p. 19. The Seventh Company.

Table 2—Trends in Hospital Utilization, 1946–1955: Average Daily Census, and Annual Admissions for All Types of Non-Federal U.S. Hospitals Compared with Non-Federal Psychiatric Hospitals

	AVERAGE DAILY CENSUS			NUMBER OF ADMISSIONS		
Year	All Non-Federal Hospitals	Non-Federal Psychiatric Hospitals	Per Cent of Total in Psychiatric Hospitals	All Non-Federal Hospitals	Non-Federal Psychiatric Hospitals	Per Cent of Total in Psychiatric Hospitals
1946	975,508	517,185	53.0	14,081,267	202,114	1.4
1947	1,040,250	558,039	53.6	16,517,732	266,366	1.6
1948	1,091,894	595,121	54.5	15,580,582	267,307	1.7
1949	1,082,886	597,061	55.1	15,956,362	269,080	1.7
1950	1,100,341	607,327	55.2	17,199,204	292,874	1.7
1951	1,126,875	635,865	56.4	17,197,164	274,671	1.6
1952	1,156,008	651,112	56.3	18,037,302	391,649	2.2
1953	1,173,823	662,939	56.5	18,625,493	290,615	1.6
1954	1,182,989	668,463	56.5	18,924,915	288,790	1.5
1955	1,205,954	677,405	56.2	19,657,727	312,422	1.6

Source: Hospitals, Administrator's Guide Issue, 1955. American Hospital Association, 29 (no. 8): 6–10, Tables 2 and 5.
Hospitals, Administrator's Guide Issue, 1956. American Hospital Association, 30 (no. 15). 14–16, Tables 1 and 3.

Table 3—Trends in Hospital Utilization, 1946–1955: Number and Type of Hospitals and of Hospital Beds in All Non-Federal U.S. Hospitals

	NUMBER OF HOSPITALS			NUMBER OF HOSPITAL BEDS		
Year	Non-Federal United States Total	Non-Federal Psychiatric	Per Cent of Total Psychiatric Treatment	Non-Federal United States Total	Non-Federal Psychiatric	Per Cent of Total Psychiatric Treatment
1946	5721	476	8.3	1,199,814	568,473	47.4
1947	5770	499	8.6	1,200,547	580,273	48.3
1948	5774	504	8.7	1,225,604	601,103	49.0
1949	5901	507	8.6	1,248,524	614,465	49.2
1950	6374	533	8.4	1,266,348	619,530	48.9
1951	6410	551	8.6	1,307,362	655,932	50.2
1952	6464	546	8.4	1,348,791	675,749	50.1
1953	6543	541	8.3	1,378,050	691,855	50.2
1954	6540	554	8.5	1,388,728	691,176	49.8
1955	6528	542	8.3	1,421,246	707,162	49.8

Source: Hospitals, Administrator's Guide Issue, 1955. American Hospital Association, 29 (no. 8): 6–10, Tables 2 and 5.

Hospitals, Administrator's Guide Issue, 1956. American Hospital Association, 30 (no. 15): 14–16, Tables 1 and 3.

Table 4—Hospital Utilization, 1946–1955: Number and Type of Hospitals and of Hospital Beds in All U.S. Hospitals

	NUMBER OF HOSPITALS			NUMBER OF BEDS		
Year	United States Total	Psychiatric Total	Per Cent of Total for Psychiatric Treatment	United States Total	Psychiatric Total	Per Cent of Total for Psychiatric Treatment
1954	6970	596	8.6	1,577,961	755,506	47.9
1955	6956	586	8.4	1,604,408	772,852	48.2

Source: Hospitals, Administrator's Guide Issue, 1955. American Hospital Association, 29 (no. 8): 10, Table 5.

Hospitals, Administrator's Guide Issue, 1956. American Hospital Association, 30 (no. 15): 16, Table 3.

Table 5—Hospital Utilization, 1954–1955: Average Daily Census, and Annual Admission Rate of All Types of U.S. Hospitals Compared with Psychiatric Hospitals

	AVERAGE DAILY CENSUS			NUMBER OF ADMISSIONS		
Year	Total United States Hospitals	Psychiatric Hospitals	Per Cent of United States Total in Psychiatric Hospitals	Total United States Hospitals	Psychiatric Hospitals	Per Cent of United States Total in Psychiatric Hospitals
1954	1,342,508	728,811	54.3	20,345,431	336,594	1.7
1955	1,363,024	740,295	54.3	21,072,521	356,377	1.7

Source: Hospitals, Administrator's Guide Issue, 1955. American Hospital Association, 29 (no. 8): 10, Table 5.

Hospitals, Administrator's Guide Issue, 1956. American Hospital Association, 30 (no. 15): 16, Table 3.

Table 6—Number of Average Daily Resident Patients in Public Mental Hospitals per 1,000 General Population, Position by States, 1956

U.S. Average	3.8
U.S. Median	2.85
1. New York	6.0
2. New Hampshire	4.8
3. Massachusetts	4.7
4. Delaware	4.3
5. New Jersey	4.1
6. Rhode Island	4.1
7. Illinois	4.0
8. Wisconsin	4.0
9. Connecticut	3.9
10. Pennsylvania	3.7
11. Colorado	3.5
12. Minnesota	3.5
13. Oklahoma	3.5
14. Vermont	3.5
15. Maryland	3.4
16. Nebraska	3.4
17. Maine	3.3
18. Georgia	3.2
19. Ohio	3.1
20. Montana	3.0
21. Virginia	3.0
22. Michigan	2.9
23. North Dakota	2.9
24. Oregon	2.9
25. California	2.8

26. Louisiana 2.8
27. Missouri 2.8
28. West Virginia 2.8
29. Arkansas 2.7
30. Washington 2.7

31. South Carolina 2.6
32. Indiana 2.5
33. Kentucky 2.5
34. Mississippi 2.5
35. Tennessee 2.4

36. Alabama 2.3
37. South Dakota 2.3
38. North Carolina 2.2
39. Florida 2.1
40. Kansas 2.1

41. Idaho 2.0
42. Wyoming 2.0
43. Iowa 1.9
44. Nevada 1.8
45. Texas 1.8

46. Arizona 1.6
47. Utah 1.6
48. New Mexico 1.2

Source: Joint Information Service of the American Psychiatric Association and the National Association for Mental Health, 1957. Thirteen indices: an aid in reviewing State mental health and hospital programs.

Table 7—Average Daily Maintenance Expenditure per Patient; Public Mental Hospitals, 1956

U.S. Average	$3.18
U.S. Median	3.11
1. Connecticut	4.73
2. Kansas	4.59
3. New Mexico	4.34
4. Michigan	4.33
5. Delaware	4.08
6. New Jersey	3.88
7. Indiana	3.83
8. Massachusetts	3.82
9. New Hampshire	3.82
10. California	3.80
11. Nebraska	3.79
12. Colorado	3.78
13. Iowa	3.64
14. Arizona	3.61
15. Maryland	3.45
16. New York	3.44
17. Wisconsin	3.40
18. Wyoming	3.36
19. Nevada	3.29
20. South Dakota	3.24
21. Vermont	3.24
22. Ohio	3.22
23. Idaho	3.17
24. Maine	3.12
25. Washington	3.10

26. Montana	3.07
27. Pennsylvania	3.06
28. Minnesota	3.01
29. Illinois	2.95
30. Oregon	2.95
31. North Carolina	2.93
32. North Dakota	2.88
33. Missouri	2.83
34. Georgia	2.73
35. Rhode Island	2.65
36. Virginia	2.63
37. Arkansas	2.60
38. Florida	2.54
39. Oklahoma	2.47
40. Utah	2.43
41. South Carolina	2.24
42. Alabama	2.13
43. Louisiana	2.08
44. Kentucky	2.07
45. Texas	2.07
46. Mississippi	2.04
47. West Virginia	1.90
48. Tennessee	1.84

Source: Joint Information Service of the American Psychiatric Association and the National Association for Mental Health, 1957. Thirteen indices: an aid in reviewing State mental health and hospital programs.

Table 8 [a]—Total Unfilled Positions for Physicians, Psychologists, and Psychometrists at State Mental Hospitals, 1956

State	PHYSICIANS			PSYCHOLOGISTS AND PSYCHOMETRISTS		
	Positions Available	Vacancy	Percentage of Vacancy	Positions Available	Vacancy	Percentage of Vacancy
Alabama	18	3	16.7	4	0	0.0
Arizona	10	1	10.0	2	0	0.0
Arkansas	22	2	9.1	4	2	50.0
California	340	47	13.8	61	4	6.6
Colorado	69	27	39.1	6	5	83.3
Connecticut	105	42	40.0	30	12	40.0
Delaware	19	6	31.6	6	1	16.7
Florida	20	2	10.0	4	1	25.0
Georgia	45	8	17.8	5	1	20.0
Idaho	11	5	45.5	8	3	37.5
Illinois	NA	NA	NA	NA	NA	NA [b]
Indiana	68	23	33.8	50	6	12.0
Iowa	33	3	9.1	19	8	42.1
Kansas	111	43	38.7	28	6	21.4
Kentucky	38	7	18.4	6	2	33.3
Louisiana	35	7	20.0	11	0	0.0
Maine	14	3	21.4	10	3	30.0
Maryland	NA	NA	NA	NA	NA	NA
Massachusetts	147	19	12.9	28	5	17.9
Michigan	168	32	19.0	36	5	13.9
Minnesota	57	7	12.3	21	3	14.3
Mississippi	NA	NA	NA	NA	NA	NA
Missouri	79	37	46.8	33	18	54.5
Montana	13	4	30.8	4	1	25.0
Nebraska	NA	NA	NA	NA	NA	NA
Nevada	1	0	0	0	0	—
New Hampshire	21	5	23.8	3	0	0.0
New Jersey	98	19	19.4	24	3	12.5
New Mexico	9	4	44.4	5	3	60.0

	PHYSICIANS			PSYCHOLOGISTS AND PSYCHOMETRISTS		
State	Positions Available	Vacancy	Percentage of Vacancy	Positions Available	Vacancy	Percentage of Vacancy
New York	649	109	16.8	48	10	20.8
North Carolina	68	18	26.5	13	1	7.7
North Dakota	11	2	18.2	8	3	37.5
Ohio	150	35	23.3	102	27	26.5
Oklahoma	47	6	12.8	11	0	0.0
Oregon	26	2	7.7	7	3	42.9
Pennsylvania	250	81	32.4	63	22	34.9
Rhode Island	32	9	28.1	4	1	25.0
South Carolina	23	4	17.4	5	0	0
South Dakota	NA	NA	NA	NA	NA	NA
Tennessee	NA	NA	NA	NA	NA	NA
Texas	NA	NA	NA	NA	NA	NA
Utah	7	3	42.9	5	1	20.0
Vermont	9	0	0	1	0	0.0
Virginia	66	29	43.9	19	1	5.3
Washington	50	18	36.0	8	2	25.0
West Virginia	22	5	22.7	6	1	16.7
Wisconsin	59	29	49.2	12	5	41.7
Wyoming	2	1	50.0	3	0	0.0
United States	3,022	707	23.4	723	169	23.4

[a] The figures contained in Tables 8–13 are incomplete, but the best available. Data supplied by the Interstate Clearing House on Mental Health, Council of State Governments, have been supplemented by data from the National Institute of Mental Health. As no data on positions available were included in the NIMH data, these figures were estimated by assuming that each of the seven states missing from the CSG data had the same percentage of vacancies as was the average of the other forty-one states. The tables do not include data for the District of Columbia. In several instances, the data reported by individual states are incomplete, and the reader is referred to the original sources for further qualifications.

[b] NA: Figures not available.

Source: Council of State Governments, Interstate Clearing House on Mental Health, 1957. The manpower situation in State mental hospitals, April. Note qualification about these data in footnote 2.

Table 9 [a]—Total Unfilled Positions for Social Workers at State Mental Hospitals, 1956

State	PSYCHIATRIC SOCIAL WORKERS			NONPSYCHIATRIC SOCIAL WORKERS (INCLUDES FIELD WORKERS)		
	Positions Available	Vacancy	Percentage of Vacancy	Positions Available	Vacancy	Percentage of Vacancy
Alabama	1	0	0.0	4	0	0.0
Arizona	4	0	0.0	0	0	—
Arkansas	5	4	80.0	2	1	50.0
California	125	12	9.6	0	0	—
Colorado	5	1	20.0	0	0	—
Connecticut	36	10	27.8	6	6	100.0
Delaware	7	2	28.6	2	0	0.0
Florida	4	1	25.0	0	0	—
Georgia	5	0	0.0	0	0	—
Idaho	5	4	80.0	3	0	0.0
Illinois	NA	NA	NA	NA	NA	NA [b]
Indiana	70	9	12.9	1	0	0.0
Iowa	18	3	16.7	3	1	33.3
Kansas	36	6	16.7	1	0	0.0
Kentucky	13	10	76.9	17	9	52.9
Louisiana	11	1	9.1	8	1	12.5
Maine	9	1	11.1	0	0	—
Maryland	NA	NA	NA	NA	NA	NA
Massachusetts	64	5	7.8	28	2	7.1
Michigan	83	8	9.6	33	1	3.0
Minnesota	10	2	20.0	7	0	0.0
Mississippi	NA	NA	NA	NA	NA	NA
Missouri	27	16	59.3	9	3	33.3
Montana	5	1	20.0	1	0	0.0
Nebraska	NA	NA	NA	NA	NA	NA
Nevada	0	0	—	0	0	—
New Hampshire	5	0	0.0	0	0	—

State	PSYCHIATRIC SOCIAL WORKERS			NONPSYCHIATRIC SOCIAL WORKERS (INCLUDES FIELD WORKERS)		
	Positions Available	Vacancy	Percentage of Vacancy	Positions Available	Vacancy	Percentage of Vacancy
New Jersey	67	20	29.9	0	0	—
New Mexico	1	0	0.0	6	2	33.0
New York	211	59	28.0	0	0	—
North Carolina	14	1	7.1	0	0	—
North Dakota	2	0	0.0	4	0	0.0
Ohio	117	14	12.0	22	1	4.5
Oklahoma	8	3	37.5	9	1	11.1
Oregon	4	2	50.0	5	2	40.0
Pennsylvania	101	28	27.7	27	7	25.9
Rhode Island	12	6	50.0	0	0	—
South Carolina	5	0	0.0	5	3	60.0
South Dakota	NA	NA	NA	NA	NA	NA
Tennessee	NA	NA	NA	NA	NA	NA
Texas	NA	NA	NA	NA	NA	NA
Utah	6	2	33.3	0	0	—
Vermont	1	0	0.0	0	0	—
Virginia	16	8	50.0	13	7	53.8
Washington	4	2	50.0	12	7	58.3
West Virginia	3	0	0.0	5	1	20.0
Wisconsin	30	10	33.3	0	0	—
Wyoming	2	0	0.0	1	0	0.0
United States	1,152	251	21.8	234	55	23.5

[a] See Table 8 [a].
[b] NA: Figures not available.

Source: Council of State Governments, Interstate Clearing House on Mental Health, 1957. The manpower situation in State mental hospitals, April. Note qualification about these data in footnote 2.

Table 10 ª—Total Unfilled Positions for Registered Nurses and Special Therapists at State Mental Hospitals, 1956

	REGISTERED NURSES			SPECIAL THERAPISTS		
State	Positions Available	Vacancy	Percentage of Vacancy	Positions Available	Vacancy	Percentage of Vacancy
Alabama	36	8	22.2	41	0	0.0
Arizona	20	4	20.0	13	0	0.0
Arkansas	35	6	17.1	29	1	3.4
California	598	58	9.7	161	22	13.7
Colorado	66	36	54.5	67	27	40.3
Connecticut	298	95	31.9	178	34	19.1
Delaware	40	6	15.0	25	3	12.0
Florida	64	18	28.1	14	2	14.3
Georgia	86	20	23.3	29	1	3.4
Idaho	25	5	20.0	17	2	11.8
Illinois	NA	NA	NA	NA	NA	NA ᵇ
Indiana	183	33	18.0	105	8	7.6
Iowa	39	2	5.1	33	3	9.1
Kansas	174	107	61.5	85	10	11.8
Kentucky	67	13	19.4	29	12	41.4
Louisiana	40	7	17.5	46	3	6.5
Maine	38	1	2.6	19	1	5.3
Maryland	NA	NA	NA	NA	NA	NA
Massachusetts	579	115	19.9	173	22	12.7
Michigan	332	53	16.0	250	18	7.2
Minnesota	190	19	10.0	103	5	4.9
Mississippi	NA	NA	NA	NA	NA	NA
Missouri	76	32	42.1	98	46	46.9
Montana	23	5	21.7	11	2	18.2
Nebraska	NA	NA	NA	NA	NA	NA
Nevada	6	1	16.7	3	0	0.0
New Hampshire	55	4	7.3	17	3	17.6

	REGISTERED NURSES			SPECIAL THERAPISTS		
State	Positions Available	Vacancy	Percentage of Vacancy	Positions Available	Vacancy	Percentage of Vacancy
New Jersey	426	176	41.3	142	17	12.0
New Mexico	9	2	22.2	15	5	33.3
New York	2,055	308	15.0	688	107	15.6
North Carolina	157	37	23.6	50	6	12.0
North Dakota	21	2	9.5	18	0	0.0
Ohio	455	137	30.1	218	13	6.0
Oklahoma	65	8	12.3	43	2	4.7
Oregon	74	18	24.3	20	4	20.0
Pennsylvania	1,172	210	17.9	302	93	30.8
Rhode Island	73	36	49.3	23	6	26.1
South Carolina	49	1	2.0	3	0	0.0
South Dakota	NA	NA	NA	NA	NA	NA
Tennessee	NA	NA	NA	NA	NA	NA
Texas	NA	NA	NA	NA	NA	NA
Utah	20	9	45.0	12	3	25.0
Vermont	10	0	0	5	0	0.0
Virginia	127	53	41.7	78	22	28.2
Washington	62	15	24.2	7	1	14.3
West Virginia	37	24	64.9	26	2	7.7
Wisconsin	202	59	29.2	81	8	9.9
Wyoming	7	0	0	0	0	0.0
United States	8,091	1,743	21.5	3,277	514	15.7

[a] See Table 8 [a].
[b] NA: Figures not available.

Source: Council of State Governments, Interstate Clearing House on Mental Health, 1957. The manpower situation in State mental hospitals, April. Note qualification about these data in footnote 2.

Table 11 ª—Total Unfilled Positions for Nonregistered Nurses and Attendants at State Mental Hospitals, 1956

State	NONREGISTERED NURSES (INCLUDES STUDENT NURSES) Positions Available	Vacancy	Percentage of Vacancy	ATTENDANTS Positions Available	Vacancy	Percentage of Vacancy
Alabama	0	0	—	900	36	4.0
Arizona	0	0	—	302	0	0.0
Arkansas	0	0	—	864	5	0.6
California	0	0	—	6,580	239	3.6
Colorado	0	0	—	1,109	204	18.4
Connecticut	193	37	19.2	1,551	87	5.6
Delaware	0	0	—	254	33	13.0
Florida	83	30	36.1	1,115	48	4.3
Georgia	68	6	8.8	1,155	32	2.8
Idaho	15	15	100.0	209	5	2.4
Illinois	NA	NA	NA	NA	NA	NA ᵇ
Indiana	0	0	—	2,105	47	2.2
Iowa	39	0	0.0	986	30	3.0
Kansas	34	0	0.0	1,012	0	0.0
Kentucky	57	4	7.0	948	45	4.7
Louisiana	48	0	0.0	935	11	1.2
Maine	17	0	0.0	496	44	8.9
Maryland	NA	NA	NA	NA	NA	NA
Massachusetts	134	29	21.6	3,554	150	4.2
Michigan	70	0	0.0	3,822	98	2.6
Minnesota	199	0	0.0	1,518	37	2.4
Mississippi	NA	NA	NA	NA	NA	NA
Missouri	120	3	2.5	2,196	224	10.2
Montana	60	0	0.0	281	18	6.4
Nebraska	NA	NA	NA	NA	NA	NA
Nevada	1	0	0.0	51	0	0.0

State	NONREGISTERED NURSES (INCLUDES STUDENT NURSES)			ATTENDANTS		
	Positions Available	Vacancy	Percentage of Vacancy	Positions Available	Vacancy	Percentage of Vacancy
New Hampshire	103	0	0.0	388	8	2.1
New Jersey	0	0	—	3,018	254	8.4
New Mexico	8	2	25.0	237	0	0.0
New York	1,016	158	15.6	12,968	262	2.0
North Carolina	1	0	0.0	1,417	29	2.0
North Dakota	19	0	0.0	319	3	0.9
Ohio	270	4	1.5	4,170	5	0.1
Oklahoma	52	0	0.0	1,217	22	1.8
Oregon	74	0	0.0	887	17	1.9
Pennsylvania	515	26	5.0	5,917	333	5.6
Rhode Island	55	15	27.3	594	77	13.0
South Carolina	1	0	0.0	706	9	1.3
South Dakota	NA	NA	NA	NA	NA	NA
Tennessee	NA	NA	NA	NA	NA	NA
Texas	NA	NA	NA	NA	NA	NA
Utah	19	0	0.0	274	0	0.0
Vermont	2	0	0.0	196	0	0.0
Virginia	75	51	68.0	1,541	102	6.6
Washington	70	0	0.0	1,396	83	5.9
West Virginia	1	0	0.0	634	0	0.0
Wisconsin	120	1	0.8	2,044	98	4.8
Wyoming	0	0	—	62	0	0.0
United States	3,539	381	10.8	69,928	2,695	3.9

[a] See Table 8 [a].
[b] NA: Figures not available.

Source: Council of State Governments, Interstate Clearing House on Mental Health, 1957. The manpower situation in State mental hospitals, April. Note qualification about these data in footnote 2.

Table 12ᵃ—Total Manpower Vacancies in State Mental Hospitals, 1956

TOTAL EMPLOYEES

State	Positions Available	Vacancies	Per Cent of Vacancies
Alabama	1,452	86	5.9
Arizona	531	5	0.9
Arkansas	1,395	31	2.2
California	10,601	447	4.2
Colorado	2,275	540	23.7
Connecticut	3,734	407	10.9
Delaware	719	51	7.1
Florida	1,927	122	6.3
Georgia	2,104	93	4.4
Idaho	441	48	10.9
Illinois	NA	NA	NA ᵇ
Indiana	4,066	161	4.0
Iowa	1,885	77	4.1
Kansas	2,492	322	12.9
Kentucky	1,706	118	6.9
Louisiana	1,984	44	2.2
Maine	957	63	6.6
Maryland	NA	NA	NA
Massachusetts	7,490	433	5.8
Michigan	7,069	297	4.2
Minnesota	3,002	101	3.4
Mississippi	NA	NA	NA
Missouri	4,019	718	17.9
Montana	546	35	6.4
Nebraska	NA	NA	NA
Nevada	95	5	5.3
New Hampshire	847	27	3.2
New Jersey	6,042	615	10.2

TOTAL EMPLOYEES

State	Positions Available	Vacancies	Per Cent of Vacancies
New Mexico	423	20	4.7
New York	25,920	1,344	5.2
North Carolina	2,979	125	4.2
North Dakota	547	10	1.8
Ohio	8,181	347	4.2
Oklahoma	2,127	47	2.2
Oregon	1,507	56	3.7
Pennsylvania	12,693	1,266	10.0
Rhode Island	1,069	216	20.2
South Carolina	1,398	27	1.9
Souht Dakota	NA	NA	NA
Tennessee	NA	NA	NA
Texas	NA	NA	NA
Utah	454	18	4.0
Vermont	337	0	0
Virginia	2,962	400	13.5
Washington	2,232	152	6.8
West Virginia	1,103	39	3.5
Wisconsin	3,913	270	6.9
Wyoming	151	1	0.7
United States	135,375	9,184	6.8

[a] See Table 8 [a].
[b] NA: Figures not available.

Source: Council of State Governments, Interstate Clearing House on Mental Health, 1957. The manpower situation in State mental hospitals, April. Note qualification about these data in footnote 2.

**Table 13 ᵃ—Total Unfilled Positions for Professional Therapeutic
Personnel, Nonprofessional Therapeutic Personnel,
and Administrative and Maintenance Personnel at
State Mental Hospitals, 1956**

State	TOTAL PROFESSIONAL THERAPEUTIC PERSONNEL			TOTAL NON-PROFESSIONAL THERAPEUTIC PERSONNEL			TOTAL ADMIN-ISTRATIVE AND MAINTENANCE PERSONNEL		
	Positions Available	Va-cancies	Per Cent of Va-cancies	Positions Available	Va-cancies	Per Cent of Va-cancies	Positions Available	Va-cancies	Per Cent of Va-cancies
Alabama	104	11	10.6	900	36	4.0	448	39	8.7
Arizona	49	5	10.2	302	0	0.0	180	0	0.0
Arkansas	97	16	16.5	864	5	0.6	434	10	2.3
California	1,285	143	11.1	6,580	239	3.6	2,736	65	2.4
Colorado	213	96	45.1	1,109	204	18.4	953	240	25.2
Connecticut	653	199	30.5	1,744	124	7.1	1,337	84	6.3
Delaware	99	18	18.2	254	33	13.0	366	0	0.0
Florida	106	24	22.6	1,198	78	6.5	623	20	3.2
Georgia	170	30	17.6	1,223	38	3.1	711	25	3.5
Idaho	69	19	27.5	224	20	8.9	148	9	6.1
Illinois	NA	NA	NA	NA	NA	NA	NA	NA	NA ᵇ
Indiana	477	79	16.6	2,105	47	2.2	1,484	35	2.4
Iowa	145	20	13.8	1,025	30	2.9	715	27	3.8
Kansas	435	172	39.5	1,046	0	0.0	1,011	150	14.8
Kentucky	170	53	31.2	1,005	49	4.9	531	16	3.0
Louisiana	151	19	12.6	983	11	1.1	850	14	1.6
Maine	90	9	10.0	513	44	8.6	354	10	2.8
Maryland	NA	NA	NA	NA	NA	NA	NA	NA	NA
Massachusetts	1,019	168	16.5	3,688	179	4.9	2,783	86	3.1
Michigan	902	117	13.0	3,892	98	2.5	2,275	82	3.6
Minnesota	388	36	9.3	1,717	37	2.2	897	28	3.1
Mississippi	NA	NA	NA	NA	NA	NA	NA	NA	NA
Missouri	322	152	47.2	2,316	227	9.8	1,381	339	24.5
Montana	57	13	22.8	341	18	5.3	148	4	2.7
Nebraska	NA	NA	NA	NA	NA	NA	NA	NA	NA

State	TOTAL PROFESSIONAL THERAPEUTIC PERSONNEL			TOTAL NON- PROFESSIONAL THERAPEUTIC PERSONNEL			TOTAL ADMIN- ISTRATIVE AND MAINTENANCE PERSONNEL		
	Positions Available	Va- cancies	Per Cent of Va- cancies	Positions Available	Va- cancies	Per Cent of Va- cancies	Positions Available	Va- cancies	Per Cent of Va- cancies
Nevada	10	1	10.0	52	0	0.0	33	4	12.1
New Hampshire	101	12	11.9	491	8	1.6	255	7	2.7
New Jersey	757	235	31.0	3,018	254	8.4	2,267	126	5.6
New Mexico	45	16	35.6	245	2	0.8	133	2	1.5
New York	3,651	593	16.2	13,984	420	3.0	8,285	331	4.0
North Carolina	302	63	20.9	1,418	29	2.0	1,259	33	2.6
North Dakota	64	7	10.9	338	3	0.9	145	0	0.0
Ohio	1,064	227	21.3	4,440	9	0.2	2,677	111	4.1
Oklahoma	183	20	10.9	1,269	22	1.7	675	5	0.7
Oregon	136	31	22.8	961	17	1.8	410	8	2.0
Pennsylvania	1,915	441	23.0	6,432	359	5.6	4,346	466	10.7
Rhode Island	144	58	40.3	649	92	14.2	276	66	23.9
South Carolina	90	8	8.9	707	9	1.3	601	10	1.7
South Dakota	NA	NA	NA	NA	NA	NA	NA	NA	NA
Tennessee	NA	NA	NA	NA	NA	NA	NA	NA	NA
Texas	NA	NA	NA	NA	NA	NA	NA	NA	NA
Utah	50	18	36.0	293	0	0.0	111	0	0.0
Vermont	26	0	0.0	198	0	0.0	113	0	0.0
Virginia	319	120	37.6	1,616	153	9.5	1,027	127	12.4
Washington	143	45	31.5	1,466	83	5.7	623	24	3.9
West Virginia	99	33	33.3	635	0	0.0	369	6	1.6
Wisconsin	384	111	28.9	2,164	99	4.6	1,365	60	4.4
Wyoming	15	1	6.7	62	0	0.0	74	0	0.0
United States	16,499	3,439	20.8	73,467	3,076	4.2	45,409	2,669	5.9

[a] See Table 8 [a].
[b] NA: Figures not available.

Source: Council of State Governments, Interstate Clearing House on Mental Health, 1957. The man-power situation in State mental hospitals, April. Note qualification about these data in footnote 2.

Table 14 ª—Position of States According to Number of Professional Patient-Care Personnel per 100 Patients in Public Mental Hospitals, 1956

U.S. Average	2.8
U.S. Median	2.5
1. Kansas	5.7
2. Delaware	5.7
3. Connecticut	4.9
4. Nebraska	4.5
5. Massachusetts	4.0
6. Pennsylvania	3.7
7. Indiana	3.7
8. New Hampshire	3.4
9. New York	3.2
10. Colorado	3.2
11. South Dakota	3.2
12. New Jersey	3.1
13. Minnesota	3.0
14. Ohio	3.0
15. Iowa	3.0
16. North Dakota	3.0
17. New Mexico	2.9
18. California	2.8
19. Maryland	2.8
20. Michigan	2.7
21. Arizona	2.6
22. Illinois	2.6
23. Oregon	2.5
24. Rhode Island	2.5
25. Maine	2.5

26. Idaho 2.4
27. North Carolina 2.4
28. Vermont 2.3
29. Nevada 2.2
30. Utah 2.1

31. Wyoming 2.1
32. Montana 2.1
33. Kentucky 2.0
34. Oklahoma 1.9
35. Mississippi 1.8

36. Virginia 1.8
37. Washington 1.7
38. Tennessee 1.7
39. Arkansas 1.7
40. Texas 1.6

41. Louisiana 1.5
42. West Virginia 1.5
43. Wisconsin 1.5
44. South Carolina 1.4
45. Missouri 1.3

46. Florida 1.2
47. Georgia 1.2
48. Alabama 1.1

[a] The reader is referred to the original source for qualifications of these data.

Source: Joint Information Service of the American Psychiatric Association and the National Association for Mental Health, 1957. Thirteen indices: an aid in reviewing State mental health and hospital programs.

Table 15 ª—Position of States According to Number of Full-Time Employees per 100 Patients in Public Mental Hospitals, 1956

U.S. Average		27.4
U.S. Median		27.4
1. Kansas		49.0
2. Nebraska		43.7
3. New Mexico		42.8
4. Delaware		40.3
5. Connecticut		36.7
6. Iowa		35.9
7. Indiana		35.5
8. Colorado		34.2
9. New Jersey		33.9
10. New Hampshire		33.8
11. Utah		33.0
12. Oregon		32.0
13. Massachusetts		31.0
14. Washington		30.9
15. Michigan		30.1
16. Maryland		30.0
17. Arizona		29.6
18. Maine		29.2
19. North Carolina		28.6
20. South Dakota		28.1
21. Pennsylvania		27.9
22. Ohio		27.6
23. Idaho		27.6
24. Arkansas		27.6
25. California		27.2

26. Montana 27.1
27. Mississippi 27.0
28. North Dakota 26.9
29. Florida 26.9
30. Missouri 26.6

31. New York 26.5
32. Oklahoma 26.3
33. Vermont 26.3
34. Minnesota 25.4
35. Rhode Island 24.7

36. Wyoming 24.5
37. Wisconsin 24.2
38. Louisiana 24.1
39. Illinois 23.5
40. Virginia 22.8

41. South Carolina 22.6
42. Kentucky 21.5
43. Nevada 20.4
44. Texas 19.7
45. West Virginia 19.0

46. Alabama 18.3
47. Georgia 17.0
48. Tennessee 16.0

ᵃ See Table 14 ᵃ.

Source: Joint Information Service of the American Psychiatric Association and the National
Association for Mental Health, 1957. Thirteen indices: an aid in reviewing State mental
health and hospital programs.

Table 16—Professional Manpower Needs in Psychiatric Facilities of the Veterans Administration by 1960

	Needed	Employed	Vacancies Expected
In Hospitals			
Psychiatrists	850	505	345
Neurologists	111	50	61
Psychologists	825	276	549
Social Workers	600	238	362
Nurses	4,000	2,767	233
Aides	15,000	12,000	3,000
In Clinics and Examining Units			
Psychiatrists	547	315	232
Psychologists	360	124	236
Social Workers	1,400	626	774

Source: Veterans Administration, Department of Medicine and Surgery, Psychiatry and Neurology Division, 1953. *Planning in psychiatry, neurology, and clinical psychology.* Government Printing Office.

Table 17—Recommended Personnel Ratios for Public Mental Hospitals

	Admission and Intensive Treatment	Continued Treatment	Geriatric Service	Medical and Surgical	Tuberculosis Service
Physicians	1:30 patients	1:150 patients	1:150 patients	1:50 patients	1:50 patients
Clinical Psychologists	1:100	1:500	—	—	—
Registered Nurses	1:5	1:40	1:20	1:5	1:5
Attendants	1:4	1:6	1:4	1:5	1:5
Psychiatric Social Workers	One to 80 new admissions per year; one to 60 patients on convalescent status or on family care; one supervisor to every 5 case workers.				

Source: American Psychiatric Association, 1956. Standards for hospitals and clinics.

Table 18 ª—Adequacy of Physician Staff in Public Mental Hospitals, 1956, According to Minimum APA Standards

State	Total Number Needed	Number Now Employed	Additional Number Needed	Per cent Adequacy of Present Staff
U.S. Total	6,675	3,007	3,668	45.0
Alabama	88	15	73	17.0
Arizona	20	9	11	45.0
Arkansas	59	20	39	33.9
California	444	265	179	59.7
Colorado	68	54	14	79.4
Connecticut	104	68	36	65.4
Delaware	21	18	3	85.7
District of Columbia	86	69	17	80.2
Florida	97	26	71	26.8
Georgia	141	42	99	29.8
Idaho	15	4	11	26.7
Illinois	458	171	287	37.3
Indiana	132	49	83	37.1
Iowa	62	49	13	79.0
Kansas	53	80	—	150.9
Kentucky	90	34	56	37.8
Louisiana	99	31	68	31.3
Maine	36	13	23	36.1
Maryland	116	63	53	54.3
Massachusetts	274	145	129	52.9
Michigan	262	109	153	41.6
Minnesota	137	55	82	40.1
Mississippi	63	20	43	31.7
Missouri	143	44	99	30.8
Montana	23	8	15	34.8
Nebraska	57	36	21	63.2

State	Total Number Needed	Number Now Employed	Additional Number Needed	Per cent Adequacy of Present Staff
Nevada	5	2	3	40.0
New Hampshire	32	17	15	53.1
New Jersey	264	157	107	59.5
New Mexico	12	5	7	41.7
New York	1,161	576	585	49.6
North Carolina	119	50	69	42.0
North Dakota	23	12	11	52.2
Ohio	340	132	208	38.8
Oklahoma	95	43	52	45.3
Oregon	59	25	34	42.4
Pennsylvania	485	179	306	36.9
Rhode Island	41	24	17	58.5
South Carolina	73	21	52	28.8
South Dakota	19	8	11	42.1
Tennessee	100	38	62	38.0
Texas	194	81	113	41.8
Utah	16	5	11	31.3
Vermont	15	9	6	60.0
Virginia	134	39	95	29.1
Washington	87	34	53	39.1
West Virginia	66	18	48	27.3
Wisconsin	180	34	154	18.9
Wyoming	8	1	7	12.5

[a] The reader is referred to the original source for qualifications in these data. The technique used to compute professional personnel available differs somewhat from that used by other manpower sources. A detailed account of these differences is available in the original source.

Source: Joint Information Service, 1957. Fact Sheet No. 4.

Table 19 ᵃ—*Adequacy of Psychologist Staff in Public Mental Hospitals, 1956, According to Minimum APA Standards*

State	Total Number Needed	Number Now Employed	Additional Number Needed	Per cent Adequacy of Present Staff
U.S. Total	1,113	723	390	64.9
Alabama	15	4	11	26.7
Arizona	3	2	1	66.7
Arkansas	10	3	7	30.0
California	74	61	24	82.4
Colorado	11	4	7	36.3
Connecticut	17	18	—	105.8
Delaware	4	8	—	200.0
District of Columbia	14	5	9	35.7
Florida	16	3	13	18.7
Georgia	23	4	19	17.4
Idaho	3	5	—	166.7
Illinois	76	78	—	102.6
Indiana	22	44	—	200.0
Iowa	10	20	—	200.0
Kansas	9	22	—	244.5
Kentucky	15	4	11	26.6
Louisiana	17	11	6	64.7
Maine	6	9	—	150.0
Maryland	19	19	—	100.0
Massachusetts	46	24	22	52.1
Michigan	44	26	18	59.0
Minnesota	23	18	5	78.2
Mississippi	11	3	8	27.3
Missouri	24	15	9	62.5
Montana	4	3	1	75.0
Nebraska	10	12	—	120.0
Nevada	1	—	1	—
New Hampshire	5	3	2	60.0
New Jersey	44	29	15	65.9
New Mexico	2	2	—	100.0
New York	194	39	155	20.1
North Carolina	20	12	8	60.0
North Dakota	4	5	—	125.0
Ohio	57	75	—	131.5
Oklahoma	16	11	5	68.7
Oregon	10	4	6	40.0
Pennsylvania	81	41	40	50.6
Rhode Island	7	3	4	42.9
South Carolina	12	5	7	41.7
South Dakota	3	3	—	100.0
Tennessee	17	13	4	76.5
Texas	32	9	23	28.1
Utah	3	4	—	133.3
Vermont	3	1	2	33.3
Virginia	22	18	4	81.8
Washington	14	6	8	42.9
West Virginia	11	5	6	45.5
Wisconsin	30	7	23	23.3
Wyoming	1	3	—	300.0

ᵃ See Table 18 ᵃ.

Source: Joint Information Service, 1957. Fact Sheet No. 4.

Table 20 ª—Adequacy of Social Worker Staff in Public Mental Hospitals, 1956, According to Minimum APA Standards

State	Total Number Needed	Number Now Employed	Additional Number Needed	Per cent Adequacy of Present Staff
U.S. Total	3,944	1,436	2,508	36.4
Alabama	44	5	39	11.4
Arizona	19	4	15	21.1
Arkansas	44	3	41	5.6
California	370	240	130	64.9
Colorado	43	8	35	18.6
Connecticut	71	26	45	36.6
Delaware	22	8	14	36.3
District of Columbia	25	13	12	52.0
Florida	44	3	41	6.8
Georgia	84	5	79	5.9
Idaho	18	6	12	33.3
Illinois	200	73	127	36.5
Indiana	74	62	12	83.8
Iowa	49	22	27	44.9
Kansas	44	31	13	70.5
Kentucky	46	11	35	23.9
Louisiana	79	17	62	21.5
Maine	17	99	8	52.9
Maryland	89	47	42	52.8
Massachusetts	162	88	74	54.3
Michigan	181	102	79	56.4
Minnesota	84	15	69	17.9
Mississippi	54	5	49	9.3
Missouri	49	17	32	34.7
Montana	22	3	19	13.6
Nebraska	49	16	33	32.7
Nevada	5	—	5	—
New Hampshire	17	5	12	29.4
New Jersey	144	62	82	43.0
New Mexico	23	5	18	21.7
New York	515	152	363	29.5
North Carolina	83	13	70	15.8
North Dakota	23	6	17	26.1
Ohio	230	124	106	53.9
Oklahoma	47	13	34	27.7
Oregon	58	5	53	8.6
Pennsylvania	262	93	169	35.5
Rhode Island	30	6	24	20.0
South Carolina	54	7	47	12.9
South Dakota	10	4	6	40.0
Tennessee	38	10	28	26.3
Texas	139	35	104	25.2
Utah	11	4	7	36.3
Vermont	8	1	7	12.5
Virginia	78	14	64	17.8
Washington	47	7	40	14.9
West Virginia	56	8	48	14.3
Wisconsin	83	20	63	24.1
Wyoming	4	3	1	75.0

ª See Table 18 ª.

Source: Joint Information Service, 1957. Fact Sheet No. 4.

Table 21 ª—Adequacy of Registered Nursing Staff in Public Mental Hospitals, 1956, According to Minimum APA Standards

State	Total Number Needed	Number Now Employed	Additional Number Needed	Per cent Adequacy of Present Staff
U.S. Total	37,085	7,185	29,900	19.4
Alabama	488	28	460	5.7
Arizona	111	16	95	14.4
Arkansas	330	29	301	8.8
California	2,467	337	2,130	13.7
Colorado	380	77	303	20.2
Connecticut	578	203	375	35.1
Delaware	116	41	75	35.3
District of Columbia	475	290	185	61.0
Florida	536	54	482	10.0
Georgia	782	66	716	8.4
Idaho	82	12	70	14.6
Illinois	2,545	290	2,255	11.4
Indiana	733	150	583	20.5
Iowa	345	45	300	13.0
Kansas	295	67	228	22.7
Kentucky	499	54	445	10.8
Louisiana	551	33	518	5.9
Maine	200	30	170	15.0
Maryland	645	67	578	10.3
Massachusetts	1,523	476	1,047	31.3
Michigan	1,457	238	1,219	16.3
Minnesota	762	171	591	22.4
Mississippi	349	29	320	8.3
Missouri	794	44	750	5.5
Montana	127	17	110	13.4
Nebraska	316	87	229	27.5
Nevada	30	5	25	16.7
New Hampshire ª	178	51	127	28.6
New Jersey	1,468	328	1,140	22.3
New Mexico	66	7	59	10.6
New York	6,451	1,761	4,690	27.2
North Carolina	659	120	539	18.2
North Dakota	128	19	109	14.8
Ohio	1,890	318	1,572	16.8
Oklahoma	526	57	469	10.8
Oregon	330	56	261	16.9
Pennsylvania	2,693	971	1,722	36.0
Rhode Island	228	37	191	16.2
South Carolina	408	48	360	11.8
South Dakota	107	28	79	26.1
Tennessee	554	52	502	9.4
Texas	1,077	54	1,023	5.0
Utah	87	11	76	12.6
Vermont	85	12	73	14.1
Virginia	742	74	668	9.9
Washington	481	47	434	9.7
West Virginia	366	27	339	7.3
Wisconsin	1,001	144	857	14.4
Wyoming	93	7	36	16.2

ª See Table 18 ª.

Source: Joint Information Service, 1957. Fact Sheet No. 4.

Table 22 ᵃ—Adequacy of Other Nurses and Attendant Staff in Public Mental Hospitals, 1956, According to Minimum APA Standards

State	Total Number Needed	Number Now Employed	Additional Number Needed	Per cent Adequacy of Present Staff
U.S. Total	111,255	84,377	26,878	75.9
Alabama	1,464	864	600	59.0
Arizona	334	302	32	90.4
Arkansas	991	859	132	86.7
California	7,400	6,197	1,203	83.7
Colorado	1,139	943	196	82.7
Connecticut	1,734	1,620	114	93.4
Delaware	347	295	42	85.0
District of Columbia	1,424	1,254	170	88.1
Florida	1,607	1,427	180	88.8
Georgia	2,348	1,185	1,168	50.4
Idaho	245	192	53	78.4
Illinois	7,635	4,084	3,551	53.5
Indiana	2,199	2,063	136	93.8
Iowa	1,034	1,046	—	101.1
Kansas	885	1,046	—	118.1
Kentucky	1,498	956	542	63.8
Louisiana	1,652	972	680	58.5
Maine	601	482	119	80.2
Maryland	1,934	1,545	389	79.9
Massachusetts	4,570	3,730	840	81.6
Michigan	4,372	3,783	589	86.5
Minnesota	2,286	1,680	606	73.5
Mississippi	1,046	807	239	77.2
Missouri	2,382	2,014	368	84.6
Montana	381	315	66	82.7
Nebraska	948	1,242	—	131.0
Nevada	89	52	37	58.4
New Hampshire	533	426	107	80.0
New Jersey	4,403	3,785	618	85.9
New Mexico	199	243	—	122.1
New York	19,354	14,405	4,949	74.4
North Carolina	1,978	1,389	589	70.2
North Dakota	385	316	69	82.0
Ohio	5,669	4,431	1,238	78.2
Oklahoma	1,579	1,247	332	79.0
Oregon	991	944	47	95.3
Pennsylvania	8,081	6,054	2,027	74.9
Rhode Island	683	557	126	81.6
South Carolina	1,223	698	525	57.1
South Dakota	321	204	117	63.6
Tennessee	1,661	760	901	45.8
Texas	3,230	1,859	1,371	57.6
Utah	261	274	—	105.0
Vermont	256	196	60	76.6
Virginia	2,227	1,463	764	65.7
Washington	1,443	1,383	60	95.8
West Virginia	1,097	596	501	54.3
Wisconsin	3,006	2,097	909	69.8
Wyoming	130	62	68	47.7

ᵃ See Table 18 ᵃ.

Source: Joint Information Service, 1957. Fact Sheet No. 4.

Table 23 ª—Ratios of Various Personnel Groups to Patients in Public Mental Hospitals, 1956, and Position According to Personnel Ratios, by States

State	Number of Patients to Physicians		Number of Patients to Psychologists		Number of Patients to Registered Nurses		Number of Patients to Attendants		Number of Patients to Social Workers	
	Position	Number	Position	Number	Position	Number	Position	Number	Position	Number
U.S. Total		183.9		768.8		77.4		6.6		159.4
Alabama	48	488.0	44	1,830.0	47	261.4	40	8.5	43	526.2
Arizona	18	185.6	28	835.0	26	104.4	10	5.5	32	280.7
Arkansas	36	247.9	41	1,652.3	42	170.9	13	5.8	46	859.3
California	8	139.6	18	606.5	28	109.7	18	6.0	4	89.7
Colorado	5	105.5	39	1,424.0	14	74.0	19	6.0	34	318.9
Connecticut	6	127.5	13	481.6	4	42.7	9	5.4	17	157.9
Delaware	2	96.3	2	216.6	3	42.3	16	5.9	16	155.8
District of Columbia	3	103.2	40	1,424.0	1	24.6	12	5.7	10	117.8
Florida	46	309.0	48	2,678.3	38	148.8	11	5.6	47	873.0
Georgia	41	279.5	49	2,934.5	43	177.8	47	9.9	48	978.4
Idaho	45	306.8	4	245.4	24	102.3	28	6.4	21	178.8
Illinois	31	223.3	14	487.5	33	131.6	46	9.3	19	166.2
Indiana	32	224.4	5	249.9	13	73.3	8	5.3	1	70.3
Iowa	4	105.5	6	258.5	30	114.9	5	4.9	11	129.5
Kansas	1	55.3	1	201.2	10	66.1	3	4.2	3	81.0
Kentucky	29	220.3	45	1,872.5	35	138.7	38	7.8	27	241.0
Louisiana	39	266.5	24	751.1	46	250.4	41	8.5	31	264.5
Maine	34	231.1	8	333.8	22	100.1	24	6.2	9	113.1
Maryland	13	153.5	16	508.9	37	144.3	25	6.3	8	110.4
Massachusetts	14	157.6	31	952.0	5	48.0	21	6.1	7	108.9
Michigan	23	200.5	29	840.7	19	91.8	14	5.8	5	96.8
Minnesota	25	207.8	20	635.0	11	66.8	34	6.8	36	321.9
Mississippi	38	261.4	42	1,742.7	44	180.3	31	6.5	44	629.0
Missouri	40	270.7	26	794.1	48	270.7	17	5.9	18	164.2
Montana	35	238.1	21	635.0	29	112.1	20	6.0	40	422.7
Nebraska	7	131.7	11	395.1	7	54.5	1	3.8	20	170.0
Nevada	30	223.0	12	446.0	18	89.2	42	8.6	—	—
New Hampshire	12	156.9	30	889.0	6	52.3	26	6.3	23	197.0
New Jersey	9	140.2	25	759.0	12	67.1	15	5.8	12	137.9
New Mexico	21	199.4	15	498.5	36	142.4	2	4.1	28	246.2
New York	16	168.0	47	2,481.2	8	54.9	32	6.7	22	195.8
North Carolina	19	197.8	27	824.2	15	82.4	35	7.1	37	363.2
North Dakota	15	160.3	10	384.6	23	101.2	22	6.1	25	121.3
Ohio	27	214.7	9	377.9	17	89.1	29	6.4	6	107.7
Oklahoma	17	183.7	23	717.9	34	138.5	27	6.3	24	206.2
Oregon	20	198.2	37	1,239.0	16	88.5	7	5.3	45	678.2
Pennsylvania	33	225.7	32	985.3	2	41.6	33	6.7	14	154.6
Rhode Island	10	142.3	34	1,138.0	20	92.3	23	6.1	33	293.3
South Carolina	43	291.1	36	1,222.6	32	127.4	44	8.8	41	447.3
South Dakota	24	200.5	17	534.6	9	57.3	39	7.9	13	146.0
Tennessee	28	218.5	22	638.7	41	159.7	49	10.9	29	246.3
Texas	22	199.4	43	1,794.4	49	299.0	43	8.7	26	231.4
Utah	37	260.6	7	325.7	31	118.5	4	4.8	15	155.5
Vermont	11	142.3	38	1,281.0	27	106.8	30	6.5	42	526.0
Virginia	42	285.5	19	618.6	39	150.4	37	7.6	35	321.6
Washington	26	212.3	35	1,202.8	40	153.6	6	5.2	38	384.3

State	Number of Patients to Physicians		Number of Patients to Psychologists		Number of Patients to Registered Nurses		Number of Patients to Attendants		Number of Patients to Social Workers	
	Position	Number	Position	Number	Position	Number	Position	Number	Position	Number
West Virginia	44	304.8	33	1,097.2	45	203.2	45	9.2	39	409.8
Wisconsin	47	442.0	46	2,147.0	25	104.3	36	7.2	30	251.8
Wyoming	49	652.0	3	217.3	21	93.1	48	10.5	2	78.6

ᵃ See Table 18 ᵃ.

Source: Joint Information Service, 1957. Fact Sheet No. 4.

Table 24—Number of Professional Mental Health Personnel Needed for Different Clinic-to-Population Ratios with Increasing Population

	ONE CLINIC PER 100,000			TWO CLINICS PER 100,000			FOUR CLINICS PER 100,000		
	Psy-chia-trists	Clinical Psy-cholo-gists	Psy-chiatric Social Workers or Others	Psy-chia-trists	Clinical Psy-cholo-gists	Psy-chiatric Social Workers or Others	Psy-chia-trists	Clinical Psy-cholo-gists	Psy-chiatric Social Workers or Others
1955 U.S. Popuation 165.2 Million									
Total Needed	1,652	1,652	3,304	3,304	3,304	6,608	6,608	6,608	13,216
Total Short (over present)	22	296	915	1,674	1,948	4,219	4,978	5,252	10,827
1960 U.S. Popuation 177.8 Million									
Total Needed	1,778	1,778	3,556	3,556	3,556	7,112	7,112	7,112	14,224
Total Short (over present)	148	422	1,167	1,926	2,200	4,723	5,482	5,756	11,835
1965 U.S. Popuation 190.3 Million									
Total Needed	1,903	1,903	3,806	3,806	3,806	7,612	7,612	7,612	15,224
Total Short (over present)	273	547	1,417	2,176	2,450	5,223	5,982	6,256	12,835

Source: Bahn, Anita K., and Norman, Vivian B., 1957. Outpatient psychiatric clinics in the United States, 1954–1955. Public Health Monograph No. 49. Government Printing Office. Adapted from data in this monograph.

Table 25—Total Professional Personnel Needed to Bring All States up to Ratio of One Clinic to Every 100,000 Population

	Number of Professional Man-Hours per Week per 100,000 Population	Number of Professional Man-Hours Needed to Bring Ratio to 140:100,000 Population	Total Professional Personnel Needed to Bring Ratio up to 140:100,000
Continental United States	116	39,432	1,127
District of Columbia	467	—	—
New York	340	—	—
Massachusetts	293	—	—
Kansas	191	—	—
Connecticut	170	—	—
Illinois	170	—	—
Delaware	167	—	—
Rhode Island	153	—	—
Utah	130	80	2
Colorado	127	208	6
Minnesota	122	576	16
California	121	2,470	70
New Hampshire	114	156	4
Maryland	114	702	20
Ohio	113	2,403	69
New Jersey	107	1,749	50
Florida	107	1,188	34
Louisiana	102	1,102	31
Vermont	91	196	6
Pennsylvania	88	5,668	162
Michigan	88	3,796	108
Virginia	79	2,196	63
Missouri	74	2,772	79
Nebraska	72	1,022	29
Iowa	64	2,052	59

	Number of Professional Man-Hours per Week per 100,000 Population	Number of Professional Man-Hours Needed to Bring Ratio to 140:100,000 Population	Total Professional Personnel Needed to Bring Ratio up to 140:100,000
Montana	64	456	13
Idaho	62	468	13
Indiana	59	3,402	97
Oregon	54	1,462	42
Washington	52	2,288	65
Wisconsin	51	3,293	94
Arizona	37	1,030	29
North Carolina	37	4,429	127
Texas	37	8,961	256
South Carolina	34	2,438	70
West Virginia	31	2,180	62
South Dakota	30	770	22
Maine	29	999	28
Oklahoma	28	2,464	70
Arkansas	24	2,088	60
Kentucky	21	3,570	102
Georgia	17	4,551	130
Tennessee	15	4,250	121
North Dakota	14	756	22
Mississippi	11	2,709	77
New Mexico	10	1,040	30
Wyoming	10	390	11
Alabama	9	4,061	116
Nevada	0	280	8
Total		86,675	2,473

Source: Bahn, Anita K., and Norman, Vivian B., 1957. Outpatient psychiatric clinics in the United States, 1954–1955. *Public Health Monograph* No. 49. Government Printing Office. Adapted from data in this monograph.

Table 26 ª—Position of States According to Professional Man-Hours in Out-Patient Clinics per Week per 100,000 Population, 1955

U.S. Average	116 hours
U.S. Median	64

1.	New York	340
2.	Massachusetts	293
3.	Kansas	191
4.	Connecticut	170
5.	Illinois	170
6.	Delaware	167
7.	Rhode Island	153
8.	Utah	130
9.	Colorado	127
10.	Minnesota	122
11.	California	121
12.	New Hampshire	114
13.	Maryland	114
14.	Ohio	113
15.	New Jersey	107
16.	Florida	107
17.	Louisiana	102
18.	Vermont	91
19.	Pennsylvania	88
20.	Michigan	88
21.	Virginia	79
22.	Missouri	74
23.	Nebraska	72
24.	Iowa	64
25.	Montana	64

[a] See Table 14 [a].

Source: Joint Information Service of the American Psychiatric Association and the National Association for Mental Health, 1957. Thirteen indices: an aid in reviewing State mental health and hospital programs.

Table 27—Summary of Number of Staff Employed and Additional Number Needed to Meet Minimum APA Standards in Public Hospitals for the Mentally Ill in Twelve Midwest States in 1956

State	PHYSICIANS			PSYCHOLOGISTS			SOCIAL WORKERS			GRADUATE NURSES			OTHER NURSES AND ATTENDANTS		
	Em-ployees	Additional Number Needed	Per Cent Met	Em-ployees	Additional Number Needed	Per Cent Met	Em-ployees	Additional Number Needed	Per Cent Met	Em-ployees	Additional Number Needed	Per Cent Met	Em-ployees	Additional Number Needed	Per Cent Met
Illinois	171	381	31.0	78	84	45.3	73	261	21.9	290	2,627	9.9	4,084	3,130	56.6
Indiana	49	113	30.3	44	5	89.8	62	34	64.6	150	704	17.6	2,063	50	97.6
Iowa	49	27	64.5	20	3	87.0	22	52	29.7	45	354	11.3	1,046	—	106.0
Kansas	80	—	123.1	22	—	110.0	31	16	66.0	67	276	19.5	1,046	—	123.2
Michigan	109	208	34.4	26	69	27.4	102	7	93.6	238	1,437	14.2	3,783	360	91.3
Minnesota	55	113	32.8	18	32	36.0	15	93	13.9	171	715	19.3	1,680	511	76.7
Missouri	44	131	25.1	15	38	28.3	17	30	36.2	44	880	4.8	2,014	270	88.2
Nebraska	36	33	52.3	12	9	57.1	16	27	37.2	87	279	23.8	1,242	—	137.2
North Dakota	12	16	42.9	5	4	55.6	6	17	26.1	19	130	12.8	316	53	85.6
Ohio	132	284	31.7	75	50	60.0	124	145	46.1	318	1,879	14.5	4,431	1,000	81.6
South Dakota	8	16	33.3	3	4	42.9	4	15	21.1	28	96	22.6	204	103	66.4
Wisconsin	34	187	15.4	7	59	10.6	20	104	16.1	144	1,021	12.4	2,097	785	72.8
Midwest Total	779	1,491	34.3	325	356	47.7	492	810	37.8	1,601	10,397	13.3	24,006	5,667	80.9
U.S. Total	3,007	5,134	36.9	723	1,719	29.6	1,436	3,111	31.6	7,185	35,836	16.7	84,377	22,018	79.3
Per Cent of U.S. Total in Midwest	25.9	29.4	—	45.0	20.7	—	34.3	26.0	—	22.3	29.0	—	28.5	25.7	—

Source: Council of State Governments, Interstate Clearing House on Mental Health, 1958. Selected tables on public hospitals for the mentally ill in twelve midwest states, 1953, 1956, 1957.

Table 28 ª—Cities over 500,000 Inhabitants, Number of Psychiatrists, and Ratio of Psychiatrists to City Population

City	Number of Psychiatrists	Population (in 10,000's)	Ratio (1:N)
New York City	1,302	789.2	6,100
Chicago	255	362.1	14,200
Philadelphia	221	207.2	9,400
Los Angeles	151	197.0	13,000
Detroit	118	185.0	15,700
Baltimore	155	95.0	6,100
Cleveland	82	91.5	11,200
St. Louis	71	85.7	12,100
Washington, D.C.	187	80.2	4,300
Boston	180	80.1	4,500
San Francisco	160	77.5	4,800
Pittsburgh	85	67.7	8,000
Milwaukee	37	63.7	17,200
Houston	36	59.6	16,600
Buffalo	33	58.0	17,600
New Orleans	66	57.0	8,600
Minneapolis	49	52.2	10,700
Cincinnati	63	50.4	8,000
Total	3,251	2,659.1	8,200

ª The reader is reminded that, unless otherwise indicated in the source, we have used urbanization data based on 1950 census publications. This means that we have underestimated urbanization in most cases.

Source: American Psychiatric Association, 1957. List of fellows and members, 1955–1956.
    Bureau of the Census, Census of Population, 1950. Government Printing Office.

Table 29—Psychoanalysts in the Ten Most Heavily Populated Cities

City	Number of Psychoanalysts
New York City	221
Chicago	57
Philadelphia	40
Los Angeles	60
Detroit	23
Baltimore	18
Cleveland	9
St. Louis	4
Washington, D.C.	46
Boston	53
Number of psychoanalysts in the United States	695
Number of psychoanalysts in ten largest cities	531
Per cent of all psychoanalysts in the ten largest cities	76.4

Source: American Psychoanalytic Association, 1957. Roster.

Table 30—Urbanization and the Distribution of Psychiatrists

Ten States with Most Urbanization	Number of Psychiatrists	Population (in 10,000's)	Ratio (1:N)	Number of Psychiatrists per 100,000
District of Columbia	209	86.6	4,100	24.1
New Jersey	262	540.3	20,600	4.8
New York	2,141	1,619.5	7,600	13.2
Massachusetts	504	481.2	9,500	10.5
Rhode Island	41	82.8	20,200	5.0
California	1,066	1,343.3	12,600	7.9
Connecticut	252	223.2	8,900	11.3
Illinois	459	943.2	20,500	4.9
Michigan	344	751.6	21,800	4.6
Pennsylvania	587	1,096.4	18,700	5.4
Total	5,865	7,168.1	12,200	8.2
Per Cent of Total	65.8	42.9		
Ten States with Least Urbanization				
North Dakota	9	65.7	73,000	1.4
Mississippi	31	212.4	68,500	1.5
Arkansas	59	181.5	30,800	3.3
South Dakota	11	69.6	63,300	1.6
North Carolina	118	442.3	37,500	2.7
West Virginia	30	198.3	66,100	1.5
Vermont	18	37.0	20,600	4.9
South Carolina	36	235.3	65,400	1.5
Kentucky	89	301.7	33,900	2.9
Idaho	11	62.5	56,800	1.8
Total	412	1,806.3	43,800	2.3
Per Cent of Total	4.6	10.8		

Source: U.S. Bureau of the Census, 1950. Census of the Population, Vol. II, Part 1. Government Printing Office.

American Psychiatric Association, 1957. List of fellows and members, 1956–1957.

Table 31—Urbanization and the Ratio of Psychiatrists to Population

Urbanization Rank	Number of Psychiatrists	Population (in 10,000's)	Ratio (1:N)	Number of Psychiatrists per 100,000	Rank in Psychiatrists to Population
1. District of Columbia	209	86.6	4,100	24.1	1
2. New Jersey	262	540.3	20,600	4.8	14
3. New York	2,141	1,619.5	7,600	13.2	2
4. Massachusetts	504	481.2	9,500	10.5	4
5. Rhode Island	41	82.8	20,200	5.0	11
6. California	1,066	1,343.3	12,600	7.9	6
7. Connecticut	252	223.2	8,900	11.3	3
8. Illinois	459	943.2	20,500	4.9	12
9. Michigan	344	751.6	21,800	4.6	16
10. Pennsylvania	587	1,096.4	18,700	5.4	9

Urbanization Rank	Number of Psychiatrists	Population (in 10,000's)	Ratio (1:N)	Number of Psychiatrists per 100,000	Rank in Psychiatrists to Population
11. Ohio	342	909.6	26,600	3.8	20
12. Maryland	290	281.2	9,700	10.3	5
13. Florida	132	377.0	28,600	3.5	24
14. Utah	39	81.2	20,800	4.8	15
15. Washington	112	266.7	23,800	4.2	17
16. Texas	230	892.5	38,800	2.6	34
17. Colorado	80	161.2	20,200	5.0	10
18. Delaware	25	40.2	16,100	6.2	8
19. Missouri	149	425.5	28,600	3.5	23
20. Indiana	110	441.3	40,100	2.5	35
21. Wisconsin	117	376.4	32,200	3.1	26
22. New Hampshire	20	56.0	28,000	3.6	22
23. Nevada	5	24.7	49,400	2.0	39
24. Arizona	29	105.7	36,400	2.7	31
25. Louisiana	93	300.4	32,300	3.1	27
26. Minnesota	123	324.1	26,300	3.8	18
27. Oregon	53	171.8	32,400	3.1	28
28. Kansas	140	210.3	15,000	6.7	7
29. Maine	24	91.0	37,900	2.6	33
30. Oklahoma	48	223.7	46,600	2.1	37
31. New Mexico	13	81.5	62,700	1.6	43
32. Wyoming	9	32.1	35,700	2.8	30
33. Iowa	64	269.2	42,100	2.4	36
34. Virginia	138	365.1	26,500	3.8	19
35. Nebraska	53	141.4	26,700	3.7	21
36. Georgia	76	371.2	48,800	2.0	38
37. Tennessee	63	346.6	55,000	1.8	40
38. Alabama	47	313.5	66,700	1.5	47
39. Montana	11	63.8	58,000	1.7	42
40. Idaho	11	62.5	56,800	1.8	41
41. Kentucky	89	301.7	33,900	2.9	29
42. South Carolina	36	235.3	65,400	1.5	45
43. Vermont	18	37.0	20,600	4.9	13
44. West Virginia	30	198.3	66,100	1.5	46
45. North Carolina	118	442.3	37,500	2.7	32
46. South Dakota	11	69.6	63,300	1.6	44
47. Arkansas	59	181.5	30,800	3.3	25
48. Mississippi	31	212.4	68,500	1.5	48
49. North Dakota	9	65.7	73,000	1.4	49

Rho = .77

Source: U.S. Bureau of the Census, 1950. Census of the Population, Vol. II, Part 1. Government Printing Office.
American Psychiatric Association, 1957. List of fellows and members, 1956–1957.

Table 32—State Population Rank and Number of Psychiatrists

State	Population Rank	Number of Psychiatrists	Rank in Number of Psychiatrists
Alabama	19	47	32
Arizona	35	29	38
Arkansas	31	59	28
California	2	1,066	2
Colorado	33	80	24
Connecticut	27	252	10
Delaware	46	25	39
District of Columbia	37	209	12
Florida	13	132	16
Georgia	15	76	25
Idaho	44	11	45
Illinois	4	459	5
Indiana	11	110	21
Iowa	23	64	26
Kansas	29	140	14
Kentucky	20	89	23
Louisiana	21	93	22
Maine	36	24	40
Maryland	22	290	8
Massachusetts	9	504	4
Michigan	7	344	6
Minnesota	18	123	17
Mississippi	28	31	36
Missouri	12	149	13
Montana	43	11	45
Nebraska	34	53	29.5
Nevada	49	5	49
New Hampshire	45	20	41
New Jersey	8	262	9
New Mexico	39	13	43
New York	1	2,141	1
North Carolina	10	118	18
North Dakota	42	9	47.5
Ohio	5	342	7
Oklahoma	26	48	31
Oregon	32	53	29.5
Pennsylvania	3	587	3
Rhode Island	38	41	33
South Carolina	25	36	35
South Dakota	41	11	45
Tennessee	17	63	27
Texas	6	230	11
Utah	40	39	34
Vermont	47	18	42
Virginia	16	138	15
Washington	24	112	20
West Virginia	30	30	37

State	Population Rank	Number of Psychiatrists	Rank in Number of Psychiatrists
Wisconsin	14	117	19
Wyoming	48	9	47.5

Rho = .87

Source: U.S. Bureau of the Census, 1956. Provisional estimates of the total and civilian population of the states and of selected outlying areas of the United States, July, 1956. *Current Population Reports, Population Estimates,* Series T-25, No. 148, November.
American Psychiatric Association, 1957. List of fellows and members, 1956–1957.

Table 33—Urbanization of States as Related to Patient Population, Patient Load, First Admissions, Per Capita Maintenance, and Full-Time Personnel in Public Mental Institutions

States	1956 Average Daily Resident Patient Population Public Mental Hospitals	Average Daily Resident Rate per 100,000	1956 First Admissions Public Mental Hospitals	Average First Admission Rate per 100,000	Total Full Time Personnel end of 1956	1956 Ratio of Patients per Full-Time Employee	Daily 1956 Per Capita Maintenance Expenditure
Ten Most Urbanized							
District of Columbia	7,120	845	1,055	125	2,734	2.6	$5.51
New Jersey	22,013	411	5,519	103	7,474	2.9	3.89
New York	96,768	599	16,108	100	25,674	3.8	3.44
Massachusetts	22,849	479	6,044	127	7,093	3.2	3.83
Rhode Island	3,414	429	952	120	844	4.0	2.65
California	37,002	283	12,354	94	10,081	3.7	3.81
Connecticut	8,668	390	2,333	105	3,178	2.7	4.74
Illinois	38,176	407	8,465	90	8,983	4.2	2.95
Michigan	21,860	291	3,333	44	6,584	3.3	4.33
Pennsylvania	40,405	369	5,119	47	11,275	3.6	3.06
U.S. Averages	556,276	337	126,510	77	152,439	3.6	3.26
Ten Least Urbanized							
North Dakota	1,923	293	635	97	518	3.7	$2.89
Mississippi	5,228	248	1,749	83	1,409	3.7	2.04
Arkansas	4,957	276	1,400	78	1,368	3.6	2.60
South Dakota	1,604	233	508	74	451	3.6	3.24
North Carolina	9,890	228	2,341	54	2,825	3.5	2.93
West Virginia	5,486	277	1,877	95	1,045	5.2	1.90
Vermont	1,281	347	387	105	337	3.8	3.24
South Carolina	6,113	265	1,781	77	1,381	4.4	2.24
Kentucky	7,490	251	1,482	50	1,610	4.7	2.07
Idaho	1,227	198	652	105	339	3.6	3.18

Source: Calculated from a variety of sources including data supplied by the Biometrics Branch, National Institute of Mental Health; and the Interstate Clearing House on Mental Health, Council of State Governments.

Table 34—First Admission Rates, Per Capita Income, and Number of Years of School Completed by Persons Twenty-Five Years Old and Over, for Ten Most Urbanized and Ten Least Urbanized States

States	Public Mental Hospital First Admission Rate per 100,000	Rank Per Capita Income	Median Years Schooling
Ten Most Urbanized			
District of Columbia	118.9	4.5	12.0
New Jersey	96.2	4.5	9.3
New York	104.5	7	9.6
Massachusetts	106.6	13	10.9
Rhode Island	107.6	15	9.3
California	99.9	7	11.6
Connecticut	105.0	3	9.8
Illinois	94.3	7	9.3
Michigan	40.9	9	9.9
Pennsylvania	52.1	16.5	9.0
Ten Least Urbanized			
North Dakota	85.4	44.5	8.7
Mississippi	91.6	49	8.1
Arkansas	83.1	48	8.3
South Dakota	65.3	38	8.9
North Carolina	61.4	44.5	7.9
West Virginia	79.2	40.5	8.5
Vermont	91.4	36	10.0
South Carolina	75.6	47	7.6
Kentucky	54.0	42	8.4
Idaho	112.6	35	11.0

Source: Calculated from a variety of sources including data supplied by the Bureau of the Census, the Council of State Governments, the National Institute of Mental Health, and the Office of Business Economics of the U.S. Department of Commerce.

Table 35—American Psychiatric Association Membership Growth

Year	Membership Total	Per Cent of Increase
1946	4,010	—
1947	4,341	8.3
1948	4,678	7.8
1949	5,276	12.8
1950	5,856	11.0
1951	6,481	10.7
1952	7,125	9.9
1953	7,608	6.8
1954	8,347	9.7
1955	8,534	2.2
1956	9,295	8.9

Source: American Psychiatric Association, 1957. List of fellows and members of the American Psychiatric Association, 1956–1957.

Table 36—Yearly Totals Certified by the American Board of Psychiatry and Neurology

NUMBER CERTIFIED IN:

Year	Neurology	Psychiatry	Psychiatry and Neurology
1935	9	49	34
1936	8	49	46
1937	18	67	58
1938	15	57	73
1939	18	109	76
1940	9	114	72
1941	19	106	53
1942	29	170	88
1943	26	115	38
1944	17	112	44
1945	5	77	34
1946	18	370	67
1947	16	338	34
1948	19	250	16
1949	36	318	12
1950	23	329	16
1951	17	316	10
1952	24	267	17
1953	13	275	12
1954	13	264	8
1955	33	353	4
1956	23	251	5

Source: Data supplied by the American Board of Psychiatry and Neurology.

Table 37—Number of Psychiatrists Compared to Population by Regions, States, and Outlying Areas of the United States

	Population (In 10,000's)	Number of Psychiatrists	Ratio of Psychiatrists to Population	Number of Psychiatrists per 100,000
Continental U.S.	16,719.1	8,912	18,800	5.3
Regions:				
Northeast	4,227.3	3,849	11,000	9.1
North Central	4,927.8	1,921	25,700	3.9
South (minus D.C.)	5,082.8	1,505	34,000	3.0
West	2,394.5	1,428	16,800	6.0
Northeast:				
New England	971.1	859	11,300	8.8
Middle Atlantic	3,256.2	2,990	10,900	9.2
North Central:				
East North Central	3,422.1	1,372	24,900	4.0
West North Central	1,505.7	549	27,400	3.6
District of Columbia	86.6	209	4,100	24.1
South (minus D.C.):				
South Atlantic	2,310.6	845	27,300	3.7
East South Central	1,174.3	230	51,100	2.0
West South Central	1,598.0	430	37,200	2.7
West:				
Mountain	612.7	197	31,100	3.2
Pacific	1,781.8	1,231	14,500	6.9
New England:				
Maine	91.0	24	37,900	2.6
New Hampshire	56.0	20	28,000	3.6
Vermont	37.0	18	20,600	4.9
Massachusetts	481.2	504	9,500	10.5
Rhode Island	82.8	41	20,200	5.0
Connecticut	223.2	252	8,900	11.3
Middle Atlantic:				
New York	1,619.5	2,141	7,600	13.2
New Jersey	540.3	262	20,600	4.8
Pennsylvania	1,096.4	587	18,700	5.4
East North Central:				
Ohio	909.6	342	26,600	3.8
Indiana	441.3	110	40,100	2.5
Illinois	943.2	459	20,500	4.9
Michigan	751.6	344	21,800	4.6
Wisconsin	376.4	117	32,200	3.1
West North Central:				
Minnesota	324.1	123	26,300	3.8
Iowa	269.2	64	42,100	2.4
Missouri	425.5	149	28,600	3.5
North Dakota	65.7	9	73,000	1.4
South Dakota	69.6	11	63,300	1.6
Nebraska	141.4	53	26,700	3.7
Kansas	210.3	140	15,000	6.7

	Population (In 10,000's)	Number of Psychiatrists	Ratio of Psychiatrists to Population	Number of Psychiatrists per 100,000
South Atlantic:				
Delaware	40.2	25	16,100	6.2
Maryland	281.2	290	9,700	10.3
Virginia	365.1	138	26,500	3.8
West Virginia	198.3	30	66,100	1.5
North Carolina	442.3	118	37,500	2.7
South Carolina	235.3	36	65,400	1.5
Georgia	371.2	76	48,800	2.0
Florida	377.0	132	28,600	3.5
East South Central:				
Kentucky	301.7	89	33,900	2.9
Tennessee	346.6	63	55,000	1.8
Alabama	313.5	47	66,700	1.5
Mississippi	212.4	31	68,500	1.5
West South Central:				
Arkansas	181.5	59	30,800	3.3
Louisiana	300.4	93	32,300	3.1
Oklahoma	223.7	48	46,600	2.1
Texas	892.5	230	38,800	2.6
Mountain:				
Montana	63.8	11	58,000	1.7
Idaho	62.5	11	56,800	1.8
Wyoming	32.1	9	35,700	2.8
Colorado	161.2	80	20,200	5.0
New Mexico	81.5	13	62,700	1.6
Arizona	105.7	29	36,400	2.7
Utah	81.2	39	20,800	4.8
Nevada	24.7	5	49,400	2.0
Pacific:				
Washington	266.7	112	23,800	4.2
Oregon	171.8	53	32,400	3.1
California	1,343.3	1,066	12,600	7.9
Outlying Areas:				
Alaska	20.9	1	209,000	0.5
Hawaii	56.0	19	29,500	3.4
Puerto Rico	226.3	21	107,800	0.9
Canal Zone	5.3	3	17,700	5.7
Virgin Islands	2.4	0	—	0.0

Source: American Psychiatric Association, 1957. List of fellows and members of the American Psychiatric Association, 1956–1957.

U.S. Bureau of the Census, 1956. *Current Population Reports, Population Estimates,* Series T-25, No. 148, November.

Table 38—Psychiatric Residencies Filled Compared with Total Residencies Filled

Year	Total First-Year Residencies Filled	Total First-Year Psychiatric Residencies Filled	Per Cent of First-Year Residencies Filled in Psychiatry
1950	—	—	—
1951	—	—	—
1952	6,376	495	7.8
1953	7,777	833	10.7
1954	7,965	649	8.1
1955	8,644	705	8.2
1956	9,005	759	8.4
1957	9,458	857	9.1

Year	Total, All Residencies Filled	Total Residencies Filled in Psychiatry	Per Cent of All Residencies Filled that are in Psychiatry
1950	17,490	1,410	8.1
1951	14,495	1,234	8.5
1952	15,851	1,370	8.6
1953	16,867	1,784	10.6
1954	18,617	1,632	8.8
1955	20,494	1,800	8.8
1956	21,425	1,950	9.1
1957	23,012	2,166	9.4

Source: Journal of the American Medical Association, Annual internship and residency number.

Table 39 [a]—Actual and Estimated Number of Medical School Graduates and Number of First-Year Residents in Psychiatry in the Fall of the Same Year

Year	Graduates of Medical School	First-Year Residents in Psychiatry	Per Cent of Medical School Graduates in First-Year Residencies in Psychiatry
1947	6,389	—	—
1948	5,543	—	—
1949	5,094	—	—
1950	5,553	—	—
1951	6,135	—	—
1952	6,080	495	8.1
1953	6,688	833	12.5
1954	6,861	649	9.5
1955	6,977	705	10.1
1956	6,845	759	11.1
1957	6,850	706	10.3 [b]
1958	6,970	718	10.3
1959	7,120	733	10.3
1960	7,290	751	10.3

Year	Graduates of Medical School	First-Year Residents in Psychiatry	Per Cent of Medical School Graduates in First-Year Residencies in Psychiatry
1961	7,290	751	10.3
1962	7,290	751	10.3
1963	7,335	756	10.3
1964	7,360	758	10.3
1965	7,410	763	10.3

Source: *Journal of the American Medical Association,* 1956. List of number of medical school graduates, p. 1653, August 25.

[a] Our estimate of the number of medical school graduates from 1957 on is based on present enrollments in freshmen classes, on an eight per cent attrition rate, and on newly established medical schools.

[b] Five year average.

Table 40—Percentage of Available Residencies Filled in All Medical Specialties Compared with the Percentage of Available Residencies Filled in Psychiatry

Year	Per Cent of Available Residencies Filled in All Fields	Per Cent of Available Residencies Filled in Psychiatry
1950	94	84
1951	75	70
1952	77	71
1953	76	73
1954	79	70
1955	80	72
1956	81	72
1957	81	73

Source: *Journal of the American Medical Association,* Annual internship and residency number.

Table 41—Residencies in Psychiatry

	FIRST YEAR				TOTAL			
	Offered	Vacant	Filled	Per Cent Filled	Offered	Vacant	Filled	Per Cent Filled
1943	—	—	—	—	548	—	—	—
1945	—	—	—	—	742	—	—	—
1948	—	—	—	—	1,618	—	—	—
1949	—	—	—	—	1,595	—	—	—
1950	—	—	—	—	1,754	344	1,410	80
1951	—	—	—	—	1,768	534	1,234	70
1952	801	306	495	62	1,936	566	1,370	71
1953	1,133	300	833	74	2,456	672	1,784	73
1954	985	336	649	66	2,335	703	1,632	70
1955	1,028	323	705	69	2,506	706	1,800	72
1956	1,092	333	759	70	2,696	746	1,950	72
1957	1,220	363	857	70	2,968	802	2,166	73
1958								
1959								
1960								

Source: Journal of the American Medical Association, Annual internship and residency number.

Table 42—Psychiatric Residencies and Other Residencies Offered and Filled by U.S. Citizens

	PSYCHIATRY					ALL SPECIALTIES EXCLUDING PSYCHIATRY				
	Total Residencies Offered	Total Residencies Filled		Total Residencies Filled by U.S. Citizens		Total Residencies Offered	Total Residencies Filled		Total Residencies Filled by U.S. Citizens	
Year		Number	Per Cent	Number	Per Cent		Number	Per Cent	Number	Per Cent
1949–50	1,754	1,410	80	—	—	16,915	16,080	95.1	—	—
1950–51	1,768	1,234	70	1,115	90.4	17,596	13,261	75.4	12,030	90.7
1951–52	1,936	1,370	71	1,176	85.8	18,709	14,481	77.4	12,442	85.9
1952–53	2,456	1,784	73	1,552	87.0	19,836	15,083	76.0	12,280	81.4
1953–54	2,335	1,632	70	1,328	81.4	21,293	16,985	79.8	13,487	79.4
1954–55	2,506	1,800	72	1,411	78.4	22,980	18,694	81.3	14,379	76.9
1955–56	2,696	1,950	72	1,477	75.7	23,820	19,475	81.8	14,368	73.8
1956–57	2,968	2,166	73	1,657	76.5	25,560	20,846	81.6	14,586	70.0

Source: Journal of the American Medical Association, Annual internship and residency number. Health Resources Advisory Committee, unpublished data.

Table 43 ª—Per Cent of All Residencies Filled by Foreign Citizens by Year

Year	Total Residencies Offered in All Specialties	Total Residencies Filled in All Specialties	Total Residencies Filled by Foreign Citizens	
			Number	Per Cent
1950	18,669	17,490	—	—
1951	19,364	14,495	1,350	9.3
1952	20,645	15,851	2,233	14.1
1953	22,292	16,867	3,035	18.0
1954	23,628	18,617	3,802	20.4
1955	25,486	20,494	4,704	23.0
1956	26,516	21,425	5,580	26.0
1957	28,528	23,012	6,769	29.4
1958				
1959				
1960				

ª There are minor differences in available estimates in the number of foreign medical residents in various medical specialties in this country. We have obtained estimates from the Health Resources Advisory Committee, from the Institute of International Education, and from published studies in the various journals referred to. Minor discrepancies between tables are due to the use of these different sources.

Source: Journal of the American Medical Association, Annual residency issues.
Health Resources Advisory Committee, unpublished data.

Table 44 ª—Per Cent of Residencies in Psychiatry Filled by Foreign Citizens by Year

Year	Total Residencies Filled in Psychiatry	Psychiatric Residencies Filled by Foreign Citizens	Per Cent of Psychiatric Residencies Filled by Foreign Citizens
1951	1,234	119	9.6
1952	1,370	194	14.2
1953	1,784	232	13.0
1954	1,632	304	18.6
1955	1,800	389	21.6
1956	1,950	473	24.3
1957	2,166		
1958			
1959			
1960			

ª See Table 43 ª.

Source: Journal of the American Medical Association, Annual residency issues.
Health Resources Advisory Committee, unpublished data.

Table 45 ᵃ—Distribution of Alien House Staff Physicians (Interns and Residents) by Geographic Region of the United States, 1955–56

	Total House Staff	Alien Staff	Per Cent Alien Staff
Continental U.S.	29,761	7,819	28
Regions:			
Northeast	11,165	3,664	33
North Central	9,012	2,443	27
South (minus D.C.)	5,631	1,089	19
West	3,412	453	13
Northeast:			
New England	2,529	731	29
Middle Atlantic	8,636	2,933	34
North Central:			
East North Central	6,200	1,771	29
West North Central	2,812	672	24
District of Columbia	541	170	31.4
South (minus D.C.):			
South Atlantic	2,739	662	24
East South Central	1,027	184	18
West South Central	1,865	243	13
West:			
Mountain	664	148	22
Pacific	2,748	305	11

ᵃ See Table 43 ᵃ.

Source: Diehl, H. S., Crosby, E. L., and Kaetzel, T. A., 1957. Hospital house staff, 1950–55. J.A.M.A., *164* (no. 3): 273.

Table 46 ᵃ—Alien Physicians Training in AMA-Approved Programs in Hospitals in the United States and Territories (Excluding Department of Defense and Public Health Service Hospitals) as a Per Cent of Total House Staffs (1955–56 Training Year)

State and Territory	RESIDENT HOUSE STAFF			TOTAL HOUSE STAFF		
	Total Staff	Alien Staff	Per Cent	Total Staff	Alien Staff	Per Cent
TOTAL	21,213	5,580	26.3	29,993	7,873	26.2
New England	1,935	562	29.0	2,529	731	28.9
Connecticut	452	147	32.5	631	202	32.0
Maine	22	3	13.6	44	8	18.2
Massachusetts	1,288	358	27.8	1,624	460	28.3
New Hampshire	25	3	12.0	37	3	8.1
Rhode Island	92	37	40.2	126	44	34.9
Vermont	56	14	25.0	67	14	20.9
Central Atlantic	7,326	2,525	34.5	10,203	3,495	34.3
Delaware	68	22	32.4	93	24	25.8
Dist. of Columbia	399	128	32.1	541	170	31.4

State and Territory	RESIDENT HOUSE STAFF			TOTAL HOUSE STAFF		
	Total Staff	Alien Staff	Per Cent	Total Staff	Alien Staff	Per Cent
Maryland	593	228	38.4	809	293	36.2
New Jersey	396	240	60.6	769	523	68.0
New York	4,310	1,479	34.3	5,770	2,005	34.7
Pennsylvania	1,489	387	26.0	2,097	405	19.3
West Virginia	71	41	57.7	124	75	60.5
South East	2,423	328	13.5	3,528	490	13.9
Alabama	149	9	6.0	224	14	6.3
Arkansas	70	7	10.0	108	9	8.3
Florida	198	45	22.7	314	76	24.2
Georgia	293	36	12.3	408	52	12.7
Kentucky	183	44	24.0	256	76	29.7
Louisiana	462	7	1.5	680	27	4.0
Mississippi	7	1	14.3	10	1	10.0
North Carolina	298	40	13.4	403	44	10.9
South Carolina	67	7	10.4	135	8	5.9
Tennessee	381	66	17.3	537	93	17.3
Virginia	315	66	21.0	453	90	19.9
South West	797	190	23.8	1,184	251	21.2
Arizona	36	20	55.6	89	44	49.4
New Mexico	18	0	—	18	0	—
Oklahoma	120	12	10.0	188	19	10.1
Texas	623	158	25.4	889	188	21.1
East North Central	4,214	1,199	28.5	6,200	1,771	28.6
Illinois	1,237	428	34.6	1,915	710	37.1
Indiana	223	13	5.8	316	14	4.4
Michigan	1,125	240	21.3	1,557	293	18.8
Ohio	1,327	485	36.5	1,957	682	34.8
Wisconsin	302	33	10.9	455	72	15.8
West North Central	2,140	488	22.8	2,812	672	23.9
Iowa	214	40	18.7	277	54	19.5
Kansas	238	49	20.6	304	59	19.4
Minnesota	896	179	20.0	1,079	215	19.9
Missouri	706	213	30.2	1,004	315	31.4
Nebraska	78	5	6.4	110	7	6.4
North Dakota	4	2	50.0	19	9	47.4
South Dakota	4	0	—	19	13	68.4
Rocky Mountain	396	74	18.7	557	104	18.7
Colorado	287	56	19.5	395	72	18.2
Montana	5	5	100.0	9	9	100.0
Utah	104	13	12.5	153	23	15.0
Far West	1,865	178	9.5	2,748	305	11.1
California	1,566	135	8.6	2,265	233	10.3
Oregon	149	15	10.1	213	26	12.2
Washington	150	28	18.7	270	46	17.0
Territories	117	36	30.8	232	54	23.3
Canal Zone	17	5	29.4	35	6	17.1
Hawaii	45	26	57.8	73	42	57.5
Puerto Rico	55	5	9.1	124	6	4.8

ᵃ See Table 43 ᵃ.

Source: Diehl, H. S., Crosby, E. L., and Kaetzel, T. A., 1957. Hospitals, 31 (Jan. 16): 39.

Table 47—American Psychoanalytic Association Membership Growth

Year	Number
1945	247
1946	273
1947	—
1948	—
1949	343
1950	365
1951	410
1952	448
1953	485
1954	511
1955	584
1956	603
1957	632
1958	702

Source: Knight, R. P., 1953. The present status of organized psychoanalysis in the United States. J. Am. Psychoan. Assoc., 1 (no. 2): 197.
McVeigh, J., 1957. Personal communication, June 17.

Table 48—Distribution of Members of American Psychoanalytic Association and Number of Persons per Psychoanalyst by Region and State

	Number of Psychoanalysts	Number of Persons in U.S. Population to Each Analyst
Continental U.S.	695	241,000
Regions:		
Northeast	381	111,000
North Central	117	421,000
South (minus D.C.)	58	876,000
West	110	218,000
Northeast:		
New England	80	121,000
Middle Atlantic	301	108,000
North Central:		
East North Central	102	336,000
West North Central	15	1,004,000
District of Columbia	29	30,000
South (minus D.C.):		
South Atlantic	42	550,000
East South Central	2	5,872,000
West South Central	14	1,141,000
West:		
Mountain	5	1,225,000
Pacific	105	170,000
New England:		
Maine	0	—

	Number of Psychoanalysts	Number of Persons in U.S. Population to Each Analyst
New Hampshire	0	—
Vermont	1	370,000
Massachusetts	63	76,000
Rhode Island	0	—
Connecticut	16	140,000
Middle Atlantic:		
New York	243	67,000
New Jersey	8	675,000
Pennsylvania	50	219,000
East North Central:		
Ohio	13	700,000
Indiana	0	—
Illinois	57	165,000
Michigan	28	268,000
Wisconsin	4	941,000
West North Central:		
Minnesota	2	1,621,000
Iowa	0	—
Missouri	6	709,000
North Dakota	0	—
South Dakota	0	—
Nebraska	0	—
Kansas	7	300,000
South Atlantic:		
Delaware	0	—
Maryland	34	83,000
Virginia	2	1,826,000
West Virginia	0	—
North Carolina	4	1,106,000
South Carolina	0	—
Georgia	1	3,712,000
Florida	1	3,770,000
East South Central:		
Kentucky	1	3,017,000
Tennessee	0	—
Alabama	1	3,135,000
Mississippi	0	—
West South Central:		
Arkansas	0	—
Louisiana	8	376,000
Oklahoma	1	2,237,000
Texas	5	1,785,000
Mountain:		
Montana	0	—
Idaho	0	—
Wyoming	0	—
Colorado	4	430,000
New Mexico	0	—
Arizona	1	1,057,000
Utah	0	—
Nevada	0	—

	Number of Psychoanalysts	Number of Persons in U.S. Population to Each Analyst
Pacific:		
Washington	8	333,000
Oregon	1	1,718,000
California	96	140,000

Source: American Psychoanalytic Association, 1957. Roster, 1956–57.
Bureau of the Census, 1957. Population Estimates.

Table 49—Undergraduate Grade Averages of First-Year Medical Students

	PER CENT		
	A	B	C
1950–51	40	43	17
1951–52	30	55	15
1952–53	18	68	14
1953–54	21	69	10
1954–55	17	69	14
1955–56	16	71	14

Source: Journal of the American Medical Association, 1956. 161: 1659.

Table 50—Percentage of All College Graduates Who Entered Practice of Medicine, 1800–1955

1801–1820	28
1821–1840	35
1841–1860	28
1861–1880	28
1881–1900	21
1901–1905	19
1906–1910	14
1911–1915	10
1916–1920	7
1921–1925	5
1926–1930	4
1931–1935	4
1936–1940	3
1941–1945	3
1946–1950	2
1951–1955	2

Source: Wolfle, D., 1954. America's Resources of Specialized Talent. Harper.

Table 51 ª—First-Level Degrees, Medical School Applicants and Admissions, and Per Cent Applying to Medical Schools

Year	First-Level Degrees Awarded	Number of Applicants to Medical School	Number Admitted	Per Cent	Per Cent of College Graduates Applying
1947	—	18,829	6,487	35	—
1948	272,311	24,242	6,688	28	8.9
1949	366,698	24,434	7,042	29	6.7
1950	433,734	22,279	7,177	32	5.1
1951	384,352	19,920	7,436	37	5.2
1952	331,924	16,763	7,425	44	5.1
1953	304,857	14,678	7,449	51	4.8
1954	292,880	14,538	7,576	52	5.0
1955	285,138	14,937	7,742	52	5.5
1956	311,298	15,918	7,824	43	5.1
1957	347,000	17,697	—	—	5.1
1958	392,000	19,992	—	—	5.1
1959	421,000	21,471	—	—	5.1
1960	437,000	22,287	—	—	5.1
1961	450,000	22,950	—	—	5.1
1962	459,000	23,409	—	—	5.1
1963	478,000	24,378	—	—	5.1
1964	515,000	26,262	—	—	5.1
1965	567,000	28,917	—	—	5.1
1966	576,000	29,376	—	—	5.1
1967	576,000	29,376	—	—	5.1
1968	605,000	30,855	—	—	5.1
1969	728,000	37,128	—	—	5.1
1970	766,000	39,066	—	—	5.1

ª The estimates from 1957 on are based on the assumption that 5.1 per cent of all first-level degree recipients will apply to medical school (this is the rate for the period 1950–1955). Note that the applicants listed for 1948 have been referred to in other tables, as applicants in 1948–1949. They are presented as they are here to make comparisons between first-degrees awarded and number of applications that same year.

Source: U.S. Department of Health, Education, and Welfare, Office of Education, yearly. Earned degrees conferred by higher educational institutions. Government Printing Office.
   U.S. Department of Health, Education, and Welfare, Office of Education, 1957. Degree estimates dated February 19.
   Stalnaker, J. M., 1955. The study of applicants, 1954–1955. J. Med. Educ., 30: 625.
   Gee, Helen H., 1956. The study of applicants, 1955–1956. J. Med. Educ., 31 (no. 12): 863.
   Committee on Interstate and Foreign Commerce, House of Representatives, Eighty-fifth Congress, 1957. Staff Report. Medical School Inquiry. Government Printing Office.

Table 52—American Psychological Association Membership Increase

Year	Total Membership	Per Cent of Increase
1945	4,183	—
1946	4,471	6.9
1947	5,090	13.8
1948	5,754	13.0
1949	6,735	17.0
1950	7,273	8.0
1951	8,554	17.6
1952	9,871	15.4
1953	10,903	10.5
1954	12,270	12.5
1955	13,475	9.8
1956	14,700	9.1
1957	15,545	5.7
1958	16,644	7.1
1959		
1960		

Source: Hoch, E. L., 1958. Personal communication, June 1.

Table 53—Number of Psychologists Compared to Population by Regions and States of the United States

	Population (in 10,000's)	Number of Psychologists	Ratio of Psychologists to Population	Number of Psychologists per 100,000
Continental U.S.	16,719.1	14,794	11,300	8.8
Regions				
Northeast	4,227.3	5,474	7,700	12.9
North Central	4,927.8	3,890	12,700	7.9
South (minus D.C.)	5,082.8	2,553	19,900	5.0
West	2,394.5	2,570	9,300	10.7
Northeast				
New England	971.1	1,192	8,100	12.3
Middle Atlantic	3,256.2	4,282	7,600	13.2
North Central				
East North Central	3,422.1	2,854	12,000	8.3
West North Central	1,505.7	1,036	14,500	6.9
District of Columbia				
Dist. Columbia	86.6	307	2,800	35.5
South (minus D.C.)				
South Atlantic	2,310.6	1,427	16,200	6.2
East South Central	1,174.3	394	29,800	3.4
West South Central	1,598.0	732	21,800	4.6
West				
Mountain	612.7	451	13,600	7.4
Pacific	1,781.8	2,119	8,400	11.9
New England				
Maine	91.0	41	22,200	4.6
New Hampshire	56.0	39	14,400	7.0
Vermont	37.0	31	11,900	8.4
Massachusetts	481.2	645	7,500	13.4
Rhode Island	82.8	56	14,800	6.8
Connecticut	223.2	380	5,900	17.0

	Population (in 10,000's)	Number of Psychologists	Ratio of Psychologists to Population	Number of Psychologists per 100,000
Middle Atlantic				
New York	1,619.5	2,850	5,700	17.6
New Jersey	540.3	542	10,000	10.0
Pennsylvania	1,096.4	890	12,300	8.1
East North Central				
Ohio	909.6	779	11,700	8.6
Indiana	441.3	284	15,500	6.4
Illinois	943.2	951	9,900	10.1
Michigan	751.6	610	12,300	8.1
Wisconsin	376.4	230	16,400	6.1
West North Central				
Minnesota	324.1	306	10,600	9.4
Iowa	269.2	158	17,000	5.9
Missouri	425.5	237	18,000	5.6
North Dakota	65.7	22	29,900	3.3
South Dakota	69.6	17	40,900	2.4
Nebraska	141.4	78	18,100	5.5
Kansas	210.3	218	9,600	10.4
District of Columbia	86.6	307	2,800	35.5
South Atlantic				
Delaware	40.2	51	7,900	12.7
Maryland	281.2	383	7,300	13.6
Virginia	365.1	310	11,800	8.5
West Virginia	198.3	49	40,500	2.5
North Carolina	442.3	171	25,900	3.9
South Carolina	235.3	40	58,800	1.7
Georgia	371.2	134	27,700	3.6
Florida	377.0	289	13,000	7.7
East South Central				
Kentucky	301.7	112	26,900	3.7
Tennessee	346.6	158	21,900	4.6
Alabama	313.5	86	36,500	2.7
Mississippi	212.4	38	55,900	1.8
West South Central				
Arkansas	181.5	45	40,300	2.5
Louisiana	300.4	100	30,000	3.3
Oklahoma	223.7	99	22,600	4.4
Texas	892.5	488	18,300	5.5
Mountain				
Montana	63.8	24	26,600	3.8
Idaho	62.5	20	31,200	3.2
Wyoming	32.1	16	20,100	5.0
Colorado	161.2	198	8,100	12.3
New Mexico	81.5	39	20,900	4.8
Arizona	105.7	63	16,800	6.0
Utah	81.2	72	11,300	8.9
Nevada	24.7	19	13,000	7.7
Pacific				
Washington	266.7	169	15,800	6.3
Oregon	171.8	109	15,800	6.3
California	1,343.3	1,841	7,300	13.7

Source: Amrine, M., 1957. Personal communication, May 1.
   Bureau of the Census, 1956. *Current Population Reports, Population Estimates,* Series T-25, No. 148, November.

Table 54—Place of Employment for Psychologists in National Scientific Register, 1954

Type of Employer	Number	Percentage
College or University	5,120	40
Other Educational Institutions	1,183	9
International Agencies	4	—
Federal Government and Armed Forces	2,136	17
State and Local Government	1,531	12
Nonprofit Foundations, Private Hospitals and Clinics	787	6
Other Nonprofit Organizations	434	3
Self-Employed	466	4
Private Industry-Employee	864	7
No Data	300	2
Total	12,825	

Source: Hoch, E. L., 1957. Personal communication supplying data based on studies by National Scientific Register, April 1.

Table 55 [a]—Sex, Level of Education, and Specialty of Psychologists in the National Scientific Register, 1954

Specialty	SEX PERCENTAGE		DEGREE				
	Male	Female	Less than M.A.	M.A. or M.S.	Ph.D.	Total	Percentage
Psychology (nonspecialized)	69	31	18	120	50	188	1
Clinical	69	31	265	2,368	2,095	4,728	37
Counseling	80	20	43	867	739	1,649	13
Developmental	45	55	6	156	269	431	3
Educational	73	27	10	415	643	1,069	8
School	43	57	8	241	72	321	3
Experimental Comparative Physiological	87	13	31	321	871	1,226	10
Human Engineering	95	5	8	85	83	176	1
General	79	21	2	29	67	98	1
Industrial	93	7	17	157	164	338	3
Personnel	92	8	35	506	403	944	7
Personality	83	17	4	124	268	396	3
Quantitative	84	16	18	176	262	456	4
Social	86	14	19	178	416	613	5
Nonpsychological	78	22	6	49	137	192	1
Total	76	24	490	5,792	6,539	12,825	

[a] Totals do not check because of four nonrespondents for degree level. Fourteen per cent are non-APA members.

Source: Hoch, E. L., 1957. Personal communication supplying data based on studies by National Scientific Register, April 1.

Table 56—Estimates of Trends in First-Level Degrees from Various Sources

ESTIMATES

Year	Actual First Level Degrees Awarded	U.S. Office of Education	Wolfle	National Science Foundation	Goodrich	Fund for the Advancement of Education	
1944	125,863						
1946	136,174						
1948	272,311						
1949	366,698						
1950	433,734			434,000			
1951	384,352			384,000			
1952	331,924			331,000			
1953	304,857			305,000			
1954	292,880		286,000	293,000			
1955	285,138		272,000	254,000	287,401	264,000	289,100
1956	311,298		283,000	290,000	286,200	303,000	293,600
1957		347,000	288,000	308,000	292,800	321,000	313,800
1958		392,000	292,000	311,000	304,300	324,000	324,500
1959		421,000	307,000	312,000	317,800	325,000	333,000
1960		437,000	326,000	326,000	329,000	340,000	355,000
1961		450,000	329,000	332,000	342,400	346,000	369,800
1962		459,000	350,000	332,000	361,200	346,000	377,200
1963		478,000	378,000	346,000	388,800	360,000	402,800
1964		515,000	427,000	371,000	410,900	387,000	439,700
1965		567,000	454,000	424,000	433,000	442,000	512,600
1966		576,000	439,000		453,300	418,000	494,400
1967		576,000	437,000		503,900	415,000	501,200
1968		605,000	532,000		534,200	420,000	517,400
1969		728,000	608,000		571,100	580,000	726,000
1970		766,000	591,000		609,300	540,000	686,500

Source: U.S. Department of Health, Education, and Welfare, Office of Education, 1957. Estimate of degree trends dated February 19.

Wolfle, D., 1954. *America's Resources of Specialized Talent.* Harper, p. 171.

National Science Foundation, 1955. *Scientific personnel resources.* Government Printing Office.

B. F. Goodrich Company, 1956. *A Study of the scientific manpower problem of the United States,* November.

Fund for the Advancement of Education, 1956. *Teachers for tomorrow,* Fourth printing, November.

Table 57—Trends in Number of Bachelors and Doctors Degrees in Psychology

	BACHELORS AND FIRST PRO- FESSIONAL DEGREE IN PSYCHOLOGY				DOCTORATES IN PSYCHOLOGY			
	Number in Psychology			Per Cent in Psychology	Number in Psychology			Per Cent in Psychology
1911–1915	1,200			0.6	120			4.8
1916–1920	1,600			0.7	130			4.7
1921–1925	3,200			0.9	220			4.6
1926–1930	6,200			1.1	400			4.6
1931–1935	8,800			1.3	540			4.0
1936–1940	12,300			1.5	610			4.1
1941–1945	13,000			1.7	520			3.6
1946–1950	31,600			2.2	850			4.1
1951	7,819			2.03	425			5.79
1952	6,622			2.00	540			7.03
1953	5,946			1.95	583			7.02
1954	5,758			1.97	619			6.88
1955	5,532			1.94	688			7.79
		X	Y			X	Y	
1956		5,909	5,519	1.95		617	463	7.00
1957		6,767	5,616	1.95		592	462	7.00
1958		7,644	5,694	1.95		587	463	7.00
1959		8,210	5,987	1.95		683	473	7.00
1960		8,522	6,357	1.95		736	495	7.00
1961		8,775	6,416	1.95		853	526	7.00
1962		8,951	6,747	1.95		935	543	7.00
1963		9,321	7,020	1.95		980	574	7.00
1964		10,043	7,547	1.95		1,019	623	7.00
1965		11,057	8,443	1.95		1,049	698	7.00

Source: Wolfle, D., 1954. America's Resources of Specialized Talent. Harper.
   U.S. Department of Health, Education, and Welfare, Office of Education, yearly. Earned degrees conferred by higher educational institutions. Government Printing Office.

Table 58—Number of Degrees in Psychology and Per Cent of Total Degrees Which Are in Psychology

Year	BACHELORS Number	Per Cent of Total	MASTERS Number	Per Cent of Total	DOCTORS Number	Per Cent of Total
1948	6,402	2.35	1,200	2.82	154	3.86
1949	8,205	2.24	1,455	2.87	201	3.98
1950	9,582	2.21	1,316	2.26	283	4.27
1951	7,819	2.03	1,645	2.53	425	5.79
1952	6,622	2.00	1,406	2.23	540	7.03
1953	5,946	1.95	1,161	1.90	583	7.02
1954	5,758	1.97	1,254	2.21	619	6.88

	BACHELORS		MASTERS		DOCTORS	
Year	Number	Per Cent of Total	Number	Per Cent of Total	Number	Per Cent of Total
1955	5,532	1.94	1,293	2.22	688	7.79
1956	5,666	1.82	973	1.64	634	7.12
1957	6,191	1.82	1,095	1.77	550	6.28
1958						

Source: U.S. Department of Health, Education, and Welfare, Office of Education, yearly. *Earned degrees conferred by higher educational institutions.* Government Printing Office.

Table 59—Total Doctorates Awarded in Selected Fields

Year	ALL FIELDS	HUMANITIES		PHYSICAL SCIENCE		SOCIAL SCIENCE		BIO-LOGICAL SCIENCE (LESS PSYCHOLOGY)		PSYCHOLOGY		MISC.	
		Number	Per Cent	Number	Per Cent	Number	Per Cent	Number	Per Cent	Number	Per Cent	Number	Per Cent
1948	3,989	617	15	1,251	31	1,083	27	743	19	154	3.86	141	4
1949	5,050	652	13	1,679	33	1,404	28	867	17	201	3.98	247	5
1950	6,633	803	12	2,115	32	1,869	28	1,148	17	283	4.27	421	6
1951	7,338	962	13	2,433	33	2,142	29	1,307	18	425	5.79	70	1
1952	7,683	1,013	13	2,492	32	2,245	29	1,351	18	540	7.03	44	1
1953	8,309	1,056	13	2,512	30	2,471	30	1,639	20	583	7.02	48	1
1954	8,996	1,170	13	2,554	28	2,731	30	1,819	20	619	6.88	103	1
1955	8,837	1,094	12	2,610	30	2,666	30	1,751	20	688	7.79	31	0
1956	8,815												
1957	8,460												
1958	8,380												
1959	9,750												
1960	10,520												

Source: Irwin, Mary, 1956. *American Universities and Colleges,* Seventh edition. American Council on Education, p. 69.

U.S. Department of Health, Education, and Welfare, Office of Education, yearly. *Earned degrees conferred by higher educational institutions.* Government Printing Office.

U.S. Department of Health, Education, and Welfare, Office of Education, 1957. Projections of earned doctor's degrees conferred in institutions of higher education in continental United States: 1955–56 to 1970–71. February 19, mimeographed.

National Science Foundation, 1955. *Scientific personnel resources,* p. 58. Government Printing Office.

Table 60—Estimate of Trends in Doctoral Level Degrees from Various Sources

ESTIMATES

Year	Actual Doctoral Level Degrees Awarded	U.S. Office of Education	Wolfle	National Science Foundation	Fund for the Advancement of Education	
					A	B
1944	2,305					
1946	1,966					
1948	3,989					
1949	5,050					
1950	6,633					
1951	7,338					
1952	7,683					
1953	8,309					
1954	8,996					
1955	8,837			7,500	8,500	7,085
1956		8,815		6,700	7,620	6,610
1957		8,460		6,100	6,880	6,600
1958		8,380		5,400	6,100	6,615
1959		9,750		6,200	7,010	6,750
1960		10,520	6,600	6,600	7,460	7,070
1961		12,180		6,700	7,550	7,520
1962		13,360		6,700	7,540	7,755
1963		14,000		7,000	7,890	8,205
1964		14,550		7,100	8,030	8,900
1965		14,980		7,100	7,990	9,970
1966		15,750			8,360	9,895
1967		17,140			8,970	10,350
1968		19,050			10,250	11,005
1969		19,550			9,710	14,370
1970		19,720	12,000		9,640	13,755

Source: U.S. Department of Health, Education, and Welfare, Office of Education, 1957. Estimate of degree trends, February 19.

Wolfle, D., 1954. America's Resources of Specialized Talent. Harper, p. 43.

National Science Foundation, 1955. Scientific personnel resources. Government Printing Office, p. 7.

Fund for the Advancement of Education, 1956. Teachers for tomorrow, Fourth printing, November, p. 59.

Table 61—Highest and Lowest Estimates of All First-Level and All Doctorate Level Degrees to 1965 and Estimates of Number of Degrees in Psychology

Year	FIRST-LEVEL DEGREES Highest Estimate	Lowest Estimate	Estimate for Psychology High	Low	DOCTORATE LEVEL DEGREES Highest Estimate	Lowest Estimate	Estimate Psychology High	Low
1956	303,000	283,000	5,909	5,519	8,815	6,610	617	463
1957	347,000	288,000	6,767	5,616	8,460	6,600	592	462
1958	392,000	292,000	7,644	5,694	8,380	6,615	587	463
1959	421,000	307,000	8,210	5,987	9,750	6,750	683	473
1960	437,000	326,000	8,522	6,357	10,520	7,070	736	495
1961	450,000	329,000	8,775	6,416	12,180	7,520	853	526
1962	459,000	346,000	8,951	6,747	13,360	7,755	935	543
1963	478,000	360,000	9,321	7,020	14,000	8,205	980	574
1964	515,000	387,000	10,043	7,547	14,550	8,900	1,019	623
1965	567,000	433,000	11,057	8,443	14,980	9,970	1,049	698

Source: See previous tables. This table is calculated from the others.

Table 62 ª—Number and Per Cent of Social Work Students in Different Types of Field Work Placements

Year	TOTAL STUDENTS EACH YEAR IN FIELDS INCLUDED	GROUP WORK Number	GROUP WORK Per Cent	MEDICAL SOCIAL WORK Number	MEDICAL SOCIAL WORK Per Cent	PSY-CHIATRIC SOCIAL WORK Number	PSY-CHIATRIC SOCIAL WORK Per Cent	SCHOOL SOCIAL WORK Number	SCHOOL SOCIAL WORK Per Cent	ALL OTHER CASE-WORK Number	ALL OTHER CASE-WORK Per Cent	ADMIN-ISTRATION Number	ADMIN-ISTRATION Per Cent	COM-MUNITY ORGAN-IZATION Number	COM-MUNITY ORGAN-IZATION Per Cent
1954	1,548	163	10.5	185	12.0	569	36.8	42	2.7	528	34.1	18	1.2	43	2.8
1955	1,574	178	11.3	199	12.6	630	40.0	25	1.6	501	31.8	9	0.6	32	2.0
1956	1,558	161	10.3	185	11.9	705	45.3	21	1.4	433	27.8	13	0.8	40	2.6

ª These figures apply to field work placements for second year students in the schools of social work in the United States. The figures for 1954 include five schools that reported placements of both first- and second-year students in a combined total; the figures for these schools have been divided in half to form an estimate of the field work placements of their second-year students, and the results have been added to the total.

Source: Council on Social Work Education, yearly. *Statistics on social work education.*

Table 63 ᵃ—Membership in Social Work Professional Organizations

MEMBERSHIP OF SEPARATE SOCIAL WORK ORGANIZATIONS

Year	Total Membership Social Work Organizations	Group Workers	Medical Social Workers	Psychiatric Social Workers	Social Workers American Association	Association for Study of Organization	School Social Workers	Social Work Research Group
1941	15,202	933	2,052	517	11,500		200	
1942								
1943	15,717	1,487	2,093	587	11,300		250	
1944								
1945	14,482	987	2,049	696	10,500		250	
1946								
1947	16,741	2,021	2,095	850	11,200	325	250	
1948								
1949	18,104	1,857	2,220	1,127	11,500	900	500	
1950								
1951	19,524	1,890	2,068	1,537	12,313	900	600	216
1952								
1953								
1954	21,248	2,150	2,293	1,889	13,500	555	600	261
1955								
1956								
1957	22,500	(N.A.S.W.) ᵇ						
1958								
1959								
1960								

ᵃ See Table 62 ᵃ.

ᵇ Two years ago the various social work organizations combined to form the National Association of Social Workers.

Source: Based on data contained in *Social Work Yearbooks,* Vols. 6–13.

Table 64—Number of Social Workers and Psychiatric Social Workers Compared to Population by Regions and States of the United States

	Population (in 10,000's)	Number of Social Workers	Ratio of Social Workers to Population (1:N)	Number of Social Workers per 100,000	Number of Psychiatric Social Workers	Ratio of Psychiatric Social Workers to Population (1:N)	Number of Psychiatric Social Workers per 100,000
Continental U.S.	16,719.1	20,786	8,000	12.4	2,342	71,400	1.4
Regions:							
Northeast	4,227.3	6,634	6,400	15.7	953	44,400	2.3
North Central	4,927.8	6,162	8,000	12.5	581	84,800	1.2
South (minus D.C.)	5,082.8	3,758	13,500	7.4	394	129,000	0.8
West	2,394.5	3,849	6,200	16.1	369	64,900	1.5
Northeast:							
New England	971.1	1,614	6,000	16.6	233	41,700	2.4
Middle Atlantic	3,256.2	5,020	6,500	15.4	720	45,200	2.2
North Central:							
East North Central	3,422.1	4,345	7,900	12.7	428	80,000	1.3
West North Central	1,505.7	1,817	8,300	12.1	153	98,400	1.0
District of Columbia	86.6	383	2,300	44.2	45	19,200	5.2
South (minus D.C.):							
South Atlantic	2,310.6	1,879	12,300	8.1	221	104,600	1.0
East South Central	1,174.3	658	17,800	5.6	52	225,800	0.4
West South Central	1,598.0	1,221	13,100	7.6	121	132,100	0.8
West:							
Mountain	612.7	725	8,500	11.8	56	109,400	0.9
Pacific	1,781.8	3,124	5,700	17.5	313	56,900	1.8
New England:							
Maine	91.0	40	22,800	4.4	1	910,000	0.1
New Hampshire	56.0	54	10,400	9.6	5	112,000	0.9
Vermont	37.0	48	7,700	13.0	9	41,100	2.4
Massachusetts	481.2	884	5,400	18.4	146	33,000	3.0
Rhode Island	82.8	143	5,800	17.3	10	82,800	1.2
Connecticut	223.2	445	5,000	19.9	62	36,000	2.8
Middle Atlantic:							
New York	1,619.5	3,198	5,100	19.7	485	33,400	3.0
New Jersey	540.3	495	10,900	9.2	82	65,900	1.5
Pennsylvania	1,096.4	1,327	8,300	12.1	153	71,700	1.4
East North Central:							
Ohio	909.6	1,296	7,000	14.2	128	71,100	1.4
Indiana	441.3	324	13,600	7.3	32	137,900	0.7
Illinois	943.2	1,302	7,200	13.8	135	69,900	1.4
Michigan	751.6	951	7,900	12.7	103	73,000	1.4
Wisconsin	376.4	472	8,000	12.5	30	125,500	0.8
West North Central:							
Minnesota	324.1	588	5,500	18.1	37	87,600	1.1
Iowa	269.2	167	16,100	6.2	12	224,300	0.4
Missouri	425.5	660	6,400	15.5	51	83,400	1.2
North Dakota	65.7	22	29,900	3.3	1	657,000	0.2
South Dakota	69.6	38	18,300	5.5	3	232,000	0.4
Nebraska	141.4	152	9,300	10.7	14	101,000	1.0
Kansas	210.3	190	11,100	9.0	35	60,100	1.7

	Population (in 10,000's)	Number of Social Workers	Ratio of Social Workers to Population (1:N)	Number of Social Workers per 100,000	Number of Psychiatric Social Workers	Ratio of Psychiatric Social Workers to Population (1:N)	Number of Psychiatric Social Workers per 100,000
South Atlantic:							
Delaware	40.2	89	4,500	22.1	4	100,500	1.0
Maryland	281.2	412	6,800	14.7	57	49,300	2.0
Virginia	365.1	388	9,400	10.6	50	73,000	1.4
West Virginia	198.3	69	28,700	3.5	6	330,500	0.3
North Carolina	442.3	244	18,100	5.5	30	147,400	0.7
South Carolina	235.3	99	23,800	4.2	10	235,300	0.4
Georgia	371.2	225	16,500	6.1	18	206,200	0.5
Florida	377.0	353	10,700	9.4	46	82,000	1.2
East South Central:							
Kentucky	301.7	172	17,500	5.7	19	158,800	0.6
Tennessee	346.6	304	11,400	8.8	18	192,600	0.5
Alabama	313.5	116	27,000	3.7	10	313,500	0.3
Mississippi	212.4	66	32,200	3.1	5	424,800	0.2
West South Central:							
Arkansas	181.5	53	34,200	2.9	5	363,000	0.3
Louisiana	300.4	355	8,500	11.8	43	69,900	1.4
Oklahoma	223.7	184	12,200	8.2	19	117,400	0.8
Texas	892.5	629	14,200	7.0	54	165,300	0.6
Mountain:							
Montana	63.8	38	16,800	6.0	2	319,000	0.3
Idaho	62.5	13	48,100	2.1	1	625,000	0.2
Wyoming	32.1	23	14,000	7.2	2	161,000	0.6
Colorado	161.2	320	5,000	19.9	30	53,700	1.9
New Mexico	81.5	64	12,700	7.9	0	—	0.0
Arizona	105.7	123	8,600	11.6	4	264,300	0.4
Utah	81.2	121	6,700	14.9	16	50,800	2.0
Nevada	24.7	23	10,700	9.3	1	247,000	0.4
Pacific:							
Washington	266.7	489	5,500	18.3	26	102,600	1.0
Oregon	171.8	202	8,500	11.8	12	143,200	0.7
California	1,343.3	2,433	5,500	18.1	275	48,800	2.0
Not in Continental U.S.		456			55		

Total NASW
Membership—21,242

Total Members
NASW Psychiatric—2,397
Social Work Division

Source: National Association of Social Workers, 1957. Data from membership files.
Bureau of the Census, 1956. *Current Population Reports, Population Estimates,* Series T-25, No. 148, November.

Table 65—Relation of Number of Psychiatric Social Workers to Population and to Availability of Schools with Psychiatric Social Work Curriculum

State	Number of Psychiatric Social Workers per 100,000 Population	Number of People to Each Social Worker	Number of Schools with Curriculum in Psychiatric Social Work
United States	1.3	78,200	37
District of Columbia	5.4	18,500	2
New York	3.0	33,500	4
Massachusetts	2.8	36,300	4
Colorado	2.5	39,300	1
Maryland	2.3	43,400	
Connecticut	2.3	43,500	
Utah	2.0	50,800	
Kansas	1.8	56,200	1
California	1.7	57,900	3
New Jersey	1.7	58,600	
Virginia	1.6	63,700	1
Rhode Island	1.5	67,200	
Illinois	1.4	72,600	3
Missouri	1.4	73,600	2
Louisiana	1.3	78,100	2
Pennsylvania	1.2	81,600	3
New Hampshire	1.1	92,000	
Michigan	1.1	93,100	2
Vermont	1.1	93,500	
Ohio	0.9	105,300	1
Nevada	0.9	106,000	
Wisconsin	0.9	113,400	1
Washington	0.8	133,000	
South Dakota	0.7	134,600	
Nebraska	0.7	135,900	1
Oklahoma	0.7	145,700	
Minnesota	0.7	149,100	1
Tennessee	0.7	152,900	1
Indiana	0.6	163,100	1
Kentucky	0.6	166,300	1
Florida	0.6	178,400	
Oregon	0.5	183,100	
Delaware	0.5	184,500	
North Carolina	0.5	192,100	1
Montana	0.5	206,300	
Texas	0.5	206,400	
Iowa	0.4	266,700	
Arizona	0.3	310,000	
North Dakota	0.3	318,000	

State	Number of Psychiatric Social Workers per 100,000 Population	Number of People to Each Social Worker	Number of Schools with Curriculum in Psychiatric Social Work
Georgia	0.3	330,000	1
South Carolina	0.3	377,700	
New Mexico	0.3	384,500	
West Virginia	0.3	398,200	
Mississippi	0.2	532,800	
Arkansas	0.2	602,300	
Alabama	0.1	768,200	
Maine	0.1	901,000	
Wyoming	0.0	—	
Idaho	0.0	—	

Source: American Association of Psychiatric Social Workers, yearly. Membership lists and directories.

Wittman, M., 1957. Personal communication indicating approved programs.

Table 66—Graduates of Social Work Schools

		MEN		WOMEN	
Year	Graduates	Number	Per Cent	Number	Per Cent
1945	839	43	5.1	796	94.9
1946	1,049	147	14.0	902	86.0
1947	1,311	306	23.3	1,005	76.7
1948	1,765	496	28.1	1,269	71.9
1949	1,803	501	27.8	1,302	72.2
1950	1,804	517	28.7	1,287	71.3
1951	1,923	744	38.7	1,179	61.3
1952	1,946	786	40.4	1,160	59.6
1953	1,844	771	41.8	1,073	58.2
1954	1,651	566	34.3	1,085	65.7
1955	1,655	579	35.0	1,076	65.0
1956	1,634	515	31.5	1,119	68.5
1957	1,612				

Source: National Association of Social Workers, yearly. Statistics on Social Work Education.

Table 67—Number of Full-Time Students, Graduates, and Number of Graduates Compared to First-Level Degrees Two Years Previously for Social Work in the United States

Year	Full-Time Students	Graduates and Estimated Number of Future Graduates	Total First-Level Degrees Two Years Previously	Rate of Social Work Graduates to First-Level Degrees Two Years Previously per 10,000
1946	3,410	1,049	125,863	83
1947	3,737	1,311		
1948	3,716	1,759	136,174	129
1949	4,066	1,803		
1950	4,336	1,804	272,311	66
1951	4,195	1,923	366,698	52
1952	4,006	1,946	433,734	45
1953	3,694	1,844	384,352	48
1954	3,512	1,651	331,924	50
1955	3,644	1,655	304,857	54
1956	3,811	1,634	292,880	56
1957		1,425–1,597	285,138	50–55
1958		1,556–1,712	311,298	50–55
1959		1,735–1,908	347,000	50–55
1960		1,960–2,156	392,000	50–55
1961		2,105–2,316	421,000	50–55
1962		2,185–2,404	437,000	50–55
1963		2,250–2,475	450,000	50–55
1964		2,295–2,525	459,000	50–55
1965		2,390–2,629	478,000	50–55

Source: National Association of Social Workers, yearly. *Statistics on Social Work Education.* Council on Social Work Education, 1957. *Statistics on Social Work Education, 1955–1956.* U.S. Department of Health, Education, and Welfare, Office of Education, 1957. *Estimate of degree trends, February 19.*

Table 68—Relation Between Number of Social Work Graduates by Sex, Number of First-Level Degrees Two Years Before, and Estimates of Numbers of Future Social Work Graduates Based on Degree Projections

Year	Graduates of Two-Year Social Work Programs			College Graduates Two Years Before		Number of Social Work Graduates per 10,000 College Graduates Two Years Before	
	Male	Female	Total	Male	Female	Male	Female
1945	43	796	839				
1946	147	902	1,049	55,865	69,998	26.3	128.9
1947	306	1,005	1,311				
1948	496	1,269	1,765	58,664	77,510	84.5	163.7
1949	501	1,302	1,803	175,987	96,157	28.5	135.4

	Graduates of Two-Year Social Work Programs			College Graduates Two Years Before		Number of Social Work Graduates per 10,000 College Graduates Two Years Before	
Year	Male	Female	Total	Male	Female	Male	Female
1950	517	1,287	1,804	175,456	95,563	29.5	134.7
1951	744	1,179	1,923	264,168	102,466	28.2	115.1
1952	786	1,160	1,946	329,819	103,915	23.8	111.6
1953	771	1,073	1,844	279,343	105,009	27.6	102.2
1954	566	1,085	1,651	227,029	104,895	24.9	103.4
1955	579	1,076	1,655	200,820	104,037	28.8	103.4
1956	515	1,119	1,634	187,500	105,380	27.4	106.2
1957	493	1,068	1,561	182,463	102,675	27	104
1958	539	1,162	1,755	199,571	111,727	27	104
1959	608	1,269	1,877	225,000	122,000	27	104
1960	699	1,383	2,082	259,000	133,000	27	104
1961	761	1,446	2,207	282,000	139,000	27	104
1962	788	1,508	2,296	292,000	145,000	27	104
1963	810	1,560	2,370	300,000	150,000	27	104
1964	826	1,591	2,417	306,000	153,000	27	104
1965	859	1,664	2,523	318,000	160,000	27	104

Source: National Association of Social Workers, yearly. *Statistics on Social Work Education.* Council on Social Work Education, 1957. *Statistics on Social Work Education, 1955–1956.* U.S. Department of Health, Education, and Welfare, Office of Education, 1957. *Estimate of degree trends,* February 19.

Table 69—Distribution of Nurses in Advanced Programs, 1955

	GRADUATES		ENROLLMENTS	
	Number	Per Cent	Number	Per Cent
Medical-Surgical	210	20.1	581	18.0
Maternal-Child	104	9.9	250	7.7
Public Health	89	8.5	300	9.3
Psychiatric-Mental Health	111	10.6	357	11.0
General Clinical and Unclassified	446	42.6	1,552	48.0
Other	86	8.2	191	5.9
Total	1,046		3,231	

Source: *Nursing Outlook,* 1956. *4* (no. 9), September.

Table 70—New Students in Schools of Nursing, Actual, 1947-1954, and Estimated, 1955-1965

ENTRANTS PER 1,000

Year of Admission	Estimates of 17-Year-Old Girls	17-YEAR-OLD GIRLS		NUMBER OF ENTRANTS	
		Reported	Estimated	Reported	Estimated
1947	1,118,000	34.18	34.13	38,210	38,200
1948	1,176,000	36.88	37.03	43,373	43,500
1949	1,126,000	38.70	38.74	43,610	43,600
1950	1,101,000	40.13	39.75	44,185	43,800
1951	1,039,000	40.10	40.35	41,667	41,900
1952	1,079,000	39.02	40.70	42,103	43,900
1953	1,085,000	39.58	40.91	42,945	44,400
1954	1,066,000	41.81	41.03	44,570	43,700
1955	1,093,000	—	41.10	—	44,900
1956	1,135,000	—	41.14	—	46,700
1957	1,124,000	—	41.17	—	46,300
1958	1,167,000	—	41.18	—	48,100
1959	1,238,000	—	41.19	—	51,000
1960	1,437,000	—	41.20	—	59,200
1961	1,359,000	—	41.20	—	56,000
1962	1,349,000	—	41.20	—	55,600
1963	1,356,000	—	41.20	—	55,900
1964	1,867,000	—	41.20	—	76,900
1965	1,733,000	—	41.20	—	71,400

Source: West, Margaret D., and Crosby, E. L., 1956. Nursing students in the future. *Hospitals,* 30: 33.

Table 71—Trends in Utilization of Professional Nurses in Hospitals

Year	Number of Nurses Employed in All Types of Hospitals	Number of Nurses Employed in Nervous and Mental Hospitals	Per Cent of Nurses Employed in Nervous and Mental Hospitals
1950	238,128	11,629	4.9
1951	247,854	11,966	4.8
1952	256,626	12,348	4.8
1953	266,581	12,692	4.8
1954	275,183	12,601	4.6
1955	291,570	13,952	4.8

Source: American Nurses Association, 1956. *Facts about nursing,* 1955–56, Table 4, p. 24.
    Hospitals, Administrator's Guide Issue, 1956. American Hospital Association, 30 (no. 15): 68.

Table 72 ª—Trends in Utilization of Practical Nurses and Auxiliary Workers

Year	Number of Practical Nurses and Auxiliary Workers Employed in All Types of Hospitals	Number Employed in Nervous and Mental Hospitals	Per Cent Employed in Nervous and Mental Hospitals
1950	297,310	95,805	32.2
1951	297,466	90,343	30.4
1952	329,076	92,619	28.1
1953	347,369	98,077	28.2
1954	351,765	91,521	26.0
1955	402,210	107,937	26.8

ª The term auxiliary workers includes practical nurses, nurses' aids, attendants, ward maids, and orderlies.

Source: American Nurses Association, 1956. Facts about nursing, 1955–56, Table 4, p. 145.
    Hospitals, Administrator's Guide Issue, 1956. American Hospital Association, 30 (no. 15): 70, Table 23.

Table 73—Sources of Current Income of United States Colleges and Universities, 1953-54

AMOUNT AS PER CENT OF TOTAL CURRENT INCOME

	All Institutions	Publicly Controlled Institutions	Privately Controlled Institutions
Educational and General:			
Student Fees	20.17	10.03	32.94
Federal Government	12.65	12.09	13.36
State Governments	25.34	44.18	1.66
Local Governments	2.97	5.23	.13
Endowment Earnings	4.30	.89	8.58
Private Gifts and Grants	6.45	2.33	11.61
Sales Related Activities	5.58	5.68	5.45
Other Sources	1.98	1.61	2.45
Total	79.44	82.04	76.18
Auxiliary Enterprises	19.45	17.33	22.10
For Scholarships, Prizes, etc.	1.11	.63	1.72
	100.00	100.00	100.00
Total Current Income	$2,966,244,000	$1,651,415,000	$1,314,850,000

Source: President's Committee on Education beyond the High School, 1957. Second Report to the President, July. Government Printing Office, p. 76.

Table 74—Doctors Degrees Awarded in Selected Fields

Year	All Doc-torates	PHI-LOSOPHY Num-ber	PHI-LOSOPHY Per Cent	BIOLOGY AND PHYSI-OLOGY Num-ber	BIOLOGY AND PHYSI-OLOGY Per Cent	CHEMISTRY Num-ber	CHEMISTRY Per Cent	PHYSICS Num-ber	PHYSICS Per Cent	MATHE-MATICS Num-ber	MATHE-MATICS Per Cent	SOCIOLOGY Num-ber	SOCIOLOGY Per Cent	PSY-CHOLOGY Num-ber	PSY-CHOLOGY Per Cent
1948	3,989	50	1.3	97	2.4	569	14.2	198	5.0	128	3.2	66	1.7	154	3.8
1949	5,050	79	1.6	123	2.4	749	14.8	266	5.3	126	2.5	83	1.6	201	4.0
1950	6,633	83	1.3	117	1.8	953	14.4	358	5.4	160	2.4	98	1.5	283	4.3
1951	7,338	84	1.1	215	2.9	1,046	14.3	443	6.1	184	2.5	129	1.8	425	5.8
1952	7,683	102	1.3	195	2.5	1,031	13.4	485	6.3	206	2.7	141	1.8	540	7.0
1953	8,309	107	1.3	267	3.2	999	12.0	478	5.8	241	2.9	157	1.9	583	7.0
1954	8,996	103	1.1	232	2.6	1,013	11.3	485	5.4	227	2.5	184	2.0	619	6.9
1955	8,837	84	1.0	207	2.3	1,005	11.4	511	5.8	250	2.8	167	1.9	688	7.8
1956	8,815														
1957	8,460														
1958	8,380														
1959	9,750														
1960	10,520														

Source: Irwin, Mary, 1956. American Colleges and Universities. *American Council on Education*, p. 69.

Table 75—Percentage of Youth of High Intelligence Graduating from College

Per Cent Level of Ability	Army General Classification Test Score (Intelligence)	Per Cent Graduating from College
Top 0.1	160 and higher	69
Top 1	147 " "	59
Top 5	133 " "	49
Top 10	126 " "	42
Top 20	117 " "	34

Source: Wolfle, D., 1954. *America's Resources of Specialized Talent.* Harper, p. 149.

Table 76—Summary of Number of Psychiatrists and Residency Programs

	States Above U.S. Average of Psychiatrists to Population	States Below U.S. Average of Psychiatrists to Population
Number of States	9	40
Population of States	53,819,000	113,372,000
Residency Programs:		
One year	33	27
Two years	34	26
Three years	73	75
Total	140	128
Population to Total Residency Programs	384,421	885,719
Total Residency Man-Years Offered	4,750	3,273
Population to Residency Man-Years	11,330	34,639

Source: Journal of the American Medical Association, yearly. Annual residency issues. Bureau of the Census, Population Estimates.

Appendix II

Joint Commission on Mental Illness and Health

PARTICIPATING ORGANIZATIONS

American Academy of Neurology

American Academy of Pediatrics

American Association for the Advancement of Science

American Association on Mental Deficiency

American Association of Psychiatric Clinics for Children

American College of Chest Physicians

American Hospital Association

American Legion

American Medical Association

American Nurses Association and The National League for Nursing (Coordinating Council of)

American Occupational Therapy Association

American Orthopsychiatric Association

American Personnel and Guidance Association

American Psychiatric Association

American Psychoanalytic Association

American Psychological Association

American Public Health Association

American Public Welfare Association

Association for Physical and Mental Rehabilitation

Association of American Medical Colleges

Association of State and Territorial Health Officers

Catholic Hospital Association

Central Inspection Board, American Psychiatric Association

Children's Bureau, Dept. of Health, Education and Welfare

Council of State Governments

Department of Defense, U.S.A.

National Association for Mental Health

National Association of Social Workers

National Committee Against Mental Illness

National Education Association

National Institute of Mental Health

National Medical Association

National Rehabilitation Association

Office of Vocational Rehabilitation, Department of Health, Education and Welfare

United States Department of Justice

Veterans Administration

MEMBERS

Kenneth E. Appel, M.D.
Philadelphia, Pa.
Walter H. Baer, M.D.
Peoria, Illinois
Leo H. Bartemeier, M.D.
Baltimore, Maryland
Walter E. Barton, M.D.
Boston, Massachusetts
Otto L. Bettag, M.D.
Springfield, Illinois
Mr. George Bingaman
Purcell, Oklahoma
Kathleen Black, R.N.
New York, New York
Daniel Blain, M.D.
Washington, D.C.
Francis J. Braceland, M.D.
Hartford, Connecticut
Hugh T. Carmichael, M.D.
Chicago, Illinois
J. Frank Casey, M.D.
Washington, D.C.
James M. Cunningham, M.D.
Dayton, Ohio
John E. Davis, Sc.D.
Rehoboth Beach, Delaware
Neil A. Dayton, M.D.
Mansfield Depot, Conn.
Miss Loula Dunn
Chicago, Illinois
Howard D. Fabing, M.D.
Cincinnati, Ohio
Rev. Patrick J. Frawley, Ph.D.
New York, New York
Mr. Mike Gorman
Washington, D.C.
Robert T. Hewitt, M.D.
Bethesda, Maryland
Herman E. Hilleboe, M.D.
Albany, New York
Nicholas Hobbs, Ph.D.
Nashville, Tennessee
Bartholomew W. Hogan, Rear Adm.
M.C., U.S.N., Washington, D.C.

Louis Jacobs, M.D.
Washington, D.C.
M. Ralph Kaufman, M.D.
New York, New York
William S. Langford, M.D.
New York, New York
Miss Madeleine Lay
New York, New York
Jack Masur, M.D.
Bethesda, Maryland
Berwyn F. Mattison, M.D.
New York, New York
Ernst Mayr, Ph.D.
Cambridge, Mass.
Robert T. Morse, M.D.
Washington, D.C.
Ralph H. Ojemann, Ph.D.
Iowa City, Iowa
Winfred Overholser, M.D.
Washington, D.C.
Howard W. Potter, M.D.
New York, New York
Mr. Charles Schlaifer
New York, New York
Lauren H. Smith, M.D.
Philadelphia, Pa.
M. Brewster Smith, Ph.D.
New York, New York
Mr. Sidney Spector
Chicago, Illinois
Mesrop A. Tarumianz, M.D.
Farnhurst, Delaware
David W. Tiedman, Ed.D.
Cambridge, Mass.
Harvey J. Tompkins, M.D.
New York, New York
Beatrice D. Wade, O.T.R.
Chicago, Illinois
Mr. E. B. Whitten
Washington, D.C.
Helen Witmer, Ph.D.
Washington, D.C.
Luther E. Woodward, Ph.D.
New York, New York

OFFICERS

President: Kenneth E. Appel, M.D.
    Philadelphia, Pa.
Chairman, Board of Trustees: Leo H. Bartemeier, M.D.
    Baltimore, Md.
Vice-President: M. Brewster Smith, Ph.D.
    New York, N.Y.
Secretary-Treasurer: Mr. Charles Schlaifer
    New York, N.Y.
Vice-Chairman, Board of Trustees: Nicholas Hobbs, Ph.D.
    Nashville, Tenn.

STAFF

Director: Jack R. Ewalt, M.D.
    Boston, Mass.
Consultant for Scientific Studies: Fillmore H. Sanford, Ph.D.
    Austin, Texas
Consultant in Social Sciences: Gordon W. Blackwell, Ph.D.
    Chapel Hill, North Carolina
Consultant in Epidemiology: John E. Gordon, M.D.
    Boston, Mass.
Associate Director for Administration: Richard J. Plunkett, M.D.
    Boston, Mass.
Director of Information: Greer Williams
    Boston, Mass.
Associate Director and Consultant on Law: Charles S. Brewton, LL.B.
    Boston, Mass.
Librarian: Mary R. Strovink
    Boston, Mass.

References

Albee, G. W., 1958. *Population and intelligence*. Speech to Maternal Health Association, Cleveland. (Mimeographed.)

Albee, G. W. and Dickey, Marguerite, 1957. Manpower trends in three mental health professions. *Am. Psychol., 12:* 57.

American Nurses' Association, 1956. *Facts about nursing, 1955-1956.*

American Psychiatric Association, 1956. Standards for hospitals and clinics.

American Psychiatric Association, 1957. List of fellows and members, 1955-1956.

American Psychoanalytic Association, 1957. Roster, 1956-1957.

Appel, K. E., 1957. Mental health and mental illness. *Social Work Yearbook, 1957,* Kurtz, R. H. (Ed.), National Association of Social Workers, p. 363.

Bahn, Anita K., and Norman, Vivian B., 1957. Outpatient psychiatric clinics in the United States, 1954-1955. *Public Health Monograph No. 49.* Government Printing Office.

Bennett, A. E., Hargrove, E. A., and Engle, B., 1951. Present status and future needs of psychiatric facilities in general hospitals in the United States and Canada. *Amer. J. Psychiat., 108:* 321-327.

Berkner, L. V., 1958. Wanted: a national science policy. In Lansner, K. (Ed.), *Second-rate Brains,* Doubleday.

Bestor, A., 1958. What went wrong with U.S. schools? Quoted in *U.S. News and World Report,* January 24, p. 70.

Bevis, H. L., 1957. Second interim report to the President from the Committee on Scientists and Engineers. Summary in *The New York Times,* December 1, p. 58.

B. F. Goodrich Company, 1956. *A study of the scientific manpower problem of the United States.*

Blain, D., 1956. Personnel shortages in psychiatric services: a reshift of emphasis. Paper read at the New York State Mental Health Forum.

Blain, D., 1958. Relief of shortages in mental health personnel. Speech to Midwestern State Governments Conference, Chicago, April 29.

Blain, D., and Robinson, R., 1957. Personnel shortages in psychiatric services. *New York J. Med.,* 57 (no. 2): 255.

Blau, P. M., et al., 1956. Occupational choice: a conceptual framework. *Industrial and Labor Relations Review,* 9 (no. 4): 531.

Brown, H., 1954. *The Challenge of Man's Future.* Viking.

Bruder, E. E., 1957. In Doniger, S. (Ed.), *Healing, Human and Divine.* Association Press, p. 117.

Buder, L., 1957. Rise of 50 per cent to 100 per cent in college tuition costs worries educators. *The New York Times,* January 20.

Bush, C. K., 1957. Growth of general hospital care of psychiatric patients. *Amer. J. Psychiat., 113* (no. 12): 1059.

Business aid to our colleges and universities. Undated pamphlet. McGraw-Hill.

Carnegie Corporation of New York, 1957. *Quarterly Report, 5* (no. 1).

Clark, K. E., 1957. *America's psychologists: a survey of a growing profession.* American Psychological Association.

Clark, M., 1958. Nation needs physicians to meet population rise. *The New York Times,* March 3.

Commission on Chronic Illness, 1957. *Chronic Illness in a Large City.* Harvard Univ. Press.

Committee on Mental Health Services, 1956. Minutes of meeting, October 19–20. Montreal, Canada.

Cornog, W. H., 1958. The perils of panic. In Lansner, K. (Ed.), *Second-rate Brains,* Doubleday.

Council of State Governments, Interstate Clearing House on Mental Health, 1957. The manpower situation in State mental hospitals. (Mimeographed.)

Council of State Governments, Interstate Clearing House on Mental Health, 1958. Selected tables on public hospitals for the mentally ill in twelve midwest states.

Council on Social Work Education, yearly. *Statistics on social work education.*

Croatman, W., 1957[a]. Are you better off than the typical G.P.? *Medical Economics, 34* (no. 4): 246.

Croatman, W., 1957[b]. How the specialties compare financially. *Medical Economics, 34* (no. 5): 115.

DelliQuadri, F., 1957. Child welfare. *Social Work Yearbook,* 1957, Kurtz, R. H. (Ed.), National Association of Social Workers.

Derthick, L. G., 1958. The Russian race for knowledge. Speech to National Press Club, June 13.

DeWitt, N., 1958. Soviet science education and its challenge. *The Mathematics Teacher, 51* (no. 2): 68, 70.

Diehl, H. S., Crosby, E. L., and Kaetzel, P. K., 1957. Hospital house staffs, 1950–1955. *J.A.M.A., 164* (no. 3): 273.

Diehl, H. S., Crosby, E. L., and Kaetzel, P. K., 1957. *Hospitals, 31:* 39.

Dolan, Eleanor, F., 1957. Report to the American Association of University Women on members available for teaching science and mathematics, November 15.

Eaton, J. W., 1956. Whence and whither social work? A sociological analysis. *Social Work, 1:* 11.

Ebaugh, F. G., and Barnes, R. H., 1956. Psychiatric education. *Amer. J. Psychiat., 112:* 561.

Educational Testing Service, 1957. Background factors relating to college plans and college enrollment among public high school students.

Ekirch, A. A., Jr., 1956. The numbers game in the colleges. American Association of University Professors *Bulletin, 42:* 714.

Fauri, F. F., 1955. The shortage of social workers—a challenge to social work education. *Proceedings,* Annual Program Meeting. Council on Social Work Education.

Federal Bureau of Investigation, 1958. *Uniform crime reports for the United States.* Government Printing Office.

Fein, R., 1958. *Economics of Mental Illness.* Basic Books.

Flexner, A., 1910. *Medical education in the United States and Canada.* Carnegie Foundation for the Advancement of Teaching.

Flexner, A., 1915. Is social work a profession? *Proceedings* of the National Conference of Charities and Correction.

Ford Foundation, 1955. *Annual report.*

Fund for the Advancement of Education, 1955. *Teachers for tomorrow.*

Funkenstein, D. H., 1955. Some myths about medical school admissions. *J. Med. Educ., 30:* 81.

Galbraith, J. K., 1958. *The Affluent Society.* Houghton Mifflin.

Gee, Helen H., 1956. The study of applicants, 1955–1956. *J. Med. Educ., 31* (no. 12): 863.

Gorman, M., 1956. *Every Other Bed.* World.

Greenwood, E., 1957. Attributes of a profession. *Social Work, 2:* 45.

Group for the Advancement of Psychiatry, 1955. Trends and issues in psychiatric residency programs. Report No. 31.

Hardin, Clara A., 1956. Supply of professional nurses in 1956. *Am. J. Nursing, 56* (no. 12): 1545.

Harris, S. E., 1957. Faculty salaries. American Association of University Professors *Bulletin, 43:* 581.

Hastings, D., 1955. The contribution of orthopsychiatry to psychiatry. *Amer. J. Orthopsychiat., 25* (no. 3): 458, 463.

Health Resources Advisory Committee, 1956. Mobilization and health manpower. II. A report of the subcommittee on paramedical personnel in rehabilitation and care of the chronically ill. Government Printing Office.

Hoch, E., 1957. Personal communication giving data obtained from the National Scientific Register's survey of psychologists, 1954.

Hogan, Admiral B. W., 1958. Letter dated August 29.

Hollingshead, A. B., and Redlich, F. C., 1958. *Social Class and Mental Illness: a Community Study.* John Wiley.

Hollis, E. V., and Taylor, Alice L., 1951. *Social Work Education in the United States.* Columbia Univ. Press.

Holt, R. R., and Luborsky, L. B., 1958. *Personality Patterns of Psychiatrists.* Basic Books.

Hoover, H., 1957. Address to campaign dinner, United Engineering Center, Waldorf Astoria Hotel, November 21.

Hospitals, Administrator's Guide Issue, 1955. American Hospital Association. *29* (no. 8): 6.

Hospitals, Administrator's Guide Issue, 1956. American Hospital Association. *30* (no. 15).

Houtchens, M., 1958. Personal communication, July 15.

Iffert, R. E., 1958. Retention and withdrawal of college students. U.S. Office of Education. Government Printing Office—442973.

In the field of education . . . who are today's capitalists? Undated pamphlet. McGraw-Hill.

Irwin, Mary, 1956. American universities and colleges. American Council on Education.

Jahoda, Marie, 1958. *Current Concepts of Positive Mental Health.* Basic Books.

Johnson, R. L., Jr., 1957. The monster. American Association of University Professors *Bulletin, 43:* 648.

Joint Information Service, 1957. Thirteen indices: an aid in reviewing State mental health and hospital programs. American Psychiatric Association and the National Association for Mental Health.

Joint Information Service, 1957. Fact Sheet No. 1. Changes in patient-employee ratios in public (State, county, and psychopathic) mental hospitals in all states and the United States, 1939–1955. American Psychiatric Association and National Association for Mental Health.

Joint Information Service, 1957. Fact Sheet No. 2. Number and distribution of psychiatrists, and ratios of population to psychiatrists, 1950 and 1956. American Psychiatric Association and National Association for Mental Health.

Joint Information Service, 1957. Fact Sheet No. 3. Physicians training in U.S. psychiatric training centers, August, 1956. American Psychiatric Association and National Association for Mental Health.

Joint Information Service, 1957. Fact Sheet No. 4. Adequacy of five personnel categories in public mental hospitals, 1956, according to American Psychiatric Association standards, by states. American Psychiatric Association and National Association for Mental Health.

Joint Information Service, 1958. Fact Sheet No. 5. Patient and administrative data for public mental hospitals and Veterans Administration hospitals, 1957. American Psychiatric Association and National Association for Mental Health.

Joint Information Service, 1958. Fact Sheet No. 6. Variations in organization practices among child guidance clinics, 1955. American Psychiatric Association and National Association for Mental Health.

Journal of the American Medical Association, yearly. Annual internship and residency number.

Journal of the American Medical Association, 1956. List of number of medical school graduates, *161:* 17.

Kaufman, M. R., 1950. The role of psychoanalysis in American psychiatry. *Bulletin* of the American Psychoanalytic Association, 6 (no. 1).

Kendall, Katherine A., 1954. Education for social work. *Social Work Yearbook,* Kurtz, R. H. (Ed.), American Association of Social Workers, p. 178.

Keynes, J. M., 1931. *Essays in Persuasion.* Macmillan.

Knight, R. P., 1953. The present status of organized psychoanalysis in the United States. *Journal of the American Psychoanalytic Association, 1* (no. 2): 197.

Leone, Lucile P., 1956. Trends and problems in practical nurse education. *Am. J. Nursing, 56* (no. 1): 51.

Long, E. S., 1958. *Determinants of career choice in psychiatric nursing.* Unpublished Ph.D. dissertation, Western Reserve University.

Louis, G. P., Pinnell, W. G., and Wells, H. B., 1958. Needs, resources, and priorities in higher educational planning. *Higher Education in the West, 4* (no. 3): 3.

Maas, H. S., and Wolins, M., 1954. Concepts and methods in social work research. In Kasius, Cora (Ed.), *New Directions in Social Work.* Harper.

Martin, H. W., and Simpson, Ida H., 1956. *Patterns of psychiatric nursing.* Institute for Research in Social Science, Univ. North Carolina.

McCormack, J. E., and Feraru, A., 1955. Alien interns and residents in the United States. *J.A.M.A., 158:* 1357.

McCurdy, W. B., 1957. Basic personnel counts, positions, vacancies, turnover, and change. Family Service Association of America.

McDonald urges 15,000 schools. *The New York Times,* December 1, 1957.

McKean, D. D., 1958. Council witness presents plans for Federal assistance.

Testimony reported in Higher Education and National Affairs, 7, 8, American Council on Education.

Menninger, K., 1955. Untitled comment. *The Progressive, 19* (no. 10): 15.

Millett, J. D., 1952. *Financing Higher Education in the United States.* Columbia Univ. Press.

Million, E. G., 1957. The ministerial crisis—two decades ahead will require 600,000 ministers. *National Council Outlook,* May.

Mumm, Louise N., 1957. The personnel of social welfare. *Social Work Yearbook,* Kurtz, R. H. (Ed.), National Association of Social Workers.

National Council of Churches of Christ in the U.S.A., Department of Pastoral Services, 1958. Opportunities for study, training, and experience in pastoral psychology—1958. *Pastoral Psychology,* January, p. 19.

National Education Association, Research Division, 1957. Teacher supply and demand in colleges and universities, 1955–1956 and 1956–1957. Pamphlet.

National Education Association, Research Division, 1958. Teacher supply and demand in the public schools. Pamphlet.

National League for Nursing, 1956. Preparation of nursing leaders. *Nursing Outlook, 4* (no. 9): 517.

National League for Nursing, 1957. Nurses for a growing nation. Pamphlet.

National Manpower Council, 1957. *Womanpower.* Columbia Univ. Press.

National Mental Health Committee, 1956. What are the facts about mental illness in the United States? National Mental Health Committee.

National Science Foundation, 1955. *Scientific personnel resources.* Government Printing Office.

Norton, J. K., 1958. Speech at the University of Pittsburgh quoted in *The New York Times,* July 20, 1958, IV, p. 9.

Nowakowski, Aurelie J., 1950. Inventory and qualifications of psychiatric nurses. National League of Nursing Education.

Oberndorf, C. P., 1953. *A History of Psychoanalysis in America.* Grune.

Perrott, G. St. J., and Pennell, Maryland Y., 1957. *Health manpower chart book.* U.S. Department of Health, Education, and Welfare, Public Health Service. Government Printing Office.

Potter, H. W., Klein, Henriette R., and Goodenough, D. R., 1957. Problems related to the personal costs of psychiatric and psychoanalytic training. *Amer. J. Psychiat., 113* (no. 11): 1013.

President's Committee on Education beyond the High School, 1957. Second Report to the President. Government Printing Office.

Public Health Reports, 1957. Mental patient data for fiscal year 1956. 72 (no. 1): 14.

Rickover, H. G., 1957. Education in the nuclear age. Speech delivered at New London, Connecticut, December 6.

Rusk, H. A., 1958. Recruiting for health. *The New York Times,* April 20, 1958, p. 77.

Rusk, H. A. and Switzer, Mary E., 1953. Doing something for the disabled. Pamphlet No. 197, Public Affairs Committee.

Selden, W. K., 1956. Accrediting—what is it? American Association of University Professors *Bulletin, 42* (no. 4).

Southern Regional Educational Board, 1954. Mental health training and research in the southern states; a report to the Southern Governors' Conference.

Southern Regional Education Board, 1956. Psychiatrists for mental health programs.

Stalnaker, J. M., 1955. The study of applicants, 1954–1955. *J. Med. Educ., 30:* 625.

Tickton, S. G., 1957. *Rebuilding Human Lives: the Rehabilitation of the Handicapped.* The Seventh Company, Inc.

Time, August 22, 1955. Mental health rivalry, p. 39.

Toynbee, A. J., 1950. *War and Civilization.* Oxford.

Turner, E. L., 1955. The facts about medical students. *J.A.M.A., 157:* 903.

Turner, E. L., Wiggins, W. S., and Tipner, Anne, 1955. Medical education in the United States and Canada. *J.A.M.A., 159:* 563.

U.S. Bureau of the Census, 1950. Census of the population. Vol. II, Part 1. Government Printing Office.

U.S. Bureau of the Census, 1956. Provisional estimates of the total and civilian population of the states and of selected outlying areas of the United States, July, 1956. Current Population Reports, Population Estimates, Series T-25, No. 148, November. Government Printing Office.

U.S. Bureau of the Census, 1956. *Statistical abstracts of the United States,* Seventy-seventh edition. Government Printing Office.

U.S. Congress, House Committee on Interstate and Foreign Commerce, Hearings on the causes, control, and remedies of the principal diseases of mankind, part 4, October 7, 8, and 9, 1953. Government Printing Office.

U.S. Department of Health, Education, and Welfare, National Institute of Mental Health, 1958. *The training program of the National Institute of Mental Health, 1947–1957.* Government Printing Office.

U.S. Department of Health, Education, and Welfare, Office of Education, yearly. *Earned degrees conferred by higher educational institutions.* Government Printing Office.

U.S. Department of Labor, undated. *Our manpower future—1955–1965.* Government Printing Office.

U.S. Department of Labor, Bureau of Labor Statistics, 1957. *Occupational outlook handbook.* Government Printing Office.

U.S. Employment Service, 1949. Job description for professional nurse. *Occupational Guide,* March.

U.S. Veterans Administration, Department of Medicine, Psychiatry and Neurology Division, 1953. Planning in psychiatry, neurology, and clinical psychology, a forecast 1953–60. Government Printing Office.

University of Michigan, Survey Research Center, 1956. Adolescent girls. Girl Scouts of the USA.

University of Minnesota, 1950. Conference on advanced psychiatric nursing and mental hygiene programs.

Vestermark, S. D., 1957. Speech delivered at a meeting of clinical psychology training directors, American Psychological Association.

Wertham, F., 1950. What to do till the doctor goes. *The Nation, 171* (10): 206.

West, Margaret D., and Crosby, E. L., 1956. Nursing students in the future. *Hospitals, 30,* January 16.

Western Interstate Commission for Higher Education, 1956. Mental health training and research in the western region.

Witte, E. F., 1956. Recruitment and training of professional personnel. *Journal of Jewish Communal Service, 33* (no. 1): 87.

Wittman, M., 1956. *Scholarship aid in social work education.* Unpublished Ph.D. dissertation, New York School of Social Work, Columbia University.

Wolfle, D., 1947. Across the secretary's desk. *Am. Psychol., 2:* 519.

Wolfle, D., 1954. *America's Resources of Specialized Talent.* Harper.

Wolfle, D., 1955. Comparisons between psychologists and other professional groups. *Am. Psychol., 10* (no. 6): 231.

World Health Organization, 1952. Expert Committee on Mental Health. Alcoholism Subcommittee. Second Report. Technical Report. Series No. 48, p. 15.

World Health Organization, 1956. Expert Committee on Psychiatric Nursing. First Report. Technical Report Series, No. 105.

Youngdahl, B. E., 1951. Social work as a profession. In Hodges, Margaret B. (Ed.), *Social Work Yearbook,* American Association of Social Workers, p. 493.

Index